THE COMMONWEALTH AND INTERNATIONAL LIBRARY

Joint Chairmen of the Honorary Editorial Advisory Board

SIR ROBERT ROBINSON, O.M., F.R.S., LONDON

DEAN ATHELSTAN SPILHAUS, MINNESOTA

Publisher: ROBERT MAXWELL, M.C., M.P.

SELECTED READINGS IN PHYSICS

General Editor: D. TER HAAR

TRANSISTORS

TRANSISTORS

BY

E. J. M. KENDALL

Physics Department
Lakehead University, Canada

THE QUEEN'S AWARD
TO INDUSTRY 1968

PERGAMON PRESS

OXFORD · LONDON · EDINBURGH · NEW YORK
TORONTO · SYDNEY · PARIS · BRAUNSCHWEIG

116 250

621.3815
K 33

PERGAMON PRESS LTD.,
Headington Hill Hall, Oxford
4 & 5 Fitzroy Square, London W.1

PERGAMON PRESS (SCOTLAND) LTD.,
2 & 3 Teviot Place, Edinburgh 1

PERGAMON PRESS INC.,
Maxwell House, Fairview Park, Elmsford, New York 10523

PERGAMON OF CANADA LTD.,
207 Queen's Quay West, Toronto 1

PERGAMON PRESS (AUST.) PTY. LTD.,
19a Boundary Street, Rushcutters Bay, N.S.W. 2011, Australia

PERGAMON PRESS S.A.R.L.,
24 rue des Écoles, Paris 5e

VIEWEG & SOHN GMBH,
Burgplatz 1, Braunschweig

Copyright © 1969 E. J. M. Kendall

First edition 1969

Library of Congress Catalog Card No. 70–88307

Printed in Great Britain by A. Wheaton & Co., Exeter

08 006510 4 (flexicover)
08 006511 2 (hard cover)

Contents

PREFACE   vii

PART 1

1. *Semiconductor Physics*   3
2. *Point Contact Devices*   35
3. *Junction Devices and Subsequent Developments*   49

PART 2

1. *Modulation of Conductance of Thin Films of Semi-conductors by Surface Charges.* W. SHOCKLEY and G. L. PEARSON   79
2. *Surface States and Rectification at a Metal–Semi-conductor contact.* JOHN BARDEEN   82
3. *The Transistor, a Semi-conductor Triode.* J. BARDEEN and W. H. BRATTAIN   106
4. *Nature of the Forward Current in Germanium Point Contacts.* W. H. BRATTAIN and J. BARDEEN   111
5. *Physical Principles Involved in Transistor Action.* J. BARDEEN and W. H. BRATTAIN   115
6. *The Double-surface Transistor.* J. N. SHIVE   164
7. *Investigation of Hole Injection in Transistor Action.* J. R. HAYNES and W. SHOCKLEY   168
8. *Effects of Electrical Forming on the Rectifying Barriers of* n- *and* p- *Germanium Transistors.* J. BARDEEN and W. G. PFANN   172
9. p–n *Junctions in Semiconductors.* W. SHOCKLEY   177
10. p–n *Junction Transistors.* W. SHOCKLEY, M. SPARKS and G. K. TEAL   186

11. *Theory of Alpha for* p–n–p *Diffused Junction Transistors*
    E. L. STEELE   222
12. *A High-frequency Diffused Base Germanium Transistor.*
    C. A. LEE   237
13. *Principles of the Surface-barrier Transistor.* W. E.
    BRADLEY   252
14. *Unipolar and Analog Transistors.* W. SHOCKLEY   264
15. *A Unipolar "Field-effect" Transistor.* W. SHOCKLEY   271
16. *The TFT—a New Thin-film Transistor.* P. K. WEIMER   308

INDEX   331

Preface

OVER the past two decades spectacular advances have been made in semiconductor physics and associated devices, and the advent of satellites, rocket systems and computers has spurred on this development to such an extent that the subject is now a highly developed technology. In this volume the main thread of transistor development is presented. To begin with, a résumé of the semiconductor physics pertinent to the understanding of transistors is given, since I felt that it would be advantageous to have a, hopefully, coherent although highly condensed outline of such physics alongside the transistor work.

In a subject that has been born and has grown to maturity in twenty years, the choice of papers presents a number of problems. In choosing them, besides looking for significant contributions, I have attempted to illustrate some of the many facets of transistor research and development. Because of the limited space I have of necessity omitted many worth-while and important contributions, and in particular only two sections of Shockley's classic paper on p–n junctions have been reprinted. I would like to thank the authors and publishers of the papers appearing in Part 2 for their permission to reprint them, and for the helpful suggestions that in many cases accompanied such permission.

In writing this book help from the Chancellor's fund of Lakehead University proved extremely helpful in the initial stages, enabling a thorough literature search to be made, and I would like to express my grateful appreciation to all concerned. I would like to thank Dr. ter Haar for many helpful suggestions and his encouragement in planning this book, particularly with respect to Chapter 1. I would also like to thank Dr. G. T. Wright of Birmingham University's Electronic and Electrical Engineering Depart-

vii

ment for his helpful criticism of the manuscript and his general encouragement. In conclusion I would particularly like to thank Miss Fiona Karlstedt for her unstinting help in preparing the typescript.

PART 1

Semiconductor Physics

IN ANY form of electronic device we are faced with the task of investigating and understanding the mechanisms of current flow, and how the physical properties of the material used influence this flow. In semiconductors, conduction is either "excess conduction", that is by electrons, or "defect conduction", that is by holes. The possibility that these two processes may be simultaneously and separately active in a semiconductor, affords a basis for explaining transistor action (Shockley, 1950).

The transistor itself is a device made from semiconducting material, particularly germanium or silicon, in which the conduction through the device is controlled. That is the transistor performs a similar function to the thermionic vacuum tube. In the transistor the conduction processes are a little more complicated, involving holes as well as electrons. The hole in essence is the positive counterpart of the electron. Further complications arise because there are certain bands of allowed and forbidden energies which apply to the current carriers.

Whilst a fuller discussion of holes and energy bands will be given later, a cursory explanation now will prove useful. Considering a single atom the energies of the electrons are equal to their respective orbitals. Once atoms come together to form a crystal, these energy levels become bands of many energy levels very close together. Each level may be occupied by two electrons of opposite spin. The outermost occupied orbitals of the atoms form the highest fully occupied energy band at zero degrees Kelvin. Since this band is occupied by the valence electrons it is called the *valence band*. The band above this, which at zero degrees Kelvin is empty, is called the *conduction band*, and between the two bands exists a forbidden energy band or energy gap. This energy gap is sufficiently small for thermal excitation of electrons from the valence band to the conduction band to occur at, or just above, room temperature in the case of germanium and silicon. This is particularly important since no electronic conduction can take place in a full band.

The vacated levels in the valence band are covalent bonds which have lost one electron and are hence positive. Such unsaturated bonds can move causing an electric current if an electron from a neighbouring bond jumps in the opposite direction saturating the vacated level, and simultaneously leaving an unsaturated bond. This type of conduction by *holes* can only occur within the valence band because it depends upon the properties of the rest of the electrons in the valence band.

If a semiconductor is pure, then conduction takes place by electrons and holes which are generated thermally in pairs. Such semiconductors are termed *intrinsic*. If, however, an impurity is added to provide electrons in the conduction band or holes in the valence band, the semiconductor is termed *extrinsic*.

In semiconductor devices, single crystals of material are used because polycrystalline material is not reproducible, and *grain boundaries* tend to harbour impurities. Also much greater control over the physical properties of the material is possible with a single crystal, and the theoretical considerations are much simplified. In fact in many ways the termination of the crystal and its juxtoposition with the outside world provides embarrassing problems, although it is debatable how far early transistor work would have progressed without the complicated surface properties of the crystal.

It is obviously necessary then, to consider more fully the crystal structure, electronic band structure, and the electronic conduction processes of semiconductors, particularly germanium and silicon, in order to understand the detailed operation and development of transistors.

The crystal structure of germanium and silicon consists of two interpenetrating face-centred cubic lattices, the second of which begins one-quarter of the way down the body diagonal of the first, i.e. the diamond structure (Fig. 1.1). For silicon and germanium

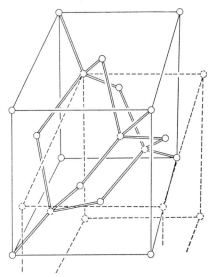

FIG. 1.1. The diamond structure; showing the two interpenetrating face-centred cubic lattices, and the tetravalent bonds.

the lattice constant a is 5·42 Å and 5·62 Å respectively, and the distance between nearest neighbours is $\sqrt{3}/16\ a$. The "density" of the structure is 8 atoms/a^3 (5·00 and 4·52 × 10^{28} atoms m^{-3}).

Silicon and germanium exhibit essentially covalent or electron-pair bonding. The hydrogen molecule is the simplest form of covalent bonding (Fig. 1.2). The common orbit shared by the

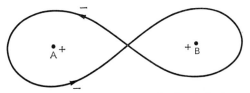

FIG. 1.2. The covalent bonding mechanism in hydrogen.

electrons results in a high probability density, that is a relatively high accumulation of charge, midway between the positive ion cores. The attractive force is fundamentally electrostatic. The Pauli exclusion principle indicates that the bond is stable when two electrons are involved, and although it is considerably weakened by the removal of one electron it is not greatly strengthened by the addition of one. For crystals of diamond, silicon and germanium, the covalent bond occurs between an atom and its four nearest neighbours, that is tetravalent bonding occurs. (Eight electrons

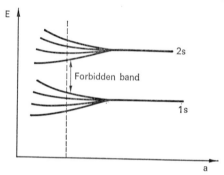

FIG. 1.3. The splitting of energy levels and the origin of the forbidden band for *four* hydrogen atoms mutually separated by distance *a*.

orbit the ionic core, four belonging to the parent atom and one to each nearest neighbour.)

Since in covalent bonding crystal atoms are close enough to *share* electrons, they are also close enough for overlap and mutual modification of their wave functions to occur. In Fig. 1.3 the resulting change in the *valence* orbit energy is shown for the case of four hydrogen atoms being brought together. Two atoms whose wave functions are ψ_1 and ψ_2 may combine in two ways corresponding to $\psi_1 \pm \psi_2$, and thus there are two energy levels formed for each energy level of an isolated atom. When four atoms are brought together there are four levels formed, and when N atoms combine N levels are formed. The splitting of energy levels is a consequence of the interaction between the positive ion cores and the overlapping parts of the electronic charge distribution. For each subshell, ns, np, nd, . . . , of the atom, a band of energy levels occurs, the width of which depends upon the strength of the interaction.

As the atomic spacing decreases splitting occurs for the higher levels. If the spacing decreases further the energy bands begin to merge, and this signals a new electronic behaviour in the crystal.

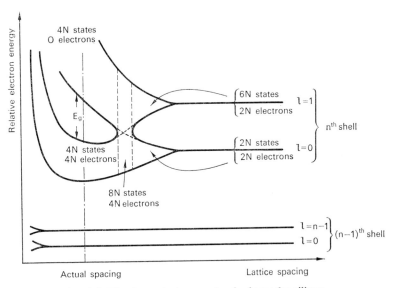

FIG. 1.4. The theoretical energy level scheme for silicon.

In Fig. 1.4 the spacing for silicon is indicated. The two energy bands of importance are separated by an energy E_g, and the lower of the energy bands, the *valence band*, has $4N$ electrons filling its $4N$ available states, provided that the electrons reside in the lowest states available. The upper energy band, the *conduction band*, is, under these circumstances, empty of electrons. The mutual repulsion of the ionic cores results in an interatomic spacing which does not correspond to the lowest energy for the electronic system, however the overall atomic system is at an energy minimum.

A different approach may be taken to the forbidden energy band. Consideration of the reflection of electron waves within crystals indicates a gap in the energies available to the current carriers, that is that there are energies for which there are no solutions to the Schrödinger equation. If in Schrödinger's equation (Rojansky, 1960; Matthews, 1963) the potential V is not constant but periodic, as it obviously is since there is a regular distribution of positive ions, then it may be shown (Bloch, 1928; Mott and Jones, 1936) that its solutions are of the form

$$\psi_k = U(\mathbf{r}) \exp (j\mathbf{k}.\mathbf{r}) \tag{1}$$

in which $U(\mathbf{r})$ is dependent upon $\mathbf{k}$ and is periodic in (x, y, z) with the period of V. Thus the plane wave $\exp (j\mathbf{k}.\mathbf{r})$ is modulated by the period of the lattice ($j = \sqrt{-1}$, $\mathbf{k}$ is the wave vector, and $\mathbf{r}$ is the position vector).

A standard proof of equation (1) is indicated below in a somewhat shortened form. In one dimension Schrödinger's equation is

$$\frac{d^2\psi}{dx^2} + \frac{2m}{\hbar^2} (E - V) \psi (x) = 0. \tag{2}$$

If the distance between the atoms is a then V has period a, and if $\psi (x)$ is a solution to equation (2) then so is $\psi (x + a)$. If $f(x)$ and $g(x)$ are two independent real solutions then

$$f (x + a) = a_1 f(x) + a_2 g(x)$$
$$g (x + a) = \beta_1 f(x) + \beta_2 g(x)$$

where a_1, a_2, β_1 and β_2 are real functions of E. It follows from this that if $\psi (x)$ is any other solution, where

$$\psi (x) = A f(x) + B g(x),$$

then

$$\psi (x + a) = (Aa_1 + B \beta_1) f(x) + (Aa_2 + B \beta_2) g(x)$$

where A and B are constants and A/B is chosen so that

$$Aa_1 + B\beta_1 = \lambda A,$$
$$Aa_2 + B\beta_2 = \lambda B, \tag{3}$$

λ is a constant. $\psi(x)$ now has the property that

$$\psi(x + a) = \lambda \psi(x). \tag{4}$$

Eliminating A and B from equation (3) one obtains

$$(a_1 - \lambda)(\beta_2 - \lambda) = a_2 \beta_1 \tag{5}$$

which has two roots λ_1 and λ_2. Each root corresponds to a ratio A/B and there are therefore only two independent functions obeying equation (4). If $V(x) = V(-x)$ it is easily shown that

$$\lambda_1 \lambda_2 = 1$$

and therefore two solutions of equation (2) exist with the form either $U_k(x) \exp \pm \mu x$ or $U_k(x) \exp \pm jkx$ where μ is a real constant. The former solutions are not bounded and do not correspond to stationary states, thus showing that there is a range of E where no electronic states exist. The latter solutions, on the other hand, do correspond to stationary states and are of the form required by Bloch's theorem.

Bloch's own proof based on elementary group theory (Bloch, 1928) is more elegant and an abbreviated form is given by Kittel (Kittel, 1965).

Since the electrons are under the influence of the periodic potential V, the effect of any external forces applied must be influenced by this potential. The electron responds to an external force as if it has an *effective mass* m^*. In general $m^* < m$, for example $m^*/m = 0 \cdot 12$ for germanium and $0 \cdot 25$ for silicon. It may be shown (Kittel, 1956) that

$$m^* = \hbar^2 \Big/ \frac{d^2E}{dk^2}, \tag{6}$$

E is the energy and $\hbar$ is Planck's constant divided by 2π.

The physical reason for effective mass lies in the interaction of the electron with the crystal lattice. If a relatively long impulse **I** is applied to the crystal, then

$$\mathbf{I} = \Delta\mathbf{P}_{\text{total}} = \Delta\mathbf{P}_{\text{lattice}} + \Delta\mathbf{P}_{\text{electron}}, \tag{7}$$

where $\Delta\mathbf{P}$ represents the resultant increase in momentum. A useful definition of effective mass is, "the mass a free electron would need in order for the velocity increment under the applied impulse to be equal to the actual velocity increment of the conduction electron under the same impulse",

i.e.
$$\frac{\Delta\mathbf{P}_{\text{el}}}{m} = \frac{\hbar\Delta\mathbf{k}}{m^*}. \tag{8}$$

In some cases when **k** is increased by an amount $\Delta\mathbf{k}$, the momentum transferred to the electron may be opposite to and less than that transferred to the lattice. That is although **k** is increased to $\mathbf{k} + \Delta\mathbf{k}$, the consequent Bragg reflections result in an overall decrease in the momentum of the electron, and the effective mass appears to be negative.

It is convenient to know the *density of energy states* $g(E)$, which is defined as *the number of energy states per unit energy range per unit volume*. If E falls within the forbidden band $g(E)$ is zero, however if it falls within an allowed band $g(E)$ is dN/dE, where dN is the number of electronic states between E and $E + dE$.

Consider $g(E)$ near the bottom edge of a band, for example the bottom edge of the conduction band. Theoretical considerations show that near the top or bottom of a band the energy varies as P^2 approximately, where $P^2 = |\mathbf{P}|$. Therefore,

$$E - E_{\text{edge}} = P^2/(2\,|\,m^*\,|) \tag{9}$$

($|m^*|$ is used to avoid complications when m^* is negative)

$$dE = \left(\frac{P}{|\,m^*\,|}\right)dP. \tag{10}$$

The volume of the spherical shell between P and $P + dP$ in P-space is $4\pi P^2 dP$ and consequently,

$$dN = \left(\frac{2}{h^3}\right)4\pi P^2 dP \tag{11}$$

since the volume per allowed point in P-space is h^3/V (Shockley, 1950), and for each point there are two quantum states, one for each spin. V is the volume of the crystal.

From equations (9), (10) and (11),

$$\left.\begin{aligned} dN &= \frac{8\pi}{h^3}\, P^2\, dP \\[2mm] &= \frac{4\pi}{h^3}\, (2\mid m^*\mid)^{3/2}\, (E - E_{\mathrm{edge}})^{\frac12}\, dE \\[2mm] &= g(E)dE \end{aligned}\right\} \qquad (12)$$

$$\therefore\ g(E) = \frac{1}{2\pi^2}\left(\frac{2\mid m^*\mid}{\hbar^2}\right)^{3/2}(E - E_{\mathrm{edge}})^{\frac12}. \qquad (13)$$

Near the top of a band $(E - E_{\mathrm{edge}})^{\frac12}$ becomes $(E_{\mathrm{edge}} - E)^{\frac12}$, or one simply writes $\mid E - E_{\mathrm{edge}}\mid^{\frac12}$. Mostly the equation appears

$$g(E) = \frac{1}{2\pi^2}\left(\frac{2\, m^*}{\hbar^2}\right)^{3/2} E^{\frac12}, \qquad (14)$$

where E is measured from the edge of the appropriate band. It is then necessary to remember that for holes, energy increases downwards away from the top of the valence band. It should be emphasized that the above equations only hold near the band edges. In equation (14), and in further equations, m^* is taken as the numerical value of the effective mass.

The probability that a given state is occupied is given by the Fermi–Dirac distribution function $f(E)$, since Fermi–Dirac statistics are used for electrons (Rushbrooke, 1955; ter Haar, 1954)

$$f(E) = \left[\exp\left(\frac{E - E_F}{kT}\right) + 1\right]^{-1} \qquad (15)$$

(see Fig. 1.5); E_F is the Fermi level. At $T = 0°\mathrm{K}$, $f(E) = 1$ for $E < E_F$ and $f(E) = 0$ for $E > E_F$, thus $E_F(0)$ is a cut-off energy above which all states are empty and below which all states are

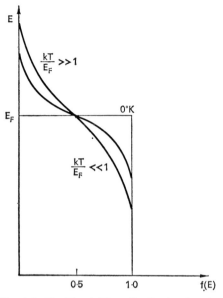

FIG. 1.5. The Fermi–Dirac distribution function.

full. For temperatures above absolute zero, the Fermi level may be defined as that energy at which $f(E) = \frac{1}{2}$; alternatively, and perhaps more pertinently, the Fermi level is simply the chemical potential of the electrons. This is a measure of how the free energy of the electron gas depends upon the electron concentration. E_F is in fact temperature dependent (Kittel, 1956) and for $kT/E_F \ll 1$,

$$E_F \simeq E_F(0) \left[1 - \frac{\pi^2}{12} \left(\frac{kT}{E_F(0)} \right)^2 \right]. \tag{16}$$

The number of electrons per unit volume with energies between E and $E + dE$ is

$$dN = f(E)\, g(E)\, dE$$

$$= \frac{1}{2\pi^2} \left(\frac{2m^*}{\hbar^2} \right)^{3/2} \frac{E^{1/2}\, dE}{\exp(E - E_F/kT) + 1}. \tag{17}$$

For substances with an energy gap, the Fermi level occurs in the gap and consequently the definition must now read: the Fermi level is that energy at which the probability of finding an electron would be one half if it were an allowed energy. Figure 1.6 shows plots of $f(E)$ and $f(E) g(E)$ against energy, as well as an *energy band* diagram. In the valence band $f(E) \sim 1$ and in the conduction band $f(E) \sim 0$.

It is appropriate at this point to consider the meaning of energy band diagrams. Such diagrams as shown in Figs. 1.5, 1.6 and 1.11

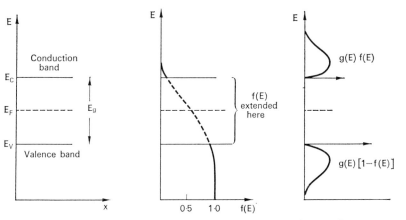

FIG. 1.6. The energy band diagram and the associated curves for a semiconductor.

are used to describe and analyse conditions where the distribution of carriers in space, as well as in energy, is important. The energy is usually represented by the *ordinate* of the diagram, whilst the *abscissa* represents distance with respect to a previously chosen origin. Any change in energy with distance is then reflected in the diagram, *cf.* the p–n junction diagrams in Chapter 2. The value E_c represents the bottom of the conduction band and the minimum electron energy, the energy for electrons increasing upwards. The value E_v represents the top of the valence band and the minimum hole energy, the energy for holes increasing downwards. $E_c - E_v$

is the minimum energy gap regardless of the complexity of the energy bands. In most cases the form of the energy bands is quite complicated, but fortunately we usually only require to know this form near the maximum and minimum values of energy, as it is only these states that contribute to the phenomena under consideration.

As we have seen the solutions to the wave equation when the potential is periodic is,

$$\psi_{\mathbf{k}} = U(\mathbf{r}) \exp (j\mathbf{k}.\mathbf{r}).$$

The energy E is then a function of $\mathbf{k}$ and the values of $\mathbf{k}$ may be restricted to a certain zone in $\mathbf{k}$-space. This Brillouin zone, as it is called, is the smallest volume in k-space centred on the origin which includes all non-equivalent values of $\mathbf{k}$, the shape of the zone depending upon the crystal structure. Let us now consider Bragg reflections within the crystal. In one dimension the Bragg equation becomes

$$k_x = \frac{n\pi}{a}$$

the first reflections occurring at $k_x = \pm\pi/a$. The first energy gap occurs at this point also, and the region in k-space from $-\pi/a$ to $+\pi/a$ is the first Brillouin zone (Fig. 1.7). Energy discontinuities occur on the zone boundaries (see Kittel, 1965), and the second Brillouin zone is defined by $-2\pi/a < k < -\pi/a$ and $\pi/a < k < 2\pi/a$.

It is no longer possible to express E as a function of a single variable, and diagrams of E as a function of $\mathbf{k}$ are drawn for the principal directions in the crystal. The simplest band structure occurs when the lowest unfilled band has a minimum at the centre of the Brillouin zone and is single valued. If in addition the crystal is cubic then m^* is isotropic, and the energy bands are termed spherical because the constant energy surfaces form spheres in k-space. Spherical energy bands are the exception rather than the rule, however, and cylindrical symmetry may occur about the x-axis of a cubic crystal when the maxima and minima occur at a

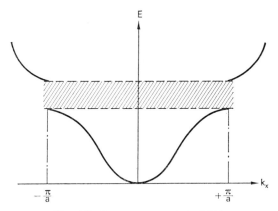

Fig. 1.7. Energy versus wave vector.

point on the surface of the Brillouin zone. m^* is then *anisotropic*, that is it is dependent upon the direction in which the electron or hole is moving. In both germanium and silicon the current carriers have anisotropic effective masses.

In considering N atoms forming N energy levels for each original atomic energy level, we noted that if the electrons reside in the lowest energy states available the conduction band is empty and the valence band full. If there are electrons in the conduction band, or if the valance band is not full, conduction is possible. The same is true if the valence band is full but overlaps the conduction band, that is when the interatomic separation is such that there is no energy gap. Considering a full valence band, the electrons in the band are moving freely in all directions but since there are no available energy levels immediately above the top of the valence band their resultant momentum is always zero, whether an external electric field is applied or not.

In copper, electronic structure $1s^22s^22p^63s^23p^63d^{10}4s^1$, each atom contributes the $4s$ electron which, because of the overlap of the $4s$ subshells, may move freely through the crystal under the influence of an applied electric field. Carbon, $1s^22s^22p^2$, has a full valence band and conduction does not occur. The same is true for silicon and germanium ($1s^2 2s^2 2p^6 3s^2 3p^2$ and $1s^2 2s^2 2p^6 3s^2 3p^6 3d^{10} 4s^2 4p^2$), but with the essential difference that the energy gap is much smaller. For diamond, $E_g = 6 \cdot 5$ eV, but for silicon and germanium $E_g = 1 \cdot 09$ eV and $0 \cdot 72$ eV respectively. It is therefore feasible to use heat energy to move electrons from the valence band to the conduction band in germanium and silicon, but not for diamond ($\sim 2000°$K would be required!). A substance is a good insulator if $E_g \gg kT$, and for an *intrinsic* semiconductor $E_g \sim kT$ at room temperatures.

When an electron leaves the valence band it creates a vacancy. The resultant motion of electrons is quite complex, but quantum mechanics shows that the vacant state is equivalent to a free positive charge in an otherwise empty band. The positive charge, or *hole*, is the counterpart of the electron obeying the same laws, but it ceases to be a valid concept outside the valence band. The existence of positive carriers is indicated by positive Hall coefficients, and from cyclotron resonance experiments (Dresselhaus, 1955) it has been established that holes and electrons "rotate" in opposite senses in a magnetic field. As mentioned in the introductory paragraphs, the vacated levels in the valence band are covalent bonds which have lost one electron and are hence positive. Such unsaturated bonds can move causing a current if an electron from a neighbouring bond jumps in the opposite direction, saturating the vacated level and simultaneously leaving an unsaturated bond.

Let us consider the valence band with one vacancy. The effect of an electric field is to move electrons in a given direction; as the one vacancy is filled another is created and so on. It is, however, superficially consistent to assign to the vacancy a positive charge and a positive mass, *or* a negative charge and a negative mass. However, since the band is filled except for, say, state E, the electrons must have a negative net velocity in order for the total velocity to be zero when the band is full. As the electrons are accelerated transporting negative charge in a given direction, the *hole* is in effect accelerated in the opposite direction. We must therefore designate the hole as carrying a positive charge, and to be consistent with the acceleration the hole must have a positive effective mass. It should be remembered that problems may be solved by considering the motion of the electrons alone, and that the *hole* is merely a convenient concept.

Heat, light or very high electric fields may be used to generate electron–hole pairs ($E_g < kT$, $E_g < h\nu$). The intrinsic conductivity, due to both electrons and holes, is given by,

$$\sigma_i = nq\mu_e + pq\mu_h \tag{18}$$

where n and p are the electron and hole densities in the conduction and valence bands respectively, q is the electronic charge and μ_e and μ_h are the electron and hole mobilities. It should be remembered that

$$\mu_{e,h} = \frac{q\tau}{m^*_{e,h}} \tag{19}$$

that is mobility is the drift velocity per unit electric field. (τ is the time for equilibrium to be restored after perturbation, or the relaxation time. For germanium at room temperature $\mu_e = 0 \cdot 39$ m²/V-sec and $\tau = 6 \times 10^{-13}$ sec.)

If carriers arise from electron–hole pair creation only, then $n = p = n_i$ and equation (18) becomes

$$\sigma_i = n_i q(\mu_e + \mu_h). \tag{20}$$

Holes and electrons move in the same physical space of course, the difference between them being energetic, and but for this difference and the restraining mechanism provided by the conservation laws, recombination would take place to a much greater extent than occurs in practice. Even so carriers do not remain at a given energy level for any extended time, but change energy quite drastically; we in fact consider a statistical equilibrium.

The probability of an energy level E being occupied by an electron is

$$f(E) = \left[1 + \exp\left(\frac{E - E_F}{kT}\right)\right]^{-1} \tag{21}$$

and of being unoccupied is

$$1 - f(E) = \left[1 + \exp\left(\frac{E_F - E}{kT}\right)\right]^{-1}. \tag{22}$$

A level that is unoccupied by an electron may be regarded as being occupied by a hole. For energies higher than $2kT$ above the Fermi level

$$f(E) \simeq \exp\left(-\frac{E - E_F}{kT}\right) \tag{23}$$

and

$$1 - f(E) \simeq \exp\left(-\frac{E_F - E}{kT}\right), \tag{24}$$

that is Maxwell–Boltzmann statistics apply to the "electron-gas" when it is non-degenerate. When degenerate ($E_c - E_F < 2kT$) Fermi–Dirac statistics must be used. Silicon and germanium are non-degenerate at room temperatures.

Under thermal equilibrium the carrier concentrations are consequently given by

$$n = \int_{E_C}^{E'} g(E) f(E) \, dE = \int_{E_C}^{E'} \frac{C_e \, E^{1/2} \, dE}{\exp\left[(E - E_F)/kT\right]}, \tag{25}$$

$$p = \int_{E''}^{E_V} g(E) \left[1 - f(E)\right] dE = \int_{E''}^{E_V} \frac{C_h \, E^{1/2} \, dE}{\exp\left[(E_F - E)/kT\right]}. \tag{26}$$

As will be seen from the nature of the functions under integration the precise values of E' and E'' are unimportant.

$$C_{e,h} = \frac{1}{2\pi^2}\left(\frac{2m_{e,h}^*}{\hbar^2}\right)^{3/2}. \tag{27}$$

It follows that

$$n = N \exp\left(-\frac{E_C - E_F}{kT}\right), \tag{28}$$

$$p = P \exp\left(-\frac{E_F - E_V}{kT}\right), \tag{29}$$

where N and P are known as the *effective densities of states* in the conduction and valence bands, where

$$N = 2 \, (2\pi m_e^* \, kT/h^2)^{3/2}, \tag{30}$$

$$P = 2 \, (2\pi m_h^* \, kT/h^2)^{3/2}. \tag{31}$$

If the effective masses of holes and electrons are the same,

$$N = P = N_i$$

and therefore $E_F - E_V = E_C - E_F = E_g/2. \tag{32}$

At absolute zero the Fermi level for intrinsic material is, therefore, situated precisely in the centre of the energy band, and will from now on be referred to as the intrinsic Fermi level E_i. Now,

$$\sigma_i = |\, q \,| \, [N_i \exp \, (- \, E_g/kT) \, (\mu_e + \mu_h)]. \tag{33}$$

If $m_e^* \neq m_h^*$

$$N_i = 2 \left[\frac{2\pi \, (m_e^* \, m_h^*)^{1/2} \, kT}{h^2} \right]^{3/2} \tag{34}$$

which slightly displaces the intrinsic Fermi level from its central position. From equations (28) and (29)

$$\ln \left(\frac{nP}{Np} \right) = - \, \frac{E_c - E_i}{kT} + \frac{E_i - E_V}{kT} \tag{35}$$

and since $n = p$ for intrinsic material, substituting from (22),

$$\ln \left(\frac{m_h^*}{m_e^*} \right)^{3/2} = - \left(\frac{E_c + E_V}{kT} \right) + \frac{2E_i}{kT}, \tag{36}$$

$$\therefore E_i = \frac{E_c - E_V}{kT} + \frac{3kT}{4} \ln \frac{m_h^*}{m_e^*} \tag{37}$$

which gives the displacement of E_i when $m_h^* \neq m_e^*$.

Over a limited range of temperature the conductivity (cf. equation (33)) is determined by the exponential term, and although mobility is temperature dependent $\ln \sigma_i$ *versus* $1/T$ is essentially a straight line (Fig. 1.8).

So far we have assumed that we are dealing with a perfect crystal of absolutely pure material, and even the most minute deviations from this state of perfection changes the electronic properties of the crystal. There are two types of impurity, the interstitial impurity which occupies a position in between the lattice sites, and the substitutional impurity which replaces an atom of the host crystal. An impurity content of 1 in 10^9 is quite sufficient to change the conductivity of the crystal. If an atom of the

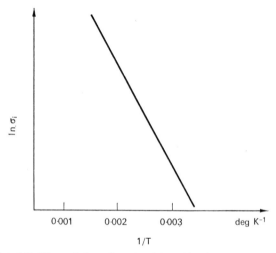

FIG. 1.8. The variation of conductivity with temperature for an intrinsic semiconductor.

host crystal is displaced to become an interstitial atom it leaves behind a vacancy. The two imperfections, the interstitial atom and the vacancy, are termed together as a *Frenkel defect*. If the displaced atom finds its way to the surface of the crystal, the remaining vacancy is known as a *Schottky defect*.

The most important deviation from perfection is the presence of a trivalent or pentavalent substitutional atom in tetravalent silicon or germanium (e.g. boron or phosphorus in silicon, indium or antimony in germanium). The process of adding controlled amounts of such impurities to a semiconductor is called doping, the doping *level* being the amount of impurity added.

As an example, let us consider pentavalent phosphorus in silicon. Four of the phosphorus' five valency electrons are required to form the bonding, and the fifth electron acts as an "orbital" electron bound to its parent ion. The combination may be considered as a quasi-hydrogen atom (Fig. 1.9). The orbital electron

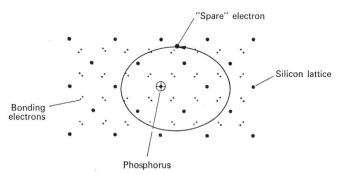

FIG. 1.9. Pentavalent phosphorus in silicon as a quasi-hydrogen atom.

is not affected by the structure of the crystal in the immediate vicinity of the impurity atom. Evoking Bohr's Theory, the first assumption states that

$$m_e^* r^2 \omega = \mathbf{n}\hbar \tag{38}$$

and therefore

$$\Delta E_D = \frac{-q^2}{4\pi\epsilon_s\epsilon_0 \, r} + \frac{1}{2} m_e^* \, r^2 \, \omega^2 \tag{39}$$

ϵ_s is the relative permittivity of the silicon and ϵ_0 the permittivity constant ($8 \cdot 85 \times 10^{-12} \text{F.m}^{-2}$), $\mathbf{n}$ is, of course, an integer equivalent to the principal quantum number. For equilibrium $F = dE/dr = 0$, consequently,

$$m_e^* \, r \, \omega^2 = \frac{q^2}{4\pi\epsilon_s\epsilon_0 \, r^2}. \tag{40}$$

Substituting for ω

$$r = \frac{4\pi\epsilon_s\epsilon_0 n^2 \hbar^2}{q\, m_e^*} \tag{41}$$

and therefore

$$\Delta E_D = -\frac{q^4\, m_e^*}{2\cdot 16\pi^2\, \epsilon_s\, \epsilon_0\, \hbar^2\, n^2}$$

$$= -\frac{q^4\, m_e^*}{2\epsilon_s\, \epsilon_0\, h^2\, n^2}. \tag{42}$$

In both silicon and germanium the effective masses are anisotropic, however considering an average for silicon, $\epsilon_s = 11\cdot 7$ and $m_e^* = 0\cdot 25\ m_e$, ΔE_D is $0\cdot 025$ eV. When the correct anisotropic considerations are taken this value becomes $0\cdot 0298$ eV. For germanium these figures are $\epsilon_g = 15\cdot 8$, $m_e^* = 0\cdot 12\ m_e$ and $\Delta E_D = 0\cdot 0065$ eV becoming $0\cdot 0091$ eV.

The energy ΔE_D is quite small, and when it is applied the "orbital" electron moves up into the conduction band. This type of impurity is a *donor* impurity, and since the *negative* electrons are now the dominant carrier the semiconductor is said to be *n*-type. In an *n*-type material we have the thermally generated electron–hole pairs plus the electrons from the donor centres, thus the more numerous electrons are called *majority* carriers whilst the relatively few holes are termed *minority* carriers.

The donor centres sit in a discrete set of energy levels $\simeq 0\cdot 04$ eV below the conduction band. The occupancy of these centres is governed by $f(E)$, and the density of occupied donors is $f(E_D)\, N_D$, and of unoccupied donors is $[1 - f(E_D)]\, N_D = N_D^+$, since unoccupied donor centres carry a positive charge. Increased concentrations of donor centres broaden the impurity band, which is initially very narrow, and thus decrease ΔE_D. This broadening is due to the overlapping of wave functions of the impurity atoms and the resultant splitting of the energy level into a band, which occurs as the concentration increases. The number of electrons in the conduction band is

$$n = p + N_D^+. \tag{43}$$

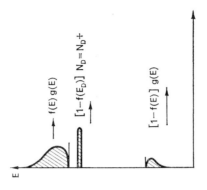

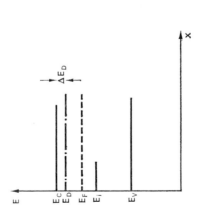

Fig. 1.10. Band diagram for a *n*-type semiconductor.

The presence of donor centres influences the position of the Fermi level which moves upward toward the conduction band to an energy at which $f(E) = \frac{1}{2}$. The shift of the Fermi level from its intrinsic value is defined as

$$\psi = E_F - E_i/kT_i. \tag{44}$$

ψ is thus a dimensionless potential energy variable, which is positive for n-type material. From equations (43) and (28),

$$n = p + N_D{}^+ = N \exp - \frac{E_c - E_F}{kT} \tag{45}$$

$$\therefore \ln\left(\frac{p + N_D{}^+}{N}\right) = -\frac{E_c - E_i + E_i - E_F}{kT} = -\frac{E_c - E_i}{kT} + \psi. \tag{46}$$

In most cases $N_D{}^+ = N_D \gg p$, that is the donor centres are completely ionized. Using the value of E_i from equation (37)

$$\psi = \frac{E_g}{2kT} - \frac{3}{4}\ln\frac{m_h^*}{m_e^*} + \ln\frac{N_D}{N}. \tag{47}$$

The second term on the right-hand side of the above equation accounts for the difference in effective masses, and the third term for the presence of donors.

For trivalent boron in silicon, the boron atom requires an extra electron for bonding; it therefore takes one from the valence band. This creates a hole in the valence band. Such impurities are termed *acceptor* impurities, and since the *positive* holes are the dominant or majority carrier, the semiconductor is said to be p-type. The previous arguments may again be pursued and $E_A \simeq 0 \cdot 06$ eV for silicon since $m_h^* \simeq 0 \cdot 50\, m_h$. The impurity atoms in this case create a discrete set of energy levels just above the valence band (Fig. 1.11).

Considering N_A acceptor atoms per unit volume then the density of occupied acceptors (by a hole!) is $f(E_A)\, N_A$, and of unoccupied acceptors is $[1 - f(E_A)]N_A = N_A{}^-$. The unoccupied

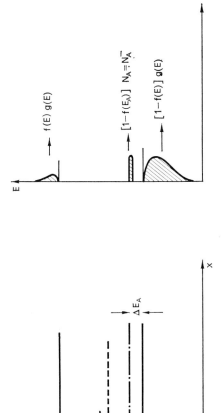

FIG. 1.11. Band diagram for a *p*-type semiconductor.

acceptor is negative since it has taken up an extra electron. The number of holes in the valence band is

$$p = n + N_A{}^-. \tag{48}$$

In this case the Fermi level moves toward the valence band and $E_F - E_i = -\psi$, where

$$-\psi = \frac{E_g}{2kT} - \frac{3}{4} \ln \frac{m_h^*}{m_n^*} + \ln \frac{N_A}{P}. \tag{49}$$

In many instances both trivalent and pentavalent impurities are present simultaneously, and donor–acceptor compensation occurs, that is the free electron from the donor atom joins the acceptor atom and hence neither the valence band nor the conduction band gains a carrier. It is then correct to use the net impurity density $|N_D - N_A|$. Except in heavily doped material $N_D{}^+ \simeq N_D$ and $N_A{}^- \simeq N_A$ at room temperature.

The following equations may be developed for impurity semi-conductors in a similar manner to the way in which equations (28) and (29) were developed (Kittel, 1956):

$$n_D = (2\,N_D)^{1/2} \left(\frac{2\pi kT m_e^*}{h^2}\right)^{3/2} \exp\left(-\,\Delta E_D/2kT\right), \tag{50}$$

$$p_A = (2\,N_A)^{1/2} \left(\frac{2kT m_h^*}{h^2}\right)^{3/2} \exp\left(-\,\Delta E_A/2kT\right) \tag{51}$$

where n_D and p_A are the densities of electrons and holes originating from impurity centres. Thus, ignoring intrinsic conductivity, the conductivity of an n-type and p-type semiconductor is given by

$$\sigma_D = |\,q\,|\,[(N_D/2)^{1/2}\,N\exp\left(-\,\Delta E_D/2kT\right)\mu_e], \tag{52}$$

$$\sigma_A = |\,q\,|\,[(N_A/2)^{1/2}\,P\exp\left(-\,\Delta E_A/2kT\right)\mu_h]. \tag{53}$$

Heating up an impurity semiconductor from a low temperature releases more and more carriers until the impurity centres are completely ionized, if the temperature at that point is not high enough to generate electron–hole pairs, then a slight decrease in conductivity occurs because of the increased effectiveness of the scattering mechanisms. This is completely swamped by the onset of electron–hole generation (cf. Fig. 1.12).

Cursory considerations would lead one to expect that doping with impurities, other than trivalent and pentavalent substances, would result in more carriers being released to the appropriate bands. Gold is an excellent example. In germanium a gold atom may exist in the following states: Au^+, Au, Au^-, Au^{2-} and Au^{3-}, depending upon the position of the Fermi level. The Fermi level may be adjusted, of course, by doping with shallow donor or acceptor impurities. Whilst these systems are of importance (see Smith, 1959), they are not immediately relevant. Table 1.1. shows the impurity levels in silicon measured from the nearest band edge for a variety of single impurities (Conwell, 1958).

Let us now consider the amount of impurity required to obtain a given resistivity. In the equations for resistivity the mobility of the carriers occurs, and this depends upon the type and effectiveness of the scattering mechanisms present. Vibrations of the crystal atoms, or *lattice vibrations*, may be regarded quantum mechanically as discrete particles or *phonons*. Carriers collide with phonons and are scattered by them. The effectiveness of the scattering increases with temperature. Besides phonon scattering, scattering can occur by imperfections, ionized and neutral impurities, as well as by electron–electron and electron–hole collisions. Whatever the mechanism the effect is to reduce the mean free path of the carriers, l, to $\sim 10^3$ m. The relaxation time is then defined by

$$\tau_r = l/v_t$$

where the thermal velocity v_t is

$$v_t = (3kT/m^*)^{1/2} \sim 10^5 \text{ m-sec}^{-1}. \tag{54}$$

In the presence of an electric field $\mathbf{E}$, the carriers assume a net momentum in a given direction. This is characterized by a drift velocity $\mathbf{v}_d$, which has a steady value in a constant field.

$$\mathbf{v}_d = -\mu\mathbf{E}. \tag{55}$$

Usually $\mu_e > \mu_h$, e.g. at room temperature for silicon $\mu_e = 0 \cdot 15$ m^2 V^{-1} sec^{-1}, $\mu_h = 0 \cdot 05$ m^2 V^{-1} sec^{-1}, and for germanium $\mu_e = 0 \cdot 34$ m^2 V^{-1} sec^{-1} and $\mu_h = 0 \cdot 19$ m^2 V^{-1} sec^{-1}.

TABLE 1.1. IMPURITY ENERGY LEVELS IN SILICON MEASURED FROM THE NEAREST BAND EDGES.

(Taken from Conwell, *Proc. I.R.E.* **46**, 1281–1300, 1958.)

Element	Energy interval, eV	Donor	Acceptor
	Conduction band edge		
Li	0·033	×	
Sb	0·039	×	
P	0·044	×	
As	0·049	×	
Bi	0·067	×	
Mn	0·530	×	
Au	0·540		×
Zn	0·550		×
Fe	0·550	×	
	Energy gap centre		
Cu	0·490		×
Au	0·350	×	
Tl	0·260		×
Cu	0·240	×	
Zn	0·083		×
Ga	0·083		×
Zn	0·078		×
Ga	0·065		×
Al	0·057		×
B	0·045		×
	Valence band edge		

If $\mathbf{J}$ is the current density, then

$$\mathbf{J} = qn\mathbf{v}_d \tag{56}$$

$$\therefore v_d = \frac{1}{q\,n\,\rho}\,\mathbf{E} \tag{57}$$

giving

$$\mu_e = \frac{1}{q\,n\,\rho} \quad \text{and} \quad \mu_h = \frac{1}{q\,p\,\rho}. \tag{58}$$

The dependence of mobility upon temperature (for a thorough discussion of mobility see Smith, 1959, 1961) is mainly governed by impurity scattering at low temperatures, and phonon scattering at high temperatures, the combination producing an observed maximum in the mobility. For most practical temperatures $\mu \propto T^{3/2}$ and the variation of conductivity is dominated by the exponential dependence of n or p on temperature. For the range of temperatures where the impurity centres are releasing their carriers, the conductivity is exponentially dependent upon temperature. Notice the maximum at about room temperature (cf. Fig. 1.12), which is due to the now constant n or p, and the still decreasing μ_e or μ_h. All the curves run into the dotted line representing intrinsic conductivity. A graph of resistivity against carrier concentration is shown in Fig. 1.13, the difference between the n- and p-type materials being due to the difference in mobilities μ_e and μ_h.

If thermal equilibrium is disturbed by the injection of carriers from a metal, or by irradiation with light, or charged particles, then after the generating system is switched off the semiconductor settles back to equilibrium, the excess electrons and holes recombining. Naturally this recombination takes place under equilibrium, but the rates of recombination and generation are equal. For small excess concentrations of carriers the recombination follows an exponential law characterized by a constant lifetime τ, where

$$\frac{dn}{dt} = -\frac{1}{\tau}\,\Delta n; \quad \frac{dp}{dt} = -\frac{1}{\tau}\,\Delta p, \tag{59}$$

Δn and Δp are the excess electrons and holes per unit volume. The values of τ differ somewhat for majority and minority carriers and is made up of a volume and a surface component, (τ_v and τ_s). τ_v is particularly sensitive to small amounts of copper, iron and nickel,

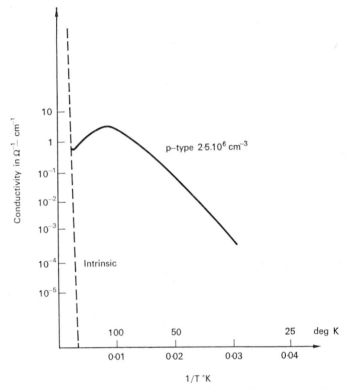

FIG. 1.12. Silicon conductivity versus temperature (for precise details see Morin and Maita, *Phys. Rev.* **96**, 28–35, 1954).

to lattice imperfections and radiation damage. These give rise to recombination centres which capture first a hole and then an electron, thus catalysing the recombination process. The process is repetitive. τ_s is sensitive to mechanical and chemical treatment of the surface, and depends upon the dimensions of the specimen

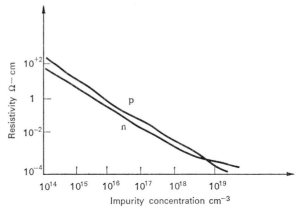

Fig. 1.13. Resistivity versus impurity concentration for silicon (for precise details see Irwin, *B.S.T.J.* **41,** 387–410, 1962).

since carriers must diffuse to the surface to recombine. The *surface velocity of recombination, s,* is defined by

$$s = \frac{\text{Recombination rate per unit area}}{\text{Excess concentration just below the surface}};$$

s varies anywhere between a few cm-sec^{-1} to 10^4 cm-sec^{-1}. To reduce s the surface is subjected to empirical polishing and etching techniques. The total recombination is given by

$$\frac{1}{\tau} = \frac{1}{\tau_v} + \frac{1}{\tau_s} \qquad (60)$$

(see Jonscher (1960) for complete treatment).

One of the most important processes in semiconductor devices is the process of diffusion† (Smith, 1959), the diffusion length L being defined as the mean distance moved in lifetime τ. The diffusion velocity v_{diff} is then defined by

$$v_{\text{diff}} = L/\tau. \qquad (61)$$

† In a semiconductor the concentration of electrons and holes may each vary considerably without the total charge density varying, and diffusion currents become extremely important, particularly in the case of the juxtaposition of *p*- and *n*-type material to form a *p–n* junction.

If we consider a point source of excess carriers, then let C_x be the concentration at a distance x from that point. The number of carriers crossing unit area per second is

$$C_x \, v_{\text{diff}} = C_x \, \frac{L}{\tau}. \tag{62}$$

The diffusion constant D is defined as

$$C_x v_{\text{diff}} = - D \frac{dC_x}{dx} \tag{63}$$

that is, D is the net flux of particles per unit concentration gradient. From the exponential decay,

$$C_x = C_0 \exp\left(-x/L\right). \tag{64}$$

From equation (63)

$$C_x = C \exp\left(-x v_{\text{diff}}/D\right), \tag{65}$$

$$\therefore \quad L v_{\text{diff}} = D, \tag{66}$$

i.e. $$L^2 = D\tau. \tag{67}$$

According to Boltzmann's distribution law, the concentration of carriers n at x is given by

$$n \propto \exp\left(-\frac{qEx}{kT}\right). \tag{68}$$

Since under equilibrium no net current flows

$$\mu n E + D \frac{dn}{dx} = 0 \tag{69}$$

and $$\therefore \quad \frac{\mu E}{D} \, dx = -\frac{dn}{n}, \tag{70}$$

hence integrating,

$$n = \exp\left(-\frac{\mu E x}{D}\right). \tag{71}$$

From (68) and (71)

$$\frac{\mu Ex}{D} = \frac{qEx}{kT}, \tag{72}$$

$$\therefore D = \frac{kT\mu}{q}, \tag{73}$$

which is the important Einstein relationship.

The surfaces of semiconductors play an extremely important role in the explanation of early transistors, and are of prime importance in current transistor work. Considering an atomically clean surface (Fig. 1.14) it may be seen that the surface atoms have

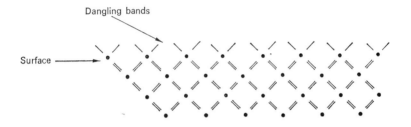

FIG. 1.14. An atomic diagram of the (100) surface of silicon.

dangling bonds, that is, there exist unfilled orbital at the surface. The atoms of one plane of a semiconductor are capable of forming covalent bonds to atoms of the next plane. If, however, the plane is a surface plane, the atoms contain unfilled orbitals which are termed *dangling bonds*, and which are capable of *accepting* electrons. These acceptor states, or Tamm states (Tamm, 1932), occur within the forbidden energy band and create a *p*-type surface. Crystal defects and absorbed foreign atoms will create other surface states, and even deep-seated impurities may act effectively as surface states. The presence of oxygen at a surface causes various oxides to form and this leads to complex surface states at the interface between the semiconductor and the oxide, and in the oxide. Various forms of chemical etching and polishing may be used to create either *n*- or *p*-type surfaces, although the whole process is still quite empirical. It is interesting to note that an atomically clean surface is the last thing that is required for transistors, since it provides a low impedance by-pass to the bulk material.

If an insulated metal plate is placed against the surface of a semiconductor, then upon the application of a voltage to this field plate or *gate*, the conductance of the specimen will change. This is due to a change in occupancy of the surface states caused by the gate bias, and it was this so called *field effect* and the consequent investigation of the surface states that proved to be the crucial step in the invention of the transistor (Bardeen, 1948).

CHAPTER 2

Point Contact Devices

AMPLIFICATION using semiconductors was first achieved using the negative temperature coefficient of resistance of certain materials. As the current through the material increases heating takes place, and the resistance begins to drop. If the current, and hence the heating, is sufficiently high the resultant decrease in resistance will actually cause a decrease in the voltage across the material, and consequently a negative differential resistance occurs. This characteristic may be used to construct networks with a net gain, provided the frequencies are low enough for the temperature to follow the current changes. Oscillators producing up to 100 kHz have been constructed using such *thermistors* (Shockley, 1950).

It was the aim of those involved in semiconductor research from 1946 to 1948 to produce a purely electronic semiconductor amplifier. The similarity between the characteristics of the then used crystal rectifiers and vacuum tubes implied that amplification should be possible by adding a "grid" to the diodes, as had been done in the case of the vacuum triode. As it happened there are few similarities between the early transistors and the vacuum triode.

The first step toward adding a "grid" was the experiment designed to investigate surface states (Shockley, 1950). Figure 2.1 shows a diagram of the experimental arrangement as well as the appropriate energy-band diagram. Because of the Tamm states the surface of an *n*-type semiconductor will be *p*-type, this *p*-type layer being called an *inversion* layer. Upon application of a positive potential to the metal field plate, electrons are attracted into the surface states and hence an increase in conductance occurs.

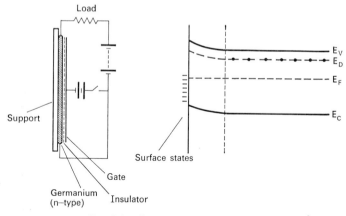

FIG. 2.1. The surface state experiment.

The voltage applied to the *gate* modulates the conductance of the specimen, and since the input requires virtually no power if a good dielectric is used, power gain will result. A field of 3×10^6 Vm^{-1} triples the electron concentration in the surface of n-type germanium, $\sigma = 42$ Ω^{-1} m^{-1} and $\mu_e = 0 \cdot 26$ m^2/V-sec, where the inversion layer is $\sim 10^{-7}$ m thick. In practice only about 10 per cent of this change is experienced (Shockley and Pearson, 1948, Paper 1).

As an explanation of the characteristics of the point-contact diode, Bardeen (1947, Paper 2) proposed a theory of surface states which may also be used to explain the reduced effectiveness of the conductance modulation mentioned above. In this theory, surface states are attributed to surface defects and absorbed foreign atoms, as well as to the more usual *dangling* bonds. Consequently a "double layer" is expected to occur at the surface of a semiconductor, formed by the charge in the surface states and the induced space charge. Electrons from the bulk of the material can become tightly bound in the surface states, and once trapped repel other electrons in the conduction band; consequently, a depletion layer is produced just below the surface. Bardeen proceeds to show that it is reasonable to suppose that 90 per cent of the charge will be fixed in the surface states when the gate is made positive, a fact verified by Shockley and Pearson (1948).

It was the consequent work on the nature of the surface states that resulted in the invention of the point-contact transistor. The transistor was first discussed in a short letter by Bardeen and Brattain (1948, Paper 3) and the essential aspects of its action, the nature of the forward current in germanium point contacts, was enlarged upon at the same time (Brattain and Bardeen, 1948, Paper 4). A complete account of the physical principles involved in transistor action appeared later (Bardeen and Brattain, 1949, Paper 5).

At this point it is pertinent to consider why, when a circuit is made involving a semiconductor and a metal, or n-type and p-type semiconductors, the Fermi levels are the same. Since the Fermi level is the chemical potential of the electrons in the semiconductor or metal, upon placing them in contact there exists initially a difference in this potential. Consequently a current will flow until the potential no longer exists, that is until the chemical potentials or the Fermi levels are the same throughout the system. This is assuming that thermal equilibrium exists. This follows essentially from the thermodynamic result that the condition for two phases to be in equilibrium with respect to any chemical species (in this case electrons), is that the chemical potential of that species should have the same value in the two phases (see Kittel, 1956, appendix IV).

Considering a metal point placed on a crystal of n-type germanium, it is apparent that electrons will flow until the Fermi levels are in equilibrium (Fig. 2.2). During this process the donor atoms lose their electrons leaving a depletion layer under the surface of the germanium. The resultant field at the contact repels electrons and pushes the bottom of the conduction band down. Since there are no carriers in the depletion layer it acts as an insulator, and under no bias conditions the barrier height is $\phi_m - \phi_s$. The application of a reverse or forward bias increases or decreases the barrier (cf. Fig. 2.2). The shapes of the potential

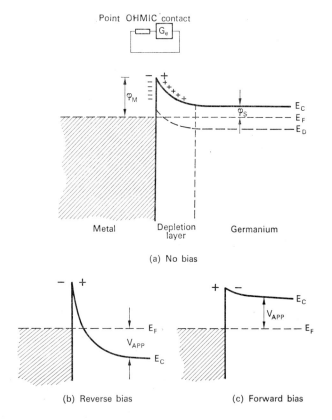

FIG. 2.2. Energy-band diagrams for a point-contact diode.

barriers suggest the asymmetrical current–voltage characteristics which give rise to the rectification properties of the device.

To find the width of the barrier, W_B, Poisson's equation must be applied, that is,

$$\frac{d^2\phi}{dx^2} = \frac{N_D^+ q}{\epsilon_0 \epsilon_G} = \frac{\rho}{\epsilon_0 \epsilon_G}, \tag{1}$$

where ϕ is the potential, N_D^+ is the ionized donor concentration and ρ is the charge density. Other symbols have their usual meanings. If $d\phi/dx = 0$ when $x = 0$, then

$$\phi = \frac{N_D^+ q \, x^2}{2\epsilon_0\epsilon_G} = \frac{\rho x^2}{2\epsilon_0\epsilon_G}, \tag{2}$$

$$W_B = \left[\frac{2\epsilon_0\epsilon_G \, (\phi_m - \phi_s)}{\rho}\right]^{\frac{1}{2}}, \tag{3}$$

since $\phi = \phi_m - \phi_s$ when $x = W_B$ for zero bias conditions ($W_B \sim 10^{-6}$ m). An applied bias (V_{app}) is reflected in ($\phi_m - \phi_s$), and there is a variation of capacitance with bias since the capacitance per unit area across the depletion layer is

$$C_B = \frac{\epsilon_0\epsilon_G}{W_B} = \left[\frac{\rho \, \epsilon_0\epsilon_G}{2\phi_B}\right]^{\frac{1}{2}}, \tag{4}$$

where $\phi_B = \phi_m - \phi_s$.

The voltage–current relationship may be derived using either the diode theory (Dilworth, 1948), in which the electrons are assumed to have a large mean free path, or on the diffusion theory in which they have a small mean free path and suffer many collisions (Fig. 2.3). On the diode theory, because we assume relatively few collisions, we may make use of the kinetic theory. Thus the number of electrons crossing unit area normal to the line of motion in 1 second is $\frac{1}{2}n \, v_x$, where n is the electron concentration and v_x is the appropriate average electron velocity. The probability that an electron will cross the barrier from the metal, that is that it will have energy in excess of $q\phi_B$, is $\exp -q\phi_B/kT$. The probability that an electron will cross the barrier in the opposite direction is $\exp -q(\phi_B - V_{app})/kT$ where V_{app} is the applied voltage. Thus the current density is given by

$$J = \tfrac{1}{2}n \, q \, v_x \exp(-q\phi_B/kT)[\exp(q \, V_{app}/kT)-1.] \tag{5}$$

Using the diffusion theory,

$$J = - \mu_e \, n_x \frac{d\phi}{dx} - qD \frac{dn_x}{dx} \tag{6}$$

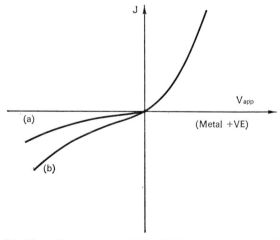

FIG. 2.3. The voltage–current relationship for a point-contact diode. (a) Using the diode theory. (b) Using the diffusion theory.

where n_x is the electron density at a distance x from the point. Using Einstein's relationship, however,

$$J = - \mu_e \, n_x \frac{d\phi}{dx} - \mu_e \, kT \frac{dn_x}{dx}, \qquad (7)$$

and integratating this gives

$$J = \sigma \left[\frac{8\pi n q}{\epsilon_0 \epsilon_G} (\phi_B + V_{app}) \right]^{\frac{1}{2}} \left[\exp\left(\frac{q \, V_{app}}{kT} \right) - 1 \right] \exp\left(-\frac{q \, \phi_B}{kT} \right). \quad (8)$$

Scattering processes in the barrier region have been proved to be negligible, and hence the diode theory appears to be the correct one (Torrey and Whitmer, 1948). In practice, there is no appreciable change in the characteristics of the device when different metals are used, and this does not agree with either theory ($\sim 0 \cdot 5$ volt change in the work function of the metal should give $\sim 10^8$ change in J). Figure 2.4 shows the I–V characteristics of a typical point contact diode.

To explain these discrepancies, Bardeen and Brattain (1949)

postulated the presence of inversion layers on the surfaces of semi-conductors, that is a *p*-type layer on *n*-type material and an *n*-type layer on *p*-type material. In fact it is possible to obtain either an *n*-type or *p*-type layer on any surface depending upon the chemical treatment of the surface. The surface treatment is quite empirical (Holmes, 1962), but the presence of an inversion layer is essential

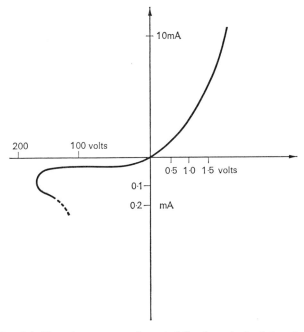

FIG. 2.4. The voltage–current characteristic of an actual point-contact diode.

to the Bardeen theory, since the metal point merely makes contact with the inversion layers and the characteristics of the diode are determined by the inversion layer–bulk junction.

In the forward direction for the first $0 \cdot 5$ volt

$$I = I_0 [\exp (q \, V_B/kT) - 1], \qquad (9)$$

where $I_0 \sim 10^{-6}$ amp, and V_B is the voltage drop across the barrier. For reverse bias the saturation current is given by

$$I_S = -I_0 \exp (\epsilon/kT), \tag{10}$$

where $\epsilon \simeq 0\cdot7$ eV. According to the diode theory,

$$I_S = -BT^2 \exp (\epsilon/kT), \tag{11}$$

the exponential function dominating (see Paper 5).

The high forward currents in the diode is explained in terms of *hole injection*, that is in *n*-type germanium some of the current is due to minority carriers injected by the point-contact. The space

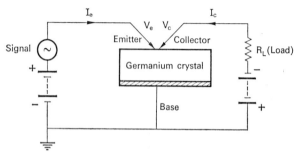

FIG. 2.5. A diagram of the point-contact transistor.

charge thus created is compensated by electrons. The injection of holes by the point-contact is also essential in the explanation of transistor action.

In Fig. 2.5 is shown a diagrammatic arrangement of one of the first point-contact transistors, the contacts being of phosphor-bronze and $\sim0\cdot01$ cm apart. The base material makes ohmic contact to the germanium. In essence there are two point-contact rectifiers; one, the emitter, is forward biased, and the other, the collector, is reverse biased. The emitter circuit is obviously of low impedance and the collector circuit of high impedance. If the collector voltage is kept constant, then as the emitter current is varied by varying the emitter voltage, changes occur in the collector current which may be greater than those in the emitter current. Besides the obvious power gain resulting from the different circuit impedances, there is a current gain a defined by,

$$a = \left[\frac{\partial I_e}{\partial I_c}\right]_{V=\text{const}}. \tag{12}$$

Overall power gains of 20 dB were initially attained and typical characteristics are shown in Fig. 2.6. Transistor action depends on the fact that the current from the emitter is composed to a large extent of holes, which are attracted to the negative collector. This

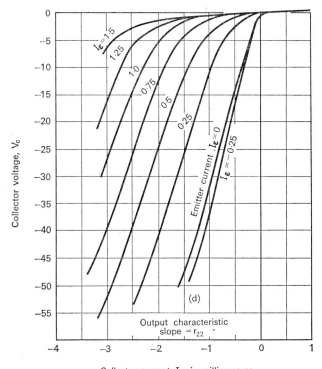

Collector current, I_c, in milliamperes

FIG. 2.6. Typical point-contact transistor characteristic (after Shockley, 1950).

flow of holes changes the space charge in the depletion layer surrounding the collector, and hence the collector voltage–current
characteristics.

Early experiments indicated that the flow of holes to the collector was mainly via the surface layer, however Shive (1949, Paper 6),
using contacts on either side of a wedge of germanium, proved
conclusively that the holes flow directly through the bulk of the
material. Haynes and Shockley (1949, Paper 7) continued the
investigation of hole flow through germanium, and found that the
mobility of the holes as measured in their experiment was in agreement with Hall effect measurements on p-type germanium. Still
later, Ryder and Shockley (1949) proved that the holes are injected
into germanium because of the nature of the barrier layer, rather
than, as previously suggested (Bray et al., 1947; Bray, 1948), as a
direct result of the electric field.

Although some form of surface "oxidation" was at first thought
essential for transistor action, Bardeen and Brattain (1949) proved
that it was rather the electrical *forming* of the collector point that
was essential. Forming is the passage of a high reverse current
pulse through the base–collector circuit. The process was later
found to be beneficial for certain emitter contacts also (Bardeen
and Pfann, 1949, Paper 8). Probing of the region around the
point–contact indicates the formation of a p-type region around
the collector, which is probably due to the rapid diffusion of
copper from the contact. The phosphorus diffuses more slowly and
sets up a heavily doped n^+ zone in the immediate vicinity of the
collector (Fig. 2.7). Holes diffuse from the emitter into the
collector area and are accelerated into the p-type region, where
they tend to accumulate since there is a barrier $(p–n^+)$ between this
region and the collector. Electrons from the collector cross the
p-type region without recombination because the width of this
region is very small, and consequently enhancement of the current
occurs, a small hole current inducing a much larger electron current
to the base region. The p-region is called the *hook* region, and
Valdes (1952), Sittner (1952) and Hogarth (1954) have discussed
its formation and the processes of forming in detail. An alternative

explanation to the *p–n* hook theory is the introduction of hole-traps around the collector, which when full create a positive charge zone. This again enhances the electron current and reduces the hole current.

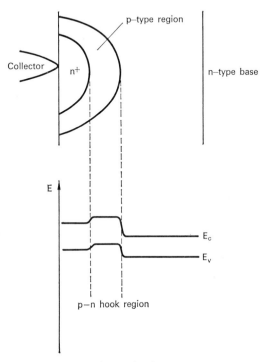

FIG. 2.7. The *p–n* hook arrangement.

One great advantage of the point contact device is its low capacitance, and consequently it is still used in some high frequency and high speed switching applications.

To describe the static characteristics of a point contact type *A* transistor, one requires two currents and two voltages, the emitter current I_e, the collector current I_c, the emitter voltage V_e and the collector voltage V_c. Now

$$V_e = f_1 (I_e, I_c), \tag{13}$$

$$V_c = f_2 (I_e, I_c); \tag{14}$$

consequently for low frequencies,

TABLE 2.1. PRELIMINARY DATA FOR TYPE-A TRANSISTOR

Typical operating conditions		Average equivalent circuit parameters (ohms)			
Emitter current	0·6 mA	$r_{11} =$	530	Emitter resistance $r_e =$	240
Emitter voltage	0·7 volt	$r_{12} =$	290	Base resistance $r_b =$	290
Collector current	−2 mA	$r_{21} =$	34,000	Collector resistance $r_c =$	19,000
Collector voltage	−40 volts	$r_{22} =$	19,000	Mutual resistance $r_m =$	34,000
		$a_e \doteqdot a \equiv r_{21}/r_{22} = 1·8$			

Maximum ratings: Not to be exceeded in continuous operation. Voltages relation to base.

Collector voltage	−70 volts
Collector dissipation	0·2 watt

Grounded base operation: Class A, working from a 500-ohm generator into a 20,000-ohm load.

Operating power gain	∼17 dB
Power output	∼5 mW

$$v_e = \frac{\partial f_1}{I_e} i_e + \frac{\partial f_1}{I_c} i_c = r_{11} i_e + r_{12} i_c \tag{15}$$

and

$$v_c = \frac{\partial f_2}{\partial I_e} i_e + \frac{\partial f_2}{\partial I_c} i_c = r_{21} i_e + r_{22} i_c, \tag{16}$$

where the small a.c. voltages v_e and v_c are produced by small a.c. currents i_e and i_c. If $r_{12} = r_{21}$ and $r_{11} > r_{12} < r_{22}$, the transistor may be represented by a passive resistance network, otherwise voltage or current generators must be introduced (Fig. 2.8).

$$a = - \left| \frac{\partial I_c}{\partial I_e} \right|_{V_c} = \frac{r_{21}}{r_{22}}, \tag{17}$$

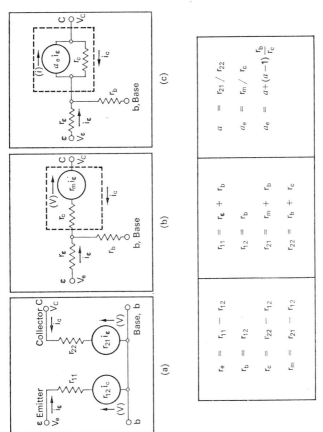

Fig. 2.8. The equivalent circuits of the point contact transistor (after Shockley, 1950).

r_{12} represents reaction at the emitter produced by the collector and is called the base resistance. If the base is grounded it represents positive feedback and thus increases gain and decreases stability. The active mutual resistance is r_m and the power gain varies as $r^2{}_m$. Table 2.1 shows some typical operating conditions.

The point contact transistor exhibits *contact* or *current noise*, for which the noise power per cycle varies inversely with frequency. One must add two voltage generators to the equivalent circuit to account for this noise. In the emitter circuit there is ~ 1 μV noise and in the collector circuit ~ 100 μV.

CHAPTER 3

Junction Devices
and Subsequent Developments

A *p–n* junction consists of an abrupt transition from a *p*-type to an *n*-type semiconductor, within a crystal lattice. The Fermi levels must be in equilibrium, and consequently there is a potential difference, qV_D, between the *p* and *n* regions greater than a distance W_D apart (see Fig. 3.1). This is because there exists a high concentration gradient of both electrons and holes across the junction, which gives rise to the diffusion of electrons from the *n*-type material, and of holes from the *p*-type material. As diffusion occurs an uncompensated space charge is developed in the junction

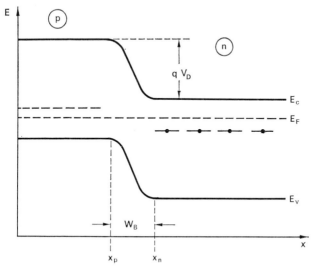

FIG. 3.1. The energy level diagram for a *p–n* diagram.

49

region, and this creates an electric field across the junction opposing the diffusion process. In equilibrium the resultant potential across the junction is termed the *diffusion potential* V_D, because it originates from the diffusion of the electrons and holes across the junction.

The application of a forward bias (i.e. *p*-region positive) facilitates the flow of holes and electrons by decreasing the potential barrier, whereas the application of a reverse bias impedes the flow of carriers by increasing the barrier height. Under reverse bias conditions no forward current flows, save for a very small minority carrier current due to minority carriers produced in the region of the junction. Thus the *p–n* junction exhibits asymmetrical properties which may be used to explain its rectification characteristics. A full treatment of the *p–n* junction has been given by Shockley (1949). This paper is a classic, and in its last section the *p–n–p* transistor is proposed.†

The junction is not only rectifying, but it is also photosensitive. It differs from the point contact in that electrons diffuse into the *p*-type region and holes diffuse into the *n*-type region. Shockley distinguishes between an abrupt and a gradual junction and he uses the word *junction* to include "all the material near the transition region in which significant contributions to the rectification process occur". Under certain conditions the major flow across the junction consists of holes, and under such conditions the *p–n* junction may be used as an *emitter* in transistor applications where the *n*-type material forms the base. Since electrons also diffuse into the *p*-type region, under different conditions it may also be used for the base (i.e. *n–p–n*).

There are then two types of the simple junction transistor, the *p–n–p* (Shockley, 1949, Paper 9) and the *n–p–n* (Shockley *et al.*, 1951, Paper 10). In the latter paper, Shockley *et al.* discuss in detail the *n–p–n* transistor, the *n*-type phototransistor with a *p–n* hook collector, and the *p–n–p–n* transistor with a *p*-type emitter and a *p–n* hook collector.

† Because of its length only sections 5 and 6 have been reproduced as Paper 9.

It is possible to consider a junction transistor as two p–n junctions sufficiently close to each other in the parent crystal to allow mutual interaction. As in the point contact transistor, the emitter circuit is forward biased, and the collector circuit is reverse biased;

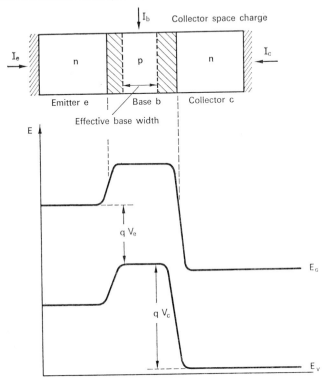

FIG. 3.2. An n–p–n transistor and its band diagram (all currents leading into the device are considered positive).

but the similarity ends there, since in the p–n junction the rectification takes place in the bulk of the material and not at the contacts. Moreover, the injected carriers diffuse rather than drift under the influence of an electric field, and under normal circumstances there is no current multiplication at the collector. Figure 3.2 shows a typical n–p–n device together with its energy band diagram. Under biased conditions the emitter injects electrons (minority carriers) into the base where they diffuse to the reverse biased base–collector junction. Those carriers that recombine give rise to a current which is supplied via the base lead. The number reaching the collector depends upon the diffusion length of the electrons in the base, L_e, and the base width W. The fraction of injected carriers reaching the collector is called the transport factor β

$$\beta = \text{sech}\,(W/L_e). \dagger \tag{1}$$

The leakage current across the base–collector junction is thus enhanced by the arrival of these electrons, and since the emitter circuit is of low impedance and the collector circuit is of high impedance, power gain results.

With reference to Fig. 3.2,

$$I_e + I_c + I_b = 0. \tag{2}$$

A proportion, γ, of the emitter current I_e is carried by minority carriers into the base, the remainder, $(1 - \gamma)I_e$, is carried by holes from the base and appears as $-(1 - \gamma)I_e$ in the base lead. The minority carriers diffusing across the base are collected by the collector, the resultant current being $\beta \gamma I_e$. There is also a leakage current in the collector circuit, $-I_c(0)$, due to thermal generation in the base, collector and intervening space charge. Thermal generation also supplies majority carriers to the base, and hence $+I_c(0)$ to the base current. A third contribution to the collector current may occur if the minority carriers arriving at the collector space-charge region cause multiplication (avalanche, or enhancement of minority carrier current in the collector) by, say, a factor α^*. α^* is often termed the "intrinsic alpha" of the collector, and for pure avalanche multiplication $\alpha^* = M$. Thus the collected current becomes $-\alpha^*\beta\gamma I_e$, and a current of $(\alpha^* - 1)\beta\gamma I_e$ appears in the base lead.

The total collector current is therefore

† For proof of this equation see Shockley *et al.* (1951) which is Paper 10 in the second half of this text.

$$I_c = -a\,I_e - I_c(0) \tag{3}$$

where $I_c(0)$ includes any multiplication of the collector leakage current, and a is the current gain of the transistor.

$$a = \gamma\,\beta\,a^* = \left[\frac{\partial I_c}{\partial I_e}\right]_{V_c}. \tag{4}$$

For a straightforward n–p–n transistor $a^* = 1$, and γ and β can be made close to unity. The total base current is

$$I_b = (a - 1)\,I_e + I_c(0). \tag{5}$$

Surface recombination has been included in β, and recombination in the emitter space-charge region has been included in γ. By increasing the collector voltage V_c, it is possible to increase the width of the collector space-charge region and thus decrease the effective base width. If the width W is small, and surface recombination is neglected,

$$\beta \simeq 1 - \tfrac{1}{2}\left(\frac{W}{L_e}\right)^2. \tag{6}$$

The important factors in transistor action are: the *diffusion* of minority carriers across the base and the avalanche or enhancement multiplication they cause in the collector space-charge region. Increased V_c can produce multiplication, however at a certain value "punch-through" occurs, that is the collector space-charge reaches the emitter and a space-charge limited current sets in. It is essential to realize that there is no electric field across the base, and the minority carriers rely entirely on diffusion to cross this region. This gives rise to a *transit* time. Also, when a current I_e flows from the emitter, a redistribution of charge occurs in the base which is analogous to the charging of a capacitance. Thus a *diffusion capacitance* is defined as

$$C_D = \frac{q}{kT}\cdot I_e \cdot \frac{W^2}{2D_m}, \tag{7}$$

where D_m is the diffusion coefficient for minority carriers in the base. The transit time, which produces a phase change between the input and output signals, and the capacitance together with the series resistance, impose serious limitations on the frequency response of the transistor. For high frequency operation one requires: small base width, low series resistance, and small cross-section area. This last requirement vies with the obvious increase in cross-section area required for greater power output.

A typical early n–p–n transistor† had a base width $\sim 0 \cdot 05$ cm, an area $\sim 0 \cdot 2$ cm² and it would deliver ~ 1 watt with a cut-off frequency of 10,000 Hz. Smaller units were operated with gains of up to 50 dB and noise figures ~ 10 dB at 1000 Hz. Even these figures represent an improvement over the point-contact transistor.

As mentioned, in a simple junction transistor $a^* = 1$ and no current multiplication is experienced. This was remedied (Shockley *et al.*, 1951, Paper 10) by introducing the p–n hook collector, thought to be the reason for current multiplication in the point-contact transistor. a^* is now increased to ~ 100 and some initial interest was shown in the development of the p–n–p–n transistor (Ebers, 1952). In a p–n–p transistor, for example, connection is made to the p-type collector via an n-type region, thus minority carriers from the base collect in the p-region and enhance the collector flow (see Fig. 3.3). The p–n–p–n transistor suffers from poor frequency response, and has not been developed to any great extent. The p–n hook mechanism is, however, used in the highly developed phototransistor.

So far we have referred to a as $[\partial I_e/\partial I_e]V_c$, but the transistor may be used with the emitter common to both the collector and base circuits, rather than the base being common to the collector and emitter circuits. Then a becomes $[\partial I_c/\partial I_b]V_c$. To distinguish between the two cases we will in future refer to $a_{ce}\, a_{cb}$ respectively. It may be shown that

$$a_{cb} \simeq \frac{a_{ce}}{1 - a_{ce}}. \tag{8}$$

Under common emitter operation the current gain is large and the signal is inserted into the base, the output as usual being taken

† Characteristics are shown in Fig. 2 of Paper 10.

from the collector. When a small base current flows it creates a small forward bias on the emitter junction, which, by nature of the emitter p–n junction, causes a large emitter current. For comparison purposes when $\alpha_{ce} = 0 \cdot 9$, $\alpha_{cb} = 9$, and when $\alpha_{ce} = 0 \cdot 999$, $\alpha_{cb} = 999$, and so on.

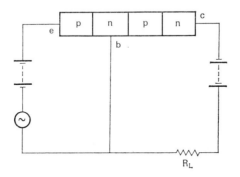

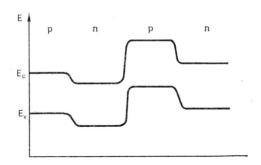

FIG. 3.3. The p–n–p–n transistor and its band diagram.

We have assumed previously that α is independent of frequency, and so it is at low frequencies. However, as the signal frequency increases α begins to decrease, the main reason being that the minority carriers diffusing through the base take different paths, and hence there is a distribution of transit times. When the transit times are of the order of the period of the emitter signal, destructive interference occurs as well as complicated phase changes. If the transit times were identical for all minority carriers then the collector current would be a delayed image of the emitter current, and α would remain constant. This is not so, and the complete solution for β is frequency dependent (Steele, 1952, Paper 11).

$$\beta = \text{sech} \left[\left(\frac{W}{L_e}\right) (1 + j\omega\tau_m)^{\frac{1}{2}} \right] \qquad (9)$$

where ω is the angular frequency of the signal, and τ_m is the minority carrier lifetime in the base. It may be proved (Evans, 1961) that the cut-off frequency f_{ca}, at which α_{ce} is 3 dB down on its low-frequency value (i.e. $0\cdot707$ of the low-frequency value), is given by

$$f_{c\alpha} = \frac{2\cdot43 D_m}{2\pi W^2}. \qquad (10)$$

If $f_{c\alpha}$ is in megaherz, then for a germanium p–n–p transistor $f_{c\alpha} = 3/W^2$ (n–p–n, $f_{ca} = 6/W^2$), and for a silicon p–n–p transistor $f_{c\alpha} = 0\cdot7/W^2$ (n–p–n, $f_{ca} = 2\cdot1/W^2$).

As observed, to improve the frequency response of a transistor it is necessary to reduce the base width, but the high-frequency response also depends upon the minority carrier lifetime in the base region, τ_m. For grounded emitter circuits τ_m is the predominant influence upon the cut-off frequency. One of the first complete treatments of the frequency dependence of α was given by Steele[†] (1952, Paper 11).

A complete equivalent circuit for a transistor would be so complicated as to be of little practical use. In Fig. 3.4 three approximate cases are shown for low, high and very high frequencies. It is desirable to reduce r_B and C_c since the time constant associated with them implies degradation. The generators are frequency dependent and the circuit parameters are themselves functions of voltage, current and temperature. Perhaps most important is the variation of α_{cb} with I_e, and with the geometry of the

† A proof of equation (9) is included in this paper.

device (Herold, 1954). [a_{ce} and hence a_{cb} is composed of three factors; cf. equation (4).] The effective base resistance is lowered for rising emitter current because of the increased concentration of holes in the base region. This reduces γ, although experimentally this reduction is found to be less in the n–p–n than in the p–n–p structures. The effect of the geometry upon a_{cb} is to be expected when one considers the importance of surface traps and so on.

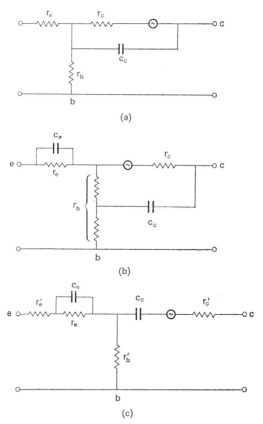

FIG. 3.4. Transistor equivalent circuits: (a) low frequency, (b) high frequency, (c) very high frequency.

At this stage in the development of the transistor, progress occurred on many fronts. New types of transistors were proposed and improvements to the existing one were made. For the sake of coherence the extensions and improvements of the p–n–p and n–p–n transistor will be dealt with first.

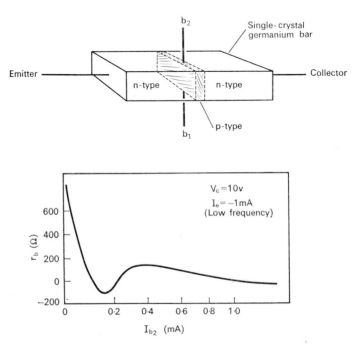

FIG. 3.5. The tetrode transistor and the variation of r_b with $I_{b_1 b_2}$.

The obvious way of increasing the cut-off frequency is to decrease the base resistance and the diffusion capacitance, that is to decrease the base width. Increasing the collector voltage V_c will increase the collector space-charge and thus decrease the effective base width, but punch-through must be avoided. The addition of a second contact to the base enabling a potential to be

applied across it, was suggested to improve the frequency characteristics (Wallace *et al.*, 1952). This *tetrode* structure reduces base
resistance, although in the same devices thinner base layers of
smaller area are used. Figure 3.5 shows the arrangement together
with a plot of r_B (base resistance) against I_{b_2}. The voltage across
$b_1 b_2$ is such that only a very small area around b_1 is correctly
biased with respect to the emitter for minority carrier injection
into the base. Consequently transistor action only takes place in
the immediate vicinity of the base, and this reduces r_B. This
electronic reduction of r_B is greater than could be achieved using
other techniques. Whilst the cut-off frequency is increased
~ 50 MHz, the device is essentially a low power one, and I_{b_2}
changes both a_{ce} and the collector resistance. In fact the cut-off
frequency is not increased that much when the tetrode bias is
applied, but the shape of the frequency response curve is altered in
a favourable way.

Perhaps the next most important step forward in transistor
work was the replacement of the alloying process by the diffusion
process. Rather more control is possible with diffusion, and by
doping from either side of a very thin wafer of material extremely
small base widths may be obtained. A typical diffusion process in
germanium would last for about 1 hour at 600–700°C to give a
base width of about 1 micron. Naturally some of the technological problems initially presented were quite formidable, but as
important as these problems were and still are, we are not concerned with them in this text.

One of the first steps toward using diffusion processes in transistor construction was made by Saby (1952), although the main
aim at that time was to increase the temperature stability of the
device. Even so the cut-off frequency was considerably increased.
Other work at the same time (Fuller, 1952; Saby and Dunlap,
1953) prompted Shockley to suggest "that the dimensional control inherent in these processes (of diffusion) be utilized to make
high frequency transistors". This led to the design and construction of germanium transistors with $a_{ce} = 0\cdot98$ and $f_{c_\alpha} = 500$ MHz
(Lee, 1955, Paper 12). Within a year of this development diffused

emitter and base transistors had been constructed using silicon (Tanenbaum and Thomas, 1956). For these units $\alpha = 0 \cdot 97$ and $f_{c\alpha} = 120$ MHz.

It would not be surprising if the penalty for such a good frequency response was a low punch-through voltage. However, in the diffused structure the base is highly doped (in the alloy type the base is relatively pure), and the depletion region moves into the purer region, that is into the collector region. Consequently breakdown is determined by avalanche in the collector region rather than punch-through.

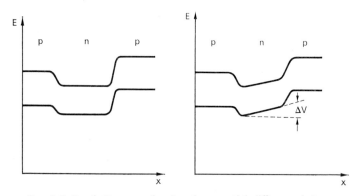

FIG. 3.6. Band diagrams showing the essential difference between the diffusion and the drift transistor.

In his paper on the diffused-base type of transistor, Lee mentions that the base has an impurity gradient and hence a "built-in" electric field. This *drift-field*, as it is called, considerably enhances the frequency response of a transistor. The idea was not a new one, and "drift-transistors" had been proposed and explored earlier (Kroemer, 1953, 1954, 1956), reaching full fruition in about 1957–8 (Kestenbaum and Ditrick, 1957).

By varying the impurity concentration in the base, there naturally arises an electric field which, if the concentration increases in the correct direction, will aid the flow of minority carriers across the base (Fig. 3.6). The consequent change in cut-off frequency is given by

$$(f_{c\alpha})_{\text{drift}} = (f_{c\alpha})_{\text{diffusion}} (\Delta V/2kT)^{3/2} \tag{11}$$

where ΔV is the built-in drift potential. There is an upper limit on the concentration gradient which limits ΔV to a maximum of less than $8kT$, however there is still a substantial improvement in $f_{c\alpha}$.

Although the decrease in base width by using diffusion processes does not carry the suspected "voltage penalty", there is a limit. One method of improving the characteristics of a p–n–p transistor is to "insert" an *intrinsic* layer between the base and the collector (Early, 1954). The resulting p–n–i–p and n–p–i–n structures show a great reduction in collector capacitance, and a high collector–voltage breakdown. The capacitance is essentially that of a capacitor whose plates are the base and collector regions, and whose dielectric is the intrinsic layer, thus

$$C_c = \frac{A_c \, \epsilon_0 \, \epsilon_i}{x_i} \tag{12}$$

where ϵ_i is the relative permittivity of the intrinsic material and x_i is its width. Likewise, the maximum collector–voltage is fixed by electric breakdown of the intrinsic region, and

$$V_{c_{\max}} = 10^5 \, x_i \tag{13}$$

for germanium where x_i is in centimetres and the constant has units V cm^{-1} (Evans, 1961). Since equation (13) does not involve the base resistivity, r_B may be considerably reduced ($\rho_B \sim 0\cdot1$ Ω-cm) without influencing $V_{c_{\max}}$. It should be noted that the collector voltage creates a high field across the intrinsic layer. Lee (1955) points to the feasibility of making transistors with a cut-off frequency ~ 1000 MHz by combining the drift and p–n–i–p techniques. To date silicon transistors with $f_{c\alpha} = 750$ MHz, $a = 45$, $C_c = 6$ pF and a power output of 300 mW have been constructed.

So far we have only considered what improvements have been made to the frequency characteristics of the early transistor, and we have not considered the developments aimed at increasing the power-handling capacity of the device. If transistors are required for R.F. and I.F. stages in common radio receivers, for example, they must be capable of handling several watts of power. A power capacity ~ 100 W would be extremely useful.

The term power transistor obviously implies high I_c and V_c, or rather high $I_c \times V_c$. Increasing I_c means increasing the emitter hole injection, and the greater concentration of holes that thus

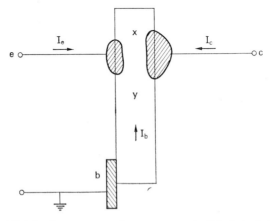

FIG. 3.7. The base current I_b causes a potential drop between X and Y in power transistors. This influences the distribution of emitter bias.

occurs in the base region reduces γ and a_{cb}. This is partly countered by increasing the emitter area and hence reducing the emitter current density, J_e. Care has to be taken not to create conditions such that there is a large change of bias between points X and Y (cf. Fig. 3.7), since in power transistors there is a large base current. Unless the base width is reasonably small, and the minority carrier lifetime in the base is as long as possible, the only part of the emitter that is at all efficient is that which is close to the base. A large emitter implies a large collector and hence an increase in $I_c(0)$ [cf. equation (3)] and thus increased temperature sensitivity.

The mounting of power transistors on large copper heat sinks helps to alleviate this problem somewhat.

In some ways a high emitter current density may be considered advantageous, since the high minority carrier concentration gradient in the base induces a high concentration gradient of majority carriers. Majority carriers tend to flow to the collector where they are reflected by the potential barrier. The presence of an electric field sufficient to prevent the flow of majority carriers clearly aids the minority carrier flow. This accounts for the initial rise in a_{cb} with I_e (Herold, 1954).

With power transistors the practical design becomes very important (Roka *et al.*, 1954), and silicon offers many of the solutions, although it also presents technological difficulties (Kendall, 1958). However, silicon power transistors are now available giving 150 watts with $f_{c\alpha} = 40$ KHz, 100 watts with $f_{c\alpha} = 30$ MHz and 15 watts with $f_{c\alpha} = 400$ MHz. It should be remembered that silicon is more temperature stable than germanium.

The overlay transistor is a good example of how design changes have aided the power transistor. It is essentially a planar n–p–n transistor. Construction begins with a silicon wafer plus an epitaxial layer, onto which is deposited a thin layer of silicon dioxide. By selective etching and vacuum deposition the electrodes and extra *dopants* are applied. The deposition masks are made by sophisticated photographic techniques.

It is possible to replace the emitter by a light source and thus create the point contact, the p–n, and the n–p–n phototransistor. The injection of minority carriers is replaced by the optical generation of carriers, otherwise the mode of operation is the same as before. The n–p–n phototransistor makes use of the p–n hook mechanism (Shive, 1953; Cummerow, 1954). Materials other than silicon and germanium are commonly used for photo-devices.

It is now appropriate to consider some of the innovations that took place at the same time as the development of the p–n–p transistor. Soon after the introduction of the tetrode transistor, a new type of device was invented, namely the surface barrier transistor (Bradley, 1953, Paper 13). This was the result of an application of a particularly beautiful electrolytic etching technique (Tiley and Williams, 1953) which was being used to reduce the base width (Fig. 3.8). Beginning with n-type germanium, an indium salt is used to etch the germanium wafer from two opposite directions, and upon reversal of the applied voltage the etching process stops and a plating process begins. Indium is then allowed to build up until contact can be made to both sides of the

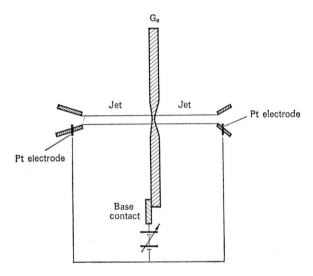

FIG. 3.8. Electrolytic etching for the surface barrier transistor.

germanium. One obvious advantage of this process is that there is no possibility of contamination of the germanium surface after etching. The transistor has an indium–germanium interface instead of an emitter and a collector, and the injection efficiency, and therefore the current gain is smaller than for the conventional units. Any attempt to increase the punch-through voltage by reducing the base resistivity lowers the injection efficiency still further. Typically, $f_{c\alpha} \sim 50$ MHz rather than the theoretical 75 MHz since the transistor is essentially non-planar (Fig. 3.9), and since the low resistivity base gives a low mobility for minority carriers.

The useful current is carried, as usual, by minority carriers (holes), which are collected and enhance the collector current. However, the holes are injected from the metal *through the surface states* into the valence band. Since the surface states are obviously important, so is the resulting insulating depletion layer which completely surrounds the germanium element. There is a high electric field across this depletion layer. If the emitter contact,

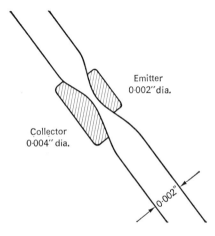

FIG. 3.9. Showing the non-planar characteristics of the surface barrier transistor.

which is of larger area than in previous transistors, is made positive, holes are repelled into the bulk of the germanium and electrons are attracted into and locked in the surface states. The holes then diffuse across the "base" to the collector, their rate of diffusion depending on the concentration gradient and very steep concentration gradients are required to make the surface barrier transistor functional. It should be noted that an increased gradient means that there is a large concentration of holes near the emitter, and this creates a positive space charge in that area which attracts electrons.

A number of interesting points occur in Bradley's paper (1953). One is the deliberate use of the surface states together with the bulk properties of the semiconductor, that is rectifying contacts are made to the germanium rather than ohmic contacts. The transistor action takes place at the contacts as in the point contact transistor. The importance of metal–semiconductor contacts is also high-lighted and certain discrepancies with previous results emphasizes their importance. For a surface barrier transistor typical parameters are, $a_{cb} \simeq 20$ when $I_c = 0 \cdot 5$ mA, $a_{cb} \simeq 12$ when $I_c = 5$ mA, dissipation ~ 50 mW, $f_{c\alpha} \simeq 50$ MHz, $C_c \simeq 5$ pF and $r_B \simeq 200$ Ω.

At the time, the surface barrier transistor represented a substantial improvement, because although the value of $f_{c\alpha}$ is only the same as that achieved using the tetrode transistor its potential was much greater. A later variant is the micro-alloy transistor (MAT) in which an indium–gallium (1 per cent) alloy is used, true alloy p–n junctions being formed at a depth of some 2 to 3 microns below the surface. Because of the gallium, the recrystallized emitter has a very low resistivity ($\sim 10^{-4}$ Ω-cm) so consequently greatly improved injector efficiency is obtained, and very low base widths may be used without substantially lowering the breakdown voltage. Whilst there is an increase in cut-off frequency, the main improvement is in a_{cb} which is increased to $\simeq 150$ at $I_c \simeq 5$ mA. This represents an increase in power dissipation. Using "diffused base" techniques $f_{c\alpha}$ may be increased to $\simeq 500$ MHz. The main disadvantages of this device are low emitter–base breakdown voltages and reduced injection efficiency (see Rittman et al., 1958; and Thornton and Angell, 1958).

In 1952 Shockley (Papers 14 and 15) proposed the unipolar class of transistors, namely the analogue and the field-effect transistors. The term *unipolar* is used in the sense that only one carrier is operative in the device. In *bipolar* transistors both minority and majority carriers are important. The field-effect transistor is probably the most important of these proposals, and

as mentioned earlier it follows on more directly from the thermionic vacuum tube or valve. The first attempt in this direction was
the modulation of the conductance of a germanium filament by
changing the occupancy of the surface states using a *field plate* or
gate (Shockley and Pearson, 1948; Shockley, 1951).

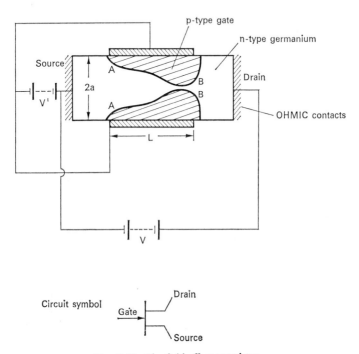

FIG. 3.10. The field-effect transistor.

In the proposed unipolar field-effect transistor (Shockley, 1952,
Paper 15) the insulated metal gate is replaced by two n^+-type sections sandwiching a p-type region. Essentially the device is a
variable resistance since both p–n junctions are reverse biased,
their space-charge regions extending into the p-region. The "useful" current is carried by holes (majority carriers) through the

p-region, and their flow is due to the applied electric field, diffusion only playing a minor role. In essence the resistance of the bulk is modulated by the reverse bias across the junctions. Figure 3.10 shows a p-type gate and an n-type filament, the terminology used being that proposed by Shockley (1952).

The width of the depletion layer surrounding the p-type gate is proportional to the reverse bias V', and so, therefore, is the *effective* cross-section area of the n-type current carrying filament.

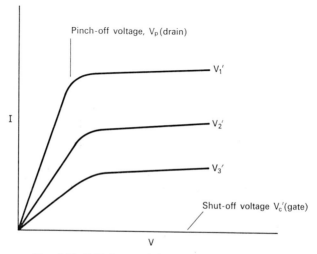

FIG. 3.11.   *I–V* characteristics of a field-effect transistor.

The unusual half-pear shape of the depletion regions is due to the fact that when a voltage V is applied to the filament and a current flows, there is a potential gradient along the filament, and points B are therefore positive with respect to points A. It may be arranged so that the resistance of the filament is proportional to V, and thus a saturation effect is obtained. Figure 3.11 shows the appropriate characteristics which resemble those of a pentode with anode resistance ~ 10 MΩ and mutual conductance ~ 1 mA V^{-1} for the early units. Two critical voltages exist; the voltage

(V_p) at which saturation sets in which is called the pinch-off voltage, and the voltage (V_c') at which the depletion layers extend completely across the filament which is called the cut-off voltage.

The advantages of the field-effect transistor are many, but probably the most important one is the high input resistance. This comes about because the input signal "sees" a reverse biased p–n junction. It also appears not to suffer from the incompatibility of the requirements of high frequency and high power, since increasing the power (V and I) does not mean increasing the dimensions in such a way as to increase the capacitance. The negative temperature coefficient of the device is also useful for compensating the positive coefficient of other transistors.

The field-effect transistor is inherently a low noise device, since the working current is carried by majority carriers only, and these pass *between* barriers rather than *across* them. Thus one of the main sources of noise, namely recombination, is eliminated. In the p–n–p transistor the main source of noise is the injection of carriers from the emitter into the base across the emitter–base barrier.

Development of the field-effect transistor was rather slow (Dacey and Ross, 1955; Handel, 1960), but has now gathered considerable momentum. The reason for this is that whilst the device is simple to understand, its construction involves some highly refined technology. The developments in material technology over the past decade and a half have enabled the FET to be developed into a commercial proposition. The so-called "Tecnetron" has an input impedance of 80 MΩ, an output impedance of 50 Ω, a mutual conductance of $0\cdot7$ mA V^{-1} at 200 MHz, and a gain of 10 dB at 200 MHz. If the suffices D, G and S are used to represent drain, gate and source respectively, the mutual conductance, or transconductance, is given by

$$g_m = \left[\frac{\partial I_D}{\partial V_g}\right]_{V_D} \tag{14}$$

and $$g_m\,(\text{max}) = 2\sigma\, a/L \tag{15}$$

where σ is the conductivity of the filament, and a and L are the dimensions shown in Fig. 3.10. The limiting frequency is given by

$$f = \frac{1}{2\pi RC} = \frac{a^2 \sigma}{4\pi L^2 \epsilon_0 \epsilon_g} \tag{16}$$

since the frequency is limited by the process of charging up the gate capacitance through the resistance of the filament channel. At present the field-effect transistor is receiving considerable attention (see Warner and Fordemwalt, 1965, chapter 8) and special enhancement mode FETs have been produced with input impedance as high as 10^{15} Ω and cut-off frequencies $\sim$ GHz, with very low noise figures and high stability. These transistors use silicon dioxide to insulate the gate from the bulk of the transistor, and are known as MOS (metal-oxide-semiconductor) field-effect transistors. The MOSFET is essentially a thin film device whose geometry is similar to the thin-film transistor discussed next. The conducting channel is situated immediately under the insulating silicon dionide and the device therefore contains an oxide–silicon interface; consequently interface states are of considerable importance. The substrate is usually silicon of about 10 Ω-cm. Recent work with high resistivity substrates, accurately aligned gates rather than gates which overlap the source and drain, and ion inplantation to form the source and drain, promises to bring the MOSFET close to its theoretical best. Noise figures have been quoted as being less than 3 dB at 100 MHz and the MOS structure is able to withstand relatively high radiation levels (e.g. $\sim 3 \times 10^{14}$ neutrons cm^{-3}).

The other major development which is occurring at present is the thin-film transistor (TFT), along with the whole subject of integrated circuits. The basic principle of the TFT is to vacuum deposit all the components, including the electrodes, onto some form of insulating glass plate. Vacuum deposition of oxides and nitrides is in fact extensively used to *passivate* or stabilize silicon and germanium surfaces, that is to reduce and control the surface states (Attalla *et al.*, 1959; Kendall, 1965; Maguire, 1966).

However, the TFT makes use of other semiconducting materials such as cadmium sulphide (Ruppel and Smith, 1959; Wright, 1960) and cadmium selenide (de Graaf, 1967). The use of materials other than silicon and germanium is not new, since diodes of

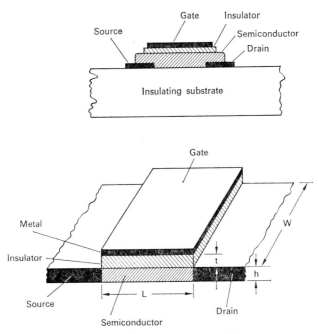

Fig. 3.12. Diagram of the thin-film transistor (TFT) with dimensions shown.

various types have been made from the gallium salts for some time, and experimental transistors have been constructed using indium phosphide which have a theoretical cut-off frequency ~ 10 GHz at low temperatures.†

In the TFT whilst the source and the drain are ohmic contacts to the semiconductor (e.g. gold on cadmium sulphide), the gate

† For a summary of the requirements of materials for transistor use see Evans, 1961, chap. 11; and Smith, 1959.

electrode is insulated from it (see Fig. 3.12), as in the MOSFET. The insulator is usually SiO, SiO_2, or Si_3N_4. The device is unipolar, and is strictly a field-effect device. Whereas in the FET, however, making the gate positive creates what may be called a *depletion mode*, in the TFT it creates an *enhancement* or *enrichment mode*; that is the drain current increases rather than decreases. A TFT may be designed to operate in either mode, but higher trans-conductances are achieved using the enrichment mode. The basic principles are the same as in the FET and in fact it is almost identical to the originally conductance modulation transistor (Shockley and Pearson, 1948; Shockley, 1951) which was pro-posed by Bardeen to investigate surface states. (The gate was also insulated in that device.) The main difference is in the dimensions and the use of a wide band-gap semiconductor. The wide energy-gap ensures that a minimum number of carriers are generated thermally, and hence that the majority carriers completely dom-inate the conduction processes. Since very thin films are used, changes in conductance greatly in excess of the originally experi-enced 10 per cent are quite feasible.

In Paper 16, Weimer (1962)† considers the effects of trapping in connection with surfaces states and bulk traps. When a small increase in gate potential, ΔV_g, is applied, Δn electrons per cubic metre are drawn into the semiconductor, where

$$\Delta n = \frac{C_g \, \Delta V_g}{q \, L \, W \, h} \tag{17}$$

(cf. Fig. 3.12). The resulting increase in source-drain current is

$$\Delta I_D = V_D \frac{Wh}{L} \Delta \sigma = V_D \frac{Wh}{L} \Delta n \, q \, \mu \tag{18}$$

where V_D is the drain-source potential difference and μ is the mobility of the Δn electrons. Consequently from equations (17) and (18) and the dimensions of the device we obtain

$$g_m = \frac{\epsilon_0 \, \epsilon_d}{t} \frac{W}{t} \cdot \frac{\mu V_D}{L} \tag{19}$$

† See also Weimer (1964).

where ϵ_d is the relative permittivity of the dielectric insulating the gate.

It is difficult to say in which direction the subject of transistors will develop. Certainly integrated circuits (Warner and Fordemwalt, 1965) are receiving the most attention. This area of work obviously includes "built-in" thin-film and field-effect transistors, as well as the more conventional components. The three-dimensional integrated circuit has still to reach optimum performance, but any consideration of such circuits is out of place in a book of this type, where the emphasis has been on the physical principles involved rather than on technical developments. The process of diffusion which enabled such advances to be made in conventional transistor development has been brought to a high degree of refinement in the integrated circuit. Surprisingly enough the principles used in semiconductor device operation are still substantially the same as they were two decades ago, only our appreciation and application of them has changed. The single transistor is giving way to the integrated circuit, and in a few years time it will only be used for special applications where a complete circuit is not required. A change in the materials used in device and circuit construction should also be expected, materials such as gallium arsenide becoming increasingly important.

References

ATTALLA, M. M. *et al.* (1959), *B.S.T.J.* **38**, 749.
BARDEEN, J. (1947) *Phys. Rev.* **71**, 717. Paper 2.
BARDEEN, J. (1948) *Phys. Rev.* **74**, 223.
BARDEEN, J. and BRATTAIN, W. H. (1948) *Phys. Rev.* **74**, 230. Paper 3.
BARDEEN, J. and BRATTAIN, W. H. (1949) *Phys. Rev.* **75**, 1208. Paper 5.
BARDEEN, J. and PFANN, W. G. (1949) *Phys. Rev.* **77**, 401. Paper 8.
BLOCH, F. (1928) *Z. Physik.* **52**, 555.
BRADLEY, W. E. (1953) *Proc. I.R.E.* **41**, 1702. Paper 13.
BRATTAIN, W. H. and BARDEEN, J. (1948) *Phys. Rev.* **74**, 231. Paper 4.
BRAY, R. *et al.* (1947) *Phys. Rev.* **72**, 530.
BRAY, R. (1948) *Phys. Rev.* **74**, 1218.
CONWELL, E. M. (1958) *Proc. I.R.E.* **46**, 1281.
CUMMEROW, A. (1954) *Phys. Rev.* **95**, 16 and 561.
DACEY, G. C. and ROSS, I. M. (1955) *B.S.T.J.* **34**, 1149.
DILWORTH, C. C. (1948) *Proc. Phys. Soc.* **60**, 315.
DRESSELHAUS, J. (1955) *Phys. Rev.* **98**, 368.
EARLY, J. M. (1954) *B.S.T.J.* **33**, No. 3, 519.
EBERS, J. J. (1952) *Proc. I.R.E.* **40**, 1361.
EVANS, J. (1961) *Fundamental Principles of Transistors*, Heywood and Co.
FULLER, C. S. (1952) *Phys. Rev.* **86**, 136.
DE GRAAF, J. (1967) *Solid-State Elec.* **10**, 51.
HANDEL, S. (1960) *Brit. Commun. Electron.* **7**, 282.
HAYNES, J. R. and SHOCKLEY, W. (1949) *Phys. Rev.* **75**, 691. Paper 7.
TER HAAR, D. (1954) *Elements of Statistical Mechanics*, Rinehart.
HEROLD, E. W. (1954) *Brit. J. Appd. Phys.* **5**, 121.
HOGARTH, C. A. (1954) *Proc. Phys. Soc.* **67B**, 636.
HOLMES, P. J. (1962), *The Electrochemistry of Semiconductors*, Academic Press.
JONSCHER, A. K. (1960), *Principles of Semiconductor Device Operation*, Chapter 2, Bell & Sons.
KENDALL, J. (1958) *Electron. Radio Engr.* **35**, 202.
KENDALL, E. J. M. (1965) *Phys. Letters*, **15**, No. 1, 28.
KENDALL, E. J. M. (1966) *Modern Physics for Electrical Engineers*, pp. 66–69, Macdonald.
KESTENBAUM, A. L. and DITRICK, N. H. (1957) *R.C.A. Review* **18**, 12.
KITTEL, C. (1956) *Introduction to Solid-State Physics*, Wiley & Sons.
KOCK, W. E. and WALLACE, R. L. (1949) *Elec. Eng.* **68**, 222.
KROEMER, H. (1953) *Naturwissenschaften* **40**, 578.
KROEMER, H. (1954) *Archiv der Elektrischen Ubertragung* **8**.

KROEMER, H. (1956) *Transistors I (R.C.A.)* 202.

LEE, C. A. (1956) *B.S.T.J.* **35**, 23. Paper 12.

MAGUIRE, T. (1966) *Electronics* (January 10th), 156.

MATTHEWS, P. T. (1963) *Introduction to Quantum Mechanics*, McGraw-Hill.

MOTT, N. F. and JONES, H. (1936) *Theory of the Properties of Metals and Alloys*, Clarendon Press, Oxford.

RITTMAN, A. D. *et al.* (1958) *I.R.E. Trans.* **ED5**, 49.

ROJANSKY, V. (1938) *Introductory Quantum Mechanics* (11th print, 1964), Prentice Hall.

RUPPEL, W. and SMITH, R. W. (1959) *R.C.A. Rev.* **20**, 702.

RUSHBROOKE, G. S. (1955) *Introduction to Statistical Mechanics*, Oxford.

SABY, J. S. (1952) *Proc. I.R.E.* **40**, 1358.

SABY, J. S. and DUNLAP, W. C. (1953) *Phys. Rev.* **90**, 630.

SHIVE, J. N. (1949) *Phys. Rev.* **75**, 689. Paper 6.

SHIVE, J. N. (1953) *Opt. Soc. Am.* **43**, 239.

SHOCKLEY, W. and PEARSON, G. L. (1948) *Phys. Rev.* **74**, 232. Paper 1.

SHOCKLEY, W. (1949) *B.S.T.J.* **28**, 435. Paper 9 (pp. 468–474 only).

SHOCKLEY, W. (1950) *Electrons and Holes in Semiconductors*, Van Nostrand.

SHOCKLEY, W. *et al.* (1951) *Phys. Rev.* **83**, No. 1, 151. Paper 10.

SHOCKLEY, W. (1952) *Proc. I.R.E.* **40**, 1311–13 (*only*). Paper 14 (pp. 1311–1313 only).

SHOCKLEY, W. (1952) *Proc. I.R.E.* **40**, 1365. Paper 15.

SITTNER, W. R. (1952) *Proc. I.R.E.* **40**, 448.

SMITH, R. A. (1959), *Semiconductors*, Cambridge.

SMITH, R. A. (1961) *Wave Mechanics of Crystalline Solids*, Chapman & Hall.

STEELE, E. L. (1952) *Proc. I.R.E.* **40**, 1424. Paper 11.

TAMM, I. (1932) *Physik Z. Sowjet* **1**, 733.

TANNENBAUM, M. M. and THOMAS, D. E. (1956) *B.S.T.J.* **35**, No. 1, 1.

THORNTON, C. G. and ANGELL, J. B. (1958) *Proc. I.R.E.* **46**, 1166.

TILEY, J. W. and WILLIAMS, R. A. (1953) *Proc. I.R.E.* **41**, 1707.

TORRY, H. C. and WHITMER, C. A. (1948) *Crystal Rectifiers*, McGraw-Hill.

VALDES, L. B. (1952) *Proc. I.R.E.* **40**, 443.

WALLACE, R. L. *et al.* (1952) *Proc. I.R.E.* **40**, 1395.

WARNER, R. M. and FORDEMWALT, J. N. (1965) (Motorola) *Integrated Circuits*, McGraw-Hill.

WEIMER, P. K. (1962) *Proc. I.R.E.* **50**, 1462. Paper 16.

WEIMER, P. K. (1964) *Physics of Thin Films* **2**, 147.

WRIGHT, G. T. (1960) *J. Brit. I.R.E.* **20**, 337.

PART 2

The following papers are published by kind permission of the authors, *The Physical Review* (Papers 1, 2, 3, 4, 5, 6, 7, 8 and 10), the Institute of Electrical and Electronic Engineers (Papers 11, 13 14, 15 and 16) and the American Telephone and Telegraph Company (Papers 9 and 12).

Modulation of Conductance of Thin Films of Semi-conductors by Surface Charges†

W. Shockley and G. L. Pearson

Bell Telephone Laboratories, Murray Hill, New Jersey

June 25, 1948

WHEN a charge is induced on the free surface of a semi-conductor, by making it one plate of a parallel plate condenser for example, some of the charge density δq goes into the surface states and some into the space charge in the barrier layer beneath the surface.[1] Figure 1 shows the energy level diagram for an N-type semi-conductor under no external field (solid lines) and under the field due to negative voltage on the other plate (dotted). If the applied field produces a change in potential δV on the surface, then δq_s, the increased charge per cm² in the surface states, will be $qN_s\delta V$ where q is the electronic charge and N_s is the number of surface states per unit area per unit voltage. The charge in the interior can be estimated from the Schottky‡ exhaustion layer theory which gives $\delta V = 4\pi\rho b\delta b/\epsilon$ where ρ is the net charge density of the impurities, ϵ the dielectric constant, and b the thickness of the exhaustion layer. This gives a charge of $\delta q_b = \rho\delta b = \epsilon\delta V/4\pi b$ per unit area, which is produced by removing conduction electrons. Hence a fraction,

$$\beta = \delta q_b/(\delta q_b + \delta q_s) = (\epsilon/4\pi b)/[qN_s + (\epsilon/4\pi b)],$$

of the total charge induced per unit area on the semi-conductor is accounted for by reduced conduction electrons in the interior.

† *The Physical Review*, **74**, 232 (1948).
‡ See Appendix I of Paper 2.
[1] J. Bardeen, *Phys. Rev.* **71**, 717 (1947). (Paper 2.)

If the semi-conductor consists of a thin layer of thickness L with exhaustion layers of thickness b on both sides, then the total charge per unit area of conduction electrons is $-\rho(L - 2b)$ and the

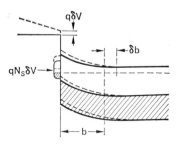

FIG. 1. Energy level diagram showing charge induced in surface states by external field.

conductance parallel to the layer is $\sigma = \rho(L - 2b)\mu$ where μ is the mobility. The applied field changes the charge by $\delta q_b = \beta \delta q$ and, therefore, changes the conductance of the layer by

$$\delta\sigma/\sigma = \pm\beta\delta q/\rho(L - 2b) = \pm\beta\delta q\mu/\sigma,$$

where the minus sign holds for N-type material (i.e., when $\delta q_b > 0$, there are less electrons and $\delta\sigma < 0$) and plus for P-type.

The charge δq on the surface is induced by using the semi-conductor as one plate of a parellel plate condenser, and the change in conductance is simultaneously determined for current flow parallel to the plate. The experimental arrangement consists of a condenser with rectangular plates about 1×2 cm of gold and semi-conductor evaporated on opposite sides of a slab of fused quartz 0.003 inch thick. The current used to measure the change in conductance flows between two additional gold electrodes evaporated on the two ends of the semi-conductor. According to the above theory, the capacity of this unit is that of the quartz C_q in series with $C_s = qN_s$ and $C_b = \epsilon/4\pi b$ in parallel, and is thus chiefly determined by C_q. The value δq is determined directly from the measured capacity per unit area and the applied voltage.

(Experiments to check the equivalent circuit for the unit, including relaxation effects, will be communicated later.)

Measurements on a number of films of P-type germanium, copper oxide, and N-type silicon show that $\delta\sigma/\sigma$ is correctly given in sign by the theory and is linear in $\delta\sigma$. Values as high as 0.11 have been obtained for Cu_2O with fields of 400,000 volts/cm. Values of β depend on the mobility, which was measured for two P-type germanium films, and give results as follows:

$\delta\sigma/\sigma\ \delta q$ cm²/coulomb	σ mhos	$\dfrac{\mu\ \text{cm}^2}{\text{volt-sec}}$	β	L cm	N_s/cm² volt
1.0×10^4	3.1×10^{-4}	33	0.10	2×10^{-5}	6×10^{13}
5.5×10^3	7.7×10^{-4}	49	0.09	5×10^{-5}	5×10^{14}

Using the exhaustion layer theory with $V = 2\pi\rho b^2/\epsilon$, the unknown values for b and ρ can be eliminated from the equations giving (for b/L and β both $\ll 1$)

$$N_s = 1.31 \times 10^{12}\ (\epsilon\mu/LV\sigma)^{\frac{1}{2}}\sigma\delta q/\delta\sigma,$$

where the units are N_s/cm² volt, μ cm²/volt-sec., L cm, V volts, σ mhos, δq coulombs/cm², $\epsilon = 19$ for Ge. The result is not sensitive to the value of V. Assuming a representative value of 0.5 volts, the value of N_s was computed. This value is comparable with that previously obtained for silicon by another method.[2]

We are indebted to many of our colleagues for discussions and advice and to R. B. Gibney, J. R. Haynes, and M. Sparks for preparation of the films.

[2] W. H. Brattain and W. Shockley, *Phys. Rev.* **72**, 345 (1947).

PAPER 2

Surface States and Rectification at a Metal–Semi-conductor Contact†

JOHN BARDEEN

Bell Telephone Laboratories, Murray Hill, New Jersey

(Received February 13, 1947)

Summary

Localized states (Tamm levels), having energies distributed in the "forbidden" range between the filled band and the conduction band, may exist at the surface of a semi-conductor. A condition of no net charge on the surface atoms may correspond to a partial filling of these states. If the density of surface levels is sufficiently high, there will be an appreciable double layer at the free surface of a semi-conductor formed from a net charge from electrons in surface states and a space charge of opposite sign, similar to that at a rectifying junction, extending into the semi-conductor. This double layer tends to make the work function independent of the height of the Fermi level in the interior (which in turn depends on impurity content). If contact is made with a metal, the difference in work function between metal and semi-conductor is compensated by surface states charge, rather than by a space charge as is ordinarily assumed, so that the space charge layer is independent of the metal. Rectification characteristics are then independent of the metal. These ideas are used to explain results of Meyerhof and others on the relation between contact potential differences and rectification.

Introduction

THE generally accepted view[1] of the nature of the rectifying contact between a metal and a semi-conductor is illustrated in Fig. 1

† *The Physical Review*, **71**, 717 (1947).

[1] See, for example, N. F. Mott and R. W. Gurney, *Electronic Processes in Ionic Crystals* (Oxford University Press, London, 1940), Chap V. The theory of rectification is due in large part to W. Schottky. The most important of his papers is *Zeits. f. Physik* **118**, 539 (1942).

which applies specifically to an excess semi-conductor. Figure 1a shows an energy level diagram of the metal and semi-conductor in equilibrium, but with the contact separated. The Fermi level is the same in both the metal and the semi-conductor. As shown, the work function of the metal, χ_1, is greater than the work function of the semi-conductor, $\chi_2{}^0$, so that there is a contact difference in potential, $\chi_1 - \chi_2{}^0$. It is assumed that when the metal

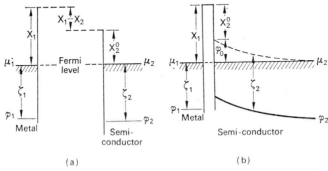

(a)   (b)

FIG. 1. Energy level diagram for metal and semi-conductor in electrical and thermal equilibrium μ_1 and μ_2 represent the Fermi levels in metal and semi-conductor, respectively, and φ_1 and φ_2 the inner potentials. ζ_1 and ζ_2 are the chemical potentials and χ_1 and $\chi_2{}^0$ the work functions. Figure 1a shows the wide gap with the contact potential difference $x_1 - x_2{}^0$. In 1b, the gap is very small. There is a space charge region in the semi-conductor which gives an electrostatic potential energy rise at the surface $\varphi_0 = \chi_1 - \chi_2{}^0$. This is the usual picture in which no surface states on the semi-conductor are assumed.

and semi-conductor are nearly joined, the potential distribution is as shown in Fig. 1b. A double layer is formed such as to give a potential drop, φ_0, from the metal to the interior of the semi-conductor equal to the contact potential difference.

This double layer is assumed to consist of a space charge region in the semi-conductor, extending to a depth of the order of 10^{-6} to 10^{-4} cm, and an induced charge on the metal surface. The space charge gives a rise in electrostatic potential energy at the surface of the semi-conductor. Electrons are depleted from the space charge region, giving a layer of high resistivity. If a potential is applied to the junction, most of the drop occurs across this barrier layer. If the potential of the semi-conductor is negative with respect to the metal, the electron energy levels in the semi-conductor are raised, and electrons may flow more easily over the potential hill into the metal. This is the direction of easy flow. On the other hand, if the semi-conductor is positive, the levels are lowered, increasing the height of the hill, and making it more difficult for electrons to travel from the semi-conductor to the metal. This is the direction of high resistance.

According to this view, the equilibrium height of the potential hill, φ_0, and therefore also the degree of rectification, depend on the work function of the metal. For an excess semi-conductor, the larger the work function of the metal, the larger is the potential rise, and the larger is the reverse resistance of the barrier. If the work function of the metal is less than that of the semi-conductor there is a potential drop instead of a potential rise, and no rectification will occur. For a defect semi-conductor, in which the current is carried by holes, just the reverse is true: low metal work function gives high rectification.

A number of investigations have been carried out which have verified these conclusions in some cases, and in other cases have not. H. Schweickert, as quoted by Schottky,[2] has found a correlation between the resistance of selenium rectifiers in the blocking direction and the work function of the metal. Selenium is a defect conductor, and high reverse resistance was found for low work function metals such as K, Na, Li, Ba, and low reverse resistance was found for such high work function metals as Ag, Au, Ni. The metal electrodes were put on by evaporation.

W. H. Brattain,[3] working in this laboratory, has found a good correlation between degree of rectification and work function for

[2] W. Schottky, *Physik Zeits.* **41,** 570 (1940).

[3] Unpublished work done at the Bell Telephone Laboratories in 1940 under the general direction of J. A. Becker. The author is indebted to Drs. Brattain and Shive for permission to quote their results.

metal contacts evaporated on cuprous oxide (a defect conductor) and on both N- and P-type silicon.[4] Metals used, listed in order of decreasing degree of rectification, were Al, Ag, and Pt on cuprous oxide; Pt, Be, Ag, Mg, and Al on N-type silicon; and Mg, Cd, Ag, and Pt on P-type silicon. He found that when contact is made to the semi-conductor by a metal junction in air, the rectification is practically independent of the work function of the metal used. Results somewhat similar to those of Schweickert have been obtained by J. N. Shive[3] who studied the rectification character-istics of a number of contacts made by evaporation of various metals on selenium. Metal contacts, listed in order of decreasing degree of rectification, are Be, Zn, Pb, and Au.

A. V. Joffe[5] has studied contact potential differences and the resistances of the contacts formed from a large number of dif-ferent semi-conductors and metals. Most gave very poor rectifica-tion characteristics. While there was some qualitative correlation of contact potential differences with contact resistance, quantita-tive agreement with theories of Schottky[1] and Davydov[6] was poor.

W. E. Meyerhof[7] has recently been making an extensive study of the relation between contact potential difference and rectification for metal point contacts applied to Si and Ge. He has determined the potential rise, φ_0, from the rectification characteristics at different temperatures and has also measured the ordinary contact potential difference, or Volta potential, by a modified Kelvin bridge method. Preliminary results show little correlation between the two sets of measurements. In fact, he has found that φ_0 is practically independent of the work function of the metal for

[4] The designations N- and P-type refer to the direction of rectification. An N-type is an excess semiconductor, and the direction of easy flow occurs when the semi-conductor is negative relative to the metal. A P-type semi-conductor is a hole conductor, and the direction of easy flow is opposite. In both cases, the direction of easy flow is that in which the carrier moves from the semi-conductor to the metal.

[5] A. V. Joffe, *J. Phys. USSR* **10,** 49 (1946).

[6] B. Davydov, *J. Phys. USSR* **4,** 355 (1941).

[7] W. E. Meyerhof, "Contact potential difference in crystal rectifiers," Technical Report No. 5, Univ. of Pennsylvania, BuShips contract NObs-34144, Aug. 10, 1946; see *Phys. Rev.* **71,** 727 (1947).

metal point—Si rectifiers. The same metal may rectify with both P- and N-type silicon, in opposite directions.

These negative results indicate that a closer analysis of the nature of the contact between a metal and semi-conductor is warranted. The main purpose of the present paper is to investigate the effect of electronic states on the surface of the semi-conductor on φ_0. There has been considerable discussion in the literature concerning the possibility of surface states,[8] but little direct evidence as to their existence.

Impurity Levels and Surface States

According to the modern theory of semi-conductors, there is an energy gap between the highest filled band of levels and the lowest state of the conduction band. In the language appropriate to excess semi-conductors, conductivity results from electrons thermally excited to the conduction band from impurity levels. The impurity levels, which are intermediate in energy between the filled band and conduction band, represent states in which the electron is localized around a foreign atom or other defect in the crystal lattice. In normal semi-conductors there may be the order of 10^{-7} to 10^{-3} impurity levels for each atom of the crystal.

In addition to the impurity levels in the interior of the crystal, there may be localized states on the surface with energies in the "forbidden" region between the filled and conduction bands. Shockley[8] and others have investigated the conditions under which surface levels may be expected on an ideal crystal. His analysis, based primarily on a one-dimensional model, indicates that "in a plot of the energy spectrum *versus* interatomic distance

[8] Surface states with energies in the "forbidden" band were studied first by I. Tamm, *Physik. Zeits. Sowjetunion* **1,** 733 (1932), and are often called Tamm states. Later theoretical work was done by R. H. Fowler, *Proc. Roy. Soc.* A141, 56 (1933), S. Rijanow, *Zeits. f. Physik* **89,** 806 (1934), A. W. Maue, *Zeits. f. Physik* **94,** 717 (1935), E. T. Goodwin, *Proc. Camb. Phil. Soc.* **35,** 205 (1939), W. G. Pollard, *Phys. Rev.* **56,** 324 (1939), and W. Shockley, *Phys. Rev.* **56,** 317 (1939). The last of these is the most critical, and shows under what conditions surface states are occupied in a normal crystal.

the surface levels appear only at lattice constants so small that the boundary curves of the allowed energy bands have crossed." The number of such surface states is equal to the number of surface atoms, and, in a neutral crystal, the surface states are half filled. The conditions for surface states are fulfilled, for example, in a diamond-type lattice.

Surface states may also result from surface imperfections, from foreign atoms on the surface, etc. On general grounds, there is good reason to suppose that the ratio of the number of surface levels to surface atoms may be much higher than the ratio of the number of impurity levels to atoms in the interior.

The energy levels corresponding to the surface states may be discrete, or they may have a continuous distribution with all energies in the gap between the filled and conduction bands. There is little evidence of either an experimental or a theoretical nature on this point. Well-defined impurity states of the same nature, sparsely distributed over the surface, would all have about the same energy and form a discrete level. If the impurity atoms are densely distributed over the surface, so that there is considerable interaction between them, a continuous distribution in energy is to be expected. A continuous distribution is also expected for surface states on clean surfaces of the type discussed by Shockley, Goodwin, and others.[8] In the analysis to follow we assume that the surface levels are continuously distributed in energy. Many of the same general conclusions would follow, however, if discrete levels had been assumed.

We will show that if there is a relatively high density of surface states, there may be a double layer on the free surface of a semiconductor resulting from a surface charge caused by electrons in surface states and a space charge of opposite sign extending into the crystal to a depth of 10^{-6} to 10^{-4} cm. The double layer tends to make the work function independent of the impurities in the interior. If contact is made to a metal, the contact potential difference is compensated largely by a true surface charge rather than by space charge, so that the height of the barrier is largely independent of the metal.

Nature of Contact

Before discussing the effect of surface states, we will give a brief review of the nature of the contact between metal and semi-conductor.

At a contact between any two electronic conductors there is an electric double layer which adjusts the potential of one relative to the other for equilibrium conditions. This potential difference may be taken as a measure of the strength of the double layer.

Some care must be taken in defining the absolute value of the potential. There is, of course, no way of measuring the potential inside a metal or semi-conductor. The potential just outside the surface can be measured, but the difference between the potential inside and outside the surface depends on the double layer at the surface. Only differences in potential between different parts of a conductor can be observed directly.

Nevertheless, it is desirable to consider the potential in the interior. The true time-average electrostatic potential is periodic, with the period of the lattice. The macroscopic potential, Φ, may be defined as the space average of the actual potential over a region large compared with atomic dimensions. This definition is somewhat arbitrary; another definition might yield a different value for the strength of the double layer at a contact or at a surface. However, only differences in double layers have direct significance, and these are independent of the way the potential in the interior is defined.

The general theory of equilibria[9] shows that when two electronic conductors are in contact and in thermal equilibrium, the electrochemical potentials, μ_1 and μ_2, must be the same in both:

$$\mu_1 = \mu_2 \text{ in equilibrium.} \tag{1}$$

In the usual picture of an electronic conductor, μ is just the Fermi

[9] An excellent discussion is given by R. H. Fowler and E. A. Guggenheim, *Statistical Thermodynamics* (Cambridge University Press, England, 1939), Chap. XI. The author is indebted to Dr. C. Herring for the method of presentation used above.

level which determines the probability, p, that a state of energy E is occupied.

$$p = 1/(1 + \exp[(E - \mu)/kT]). \qquad (2)$$

The electrochemical potential in a region may be defined thermodynamically, in a way which is independent of any particular model, by the equation:

$$\mu = \frac{\partial}{\partial n} (U - TS),$$

where n is the number of electrons in the region, and U and S are the energy and entropy. The partial differentiation corresponds to a reversible change in which the volume and temperature are held constant. The internal energy U includes an electrostatic potential energy, $-e\Phi$, per electron. The choice of the zero or reference level from which this potential energy is measured is arbitrary, and there is the same arbitrary choice in the definition of μ.

It is convenient to introduce a quantity which depends on the chemical constitution of the material, and on the electron density, but not on the electrostatic potential. This quantity, ζ, which is called the chemical potential, to distinguish it from the electrochemical potential, is defined by

$$\zeta = \mu - \varphi, \qquad (3)$$

where

$$\varphi = -e\Phi$$

is the electrostatic energy per electron.

Let φ_e be the potential energy of an electron just outside the surface of a conductor. This potential is to be evaluated at a point where the image potential is negligible, but at a distance from the surface small compared with macroscopic dimensions. The work function of the surface is then:

$$\chi_s = \varphi_e - \mu. \qquad (4)$$

This is the energy required to take an electron from the conductor and place it at rest at a point, defined as above, just outside the surface.

T.—D

The work function depends on the double layer at the surface. By replacing μ by $\zeta + \varphi$, according to Eq. (3), the work function may be expressed in the form:

$$\chi_s = \varphi_e - \varphi - \zeta, \tag{5}$$

which shows explicitly that the work function is the sum of the energy required to take an electron through the surface double layer, $\varphi_e - \varphi$, and a body term, $-\zeta$, independent of the surface.

It should be emphasized that the separation of the work function into a surface term and a body term depends on the precise way the potential energy, φ, in the interior of the conductor is defined. We have suggested above that the electrostatic potential Φ be defined as space average of the actual potential. Another definition might yield, for example, a smaller value for $\varphi_e - \varphi$ and a correspondingly larger value for $-\zeta$. Differences in double layers, such as might yield different work functions for different crystal faces of the same material, are not affected by the arbitrary definition of the inner potential. Since the double layer involves a potential difference, the value is independent of the reference level, or zero of potential, which is also arbitrary.

If two electronic conductors are in contact, and in thermal equilibrium, the electrochemical potentials must be the same in both. Thus,

$$\zeta_1 + \varphi_1 = \zeta_2 + \varphi_2,$$

or

$$\varphi_2 - \varphi_1 = \zeta_1 - \zeta_2. \tag{6}$$

The strength of the double layer at the contact, $\varphi_1 - \varphi_2$, is equal to the difference between the chemical potentials. Since the chemical potentials depend only on the internal constitutions of the two conductors, the double layer is independent of the work functions of the two surfaces before they are brought into contact.

The situation when there is a small gap between the two conductors in equilibrium is illustrated in Fig. 2. There is a double layer of strength $\varphi_{e1} - \varphi_1$ at the surface of conductor 1, a double layer of strength $\varphi_{e2} - \varphi_2$, in the opposite direction, at the surface

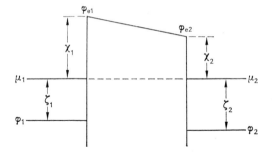

FIG. 2. Diagram to illustrate double layers at a contact between two conductors in equilibrium. There is a double layer of strength $\varphi_n - \varphi_0$ at the surface of conductor 1, a double layer of strength $\varphi_n - \varphi_2$, in the opposite direction at the surface of conductor 2 and a double layer of strength $\varphi_n - \varphi_n = -(\chi_1 - \chi_2)$ formed by surface charges on the two conductors. Total strength, $\varphi_2 - \varphi_1$, is independent of the surface double layers.

of conductor 2, and a double layer of strength $\varphi_{e2} - \varphi_{e1} = -(\chi_1 - \chi_2)$, formed by surface charges on the two conductors. The total strength of the double layer is:

$$(\varphi_{e1} - \varphi_1) + (\varphi_{e2} - \varphi_{e1}) - (\varphi_{e2} - \varphi_2) = \varphi_2 - \varphi_1. \tag{7}$$

The surface double layers drop out, as they should according to Eq. (6).

If the surfaces are in very intimate contact, so that the electron space charges of the two surfaces overlap, it is not possible to divide the total double layer into different parts which depend on the work functions of the individual surfaces. All that can be said is that the strength of the total double layer is $\varphi_2 - \varphi_1$. The work functions of the surfaces before they are brought into contact play no role.[10]

[10] H. Y. Fan, *Phys. Rev.* **61**, 365 (1942); **62**, 388 (1942), has attempted to calculate the electron space charge distribution in the double layer at the contact between two metals, and at the contact between a metal and a semi-conductor. Although his calculations are based on a highly idealized model, they may serve to give a rough picture of the charge density in the contact region. He does not consider the effect of surface states on the semi-conductor.

Usual Picture of Rectifying Contact

If one of the conductors is a semi-conductor, and the other is a metal, it has generally been assumed that as they are brought into contact, no surface charge forms on the semi-conductor.[11] Instead, there is a space charge near the surface which may extend to a depth of the order 10^{-6} to 10^{-4} cm. If the gap is small compared with this distance, but is still large enough so that there is no appreciable overlap, most of the energy drop $\chi_1 - \chi_2{}^0$ will occur in the semi-conductor rather than in the gap. This situation is illustrated in Fig. 1b. The space charge raises the energy at the surface of the semi-conductor by an amount $\chi_1 - \chi_2{}^0$. This is the usual picture which indicates that the height of the potential barrier should be equal to the difference in work functions, and is that which is discussed in the introduction.

This picture is deficient in two respects:

(a) The contact may be so intimate that a division of the double layer into one at the surface of the metal, one at the surface of the semi-conductor, and one caused by space charge may not be possible. There will be a double layer at the immediate interface, and another due to space charge, but it is not possible to say how the total strength is divided between them. A cruder way of stating this is that the work functions of the two surfaces are modified by the contact. However, if the contact is intimate, the separate work functions have no meaning.

(b) There may be electronic states localized on the surface of the semi-conductor, so that the surface atoms can become charged. An appreciable field may then exist in the gap. Part of the total drop from metal to semi-conductor will occur across the gap and part across the space charge region. If the density of surface states is sufficiently high, part of the double layer at the *free* surface of a semi-conductor may be formed by a surface states charge

---

[11] N. F. Mott, *Proc. Camb. Phil. Soc.* **34,** 568 (1938), gives a discussion of the contact between a metal and an insulator or a semi-conductor. A brief analysis is given of the effect of a surface charge resulting from electrons in surface states on the contact between a metal and an insulator. Mott assumes a discrete energy level for the surface states.

compensated by a space charge. The height of the potential barrier of a rectifier formed from the material will then be determined in part by the normal space charge of the free semi-conductor and in part by the work function of the metal.

Free Surface of Semi-conductor

We will first consider the free surface of a semi-conductor, and then discuss the rectifying contact. The notation to be used is illustrated in the energy level diagram of Fig. 3. The lowest state

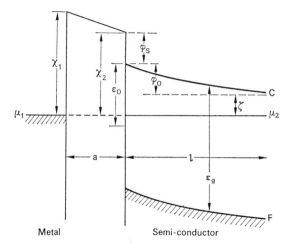

FIG. 3. Energy level diagram for metal semi-conductor contact illustrating notation used in text. The Fermi levels are μ_1 and μ_2 and the work functions χ_1 and χ_2. The lowest state of the conduction band is denoted by C and the highest level of the filled band by F. If the surface states are filled to an energy ϵ_0 below the conduction band there is no net charge on the surface atoms.

of the conduction band and the highest state of the filled band of the semi-conductor are indicated, with an energy gap ϵ_g. It is assumed that the distribution of surface states is such that the surface states give no net charge if the states are filled to an energy ϵ_0 below the conduction band.[12] Since the Fermi level cuts the surface above the level determined by ϵ_0, the surface as shown will be negatively charged, this charge resulting from electrons in states between ϵ_0 and the Fermi level. The picture applies to an excess semi-conductor.[13] In the body of the semi-conductor, the Fermi level is an energy ζ below the conduction band. The space charge region extends for an approximate distance l into the semi-conductor, giving a potential energy rise φ_0 at the surface. An energy φ_s is required to remove an electron from the lowest state of the conduction band near the surface to a point just outside the semi-conductor. The work function, χ_2, depends on φ_s as well as on φ_0:

$$\chi_2 = \varphi_s + \varphi_0 + \zeta. \tag{8}$$

The amount and extent of the space charge inside the free surface is determined by the density of surface levels. For zero external field, the positive space charge raises the potential at the surface by an amount just sufficient to give a compensating negative surface charge. The larger the positive space charge region, the larger is φ_0, and the smaller is the negative surface states charge. For some φ_0 the two will be equal in magnitude. This is the equilibrium value.

These relations are indicated in a schematic way in Fig. 4, which shows the variation of σ_i, the total space charge per unit area, of σ_s, the surface states charge, and of the surface charge, $\sigma_s + \sigma_i$, with φ_0. The other curves on the diagram will be referred to later in connection with the discussion of a metal contact. For a uniform space charge in the boundary layer, σ_i is proportional to the square root of φ_0 (see the Appendix). The plot of σ_s has a steep

[12] We refer to the net charge of the surface states as "surface states" charge to distinguish it from the total charge, including space charge, in the surface layer, which we call "surface charge."

[13] The case of an excess semi-conductor seems to be easier to visualize than that of a defect semi-conductor. All results derived for one case, of course, apply to the other with obvious changes in signs of the charges.

slope corresponding to a fairly high density of surface states. It passes through zero (point E in Fig. 4) when

$$\varphi_0 = \epsilon_0 - \zeta, \tag{9}$$

because, according to the definition of ϵ_0 the surface states will then be filled up to the level corresponding to zero surface states charge. The point A represents a value of φ_0 for which $\sigma_s + \sigma_i = 0$, which corresponds to a neutral surface. It can be seen that if the

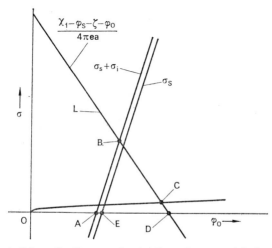

FIG. 4. Schematic diagram showing how the potential rise φ_0 is determined from the density of surface levels and the contact potential difference (see text).

density of surface states is high, this value of φ_0 will be close to that given by Eq. (9).

For the limiting case of a very high density of surface states, the line σ_s becomes vertical, points A and E coincide, and Eq. (9) must be satisfied; hence, according to Eq. (8):

$$\chi_2 = \varphi_s + \epsilon_0. \tag{10}$$

The work function is determined entirely by the surface, and is independent of the position of the Fermi level in the interior.

On the other hand, if the density of surface states is small, $\sigma_s + \sigma_i$ is approximately equal to σ_i and the condition for a neutral surface leads to a small value for φ_0. In the limiting case of vanishing surface states charge, $\varphi_0 = 0$, and the work function is

$$\chi_2 = \varphi_s + \zeta, \qquad (11)$$

which of course *does* depend on the position of the Fermi level in the interior of the semi-conductor.

Some semi-conductors can be made either excess or defect, or N- or P-type,[4] depending on the nature and concentration of impurities. The distribution of impurities in a single sample may be such as to make one end N-type and the other end P-type. Silicon and germanium are examples of materials which may behave in this way. For an N-type conductor, ζ is small; for a P-type conductor ζ is almost equal to the energy gap ϵ_g, which is the order of one electron volt for these materials.

If the density of surface states is low, a large difference in work function between N- and P-type is to be expected. The difference will be almost equal to the energy gap ϵ_g. For a high density of surface states, the difference in work function will be small. Figures 5a and b show schematic energy level diagrams of these two limiting cases. Both show the variation in potential along, and the work functions at the two ends of a sample which changes from N- to P-type from left to right along its length. Figure 5a is that corresponding to a high density of surface states. There is a space charge region at each end. The potential at the left is raised so as to bring the energy level corresponding to a neutral surface close to the Fermi level. The potential at the right is similarly lowered. The difference in work functions, $\chi_P - \chi_N$, is small. Figure 5b is the case corresponding to a small density of surface states. There are no space charge regions at the ends, and the difference in work functions is large.

A difference in work function can be detected experimentally as a difference in contact potential. Meyerhof[7] has in this way measured the differences in work functions of various samples of N- and P-type silicon and has investigated the effect of surface

treatment on these differences. He finds that the difference between N- and P-type samples is about 0.25 eV, which is considerably smaller than the energy gap of about 1.1 eV. It is quite
possible that there is a high density of surface states, either on the

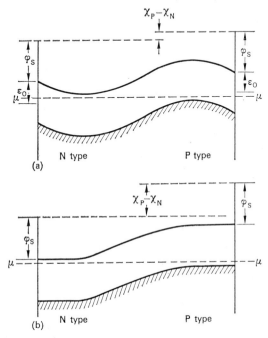

FIG. 5. Energy level diagram showing contact potential difference
between two ends of a semi-conductor which changes from N-type
to P-type along its length. (a) High density of surface states, small
contact potential difference. (b) No surface states, large contact
potential difference.

pure material or resulting from surface films or impurities, which
is sufficient to account for this discrepancy.

We have so far discussed the density of surface states in a
purely qualitative way. It is of interest to make an estimate of the
density required to produce an appreciable space charge layer at

the free surface of a semi-conductor. The density depends on the density of charged centers, or donors, in the boundary layer. If there are N such centers per unit volume, and if the thickness of the boundary layer (assumed uniform) is l, we have for the total space charge per unit area:[1]

$$\sigma_i = eNl. \tag{12}$$

The potential energy rise at the surface is

$$\varphi_0 = (2\pi/\kappa)e^2Nl^2, \tag{13}$$

where κ is the dielectric constant.

Let the number of surface states in the energy interval $d\epsilon$ be $nd\epsilon/\epsilon_0$. We assume, for simplicity, that n is a constant, which is of the order of the total number of surface levels per unit area with energies in the gap. The change in surface states charge density corresponding to a potential energy rise φ_0 at the surface is then

$$\Delta\sigma_s = en\varphi_0/\epsilon_0. \tag{14}$$

The condition for an appreciable space charge layer is that ϕ_0 be of the order of magnitude of ϵ_0 when $\Delta\sigma_s = \sigma_i$. This requires that n be the order of Nl. Taking, for example, $\kappa \sim 15$, and $N \sim 10^{17}$, Eq. (13) gives $l \sim 10^{-5}$, so that

$$n \sim Nl \sim 10^{12} \text{ states/cm}^2. \tag{15}$$

This density corresponds to about one surface state per thousand surface atoms. Other things being fixed, the limiting density of surface states is proportional to the square root of the density of charged centers in the boundary layer.

Metal Semi-conductor Contact

As a metal surface approaches that of a semi-conductor, the electrostatic field in the gap increases. There is a surface charge σ_M on the metal surface, and a charge of equal magnitude and opposite sign divided between a surface charge ,σ_s, and a space charge, σ_i (the latter has been defined as the total space charge per unit area of surface). Thus

$$\sigma_M = -(\sigma_s + \sigma_i). \qquad (16)$$

In the case of the metal, the surface charge causes only a very slight change in work function. However, the charge on the semi-conductor may cause appreciable changes in its work function, so that its value χ_2 will differ appreciably from the zero field value $\chi_2{}^0$. These changes can be analyzed with the aid of Figs. 3 and 4.

According to Fig. 3, the field in the gap between metal and semi-conductor is $(\chi_1 - \chi_2)/ea$. This is produced by the surface charge which gives a field $4\pi(\sigma_s + \sigma_i)$. Equation (8) expresses χ_2 as a function of φ_0. Equating the two expressions for the field leads to:

$$\frac{\chi_1 - \zeta - \varphi_s - \varphi_0}{4\pi ea} = \sigma_s(\varphi_0) + \sigma_i(\varphi_0). \qquad (17)$$

The left-hand side of the equation is plotted in Fig. 4 as the line "L," and is a straight line of negative slope. The solution to (17) is represented by the point B, which is the intersection of "L" with the line representing $\sigma_s + \sigma_i$. The line "L" crosses the axis at the point D, which corresponds to $\chi_2 = \chi_1$, or

$$\varphi_0 = \chi_1 - \varphi_s - \zeta. \qquad (18)$$

It can be seen that if the density of surface levels is high, so that σ_s and $\sigma_s + \sigma_i$ have steep slopes, the point B will lie close to the point A which gives the value of ϕ_0 for the free surface. In this case,

$$\varphi_0 \sim \epsilon_0 - \zeta, \qquad (19)$$

and is practically independent of the work function of the metal. This is a possible explanation of the results of Meyerhof, who found that the value of φ_0 for metal points on silicon does not depend very much on the metal used.

In the limiting case of vanishing surface states charge density, $\sigma_s = 0$, and the solution of (17) is given by the point C of Fig. 4.

The value of φ_0 is then close to that given by the intersection of the line L with the horizontal axis (point D). In this case,

$$\varphi_0 \sim \chi_1 - \varphi_s - \zeta, \tag{20}$$

and the usual picture of the contact between metal and semi-conductor applies.

As the metal is brought closer to the semi-conductor, the slope of the line "L" increases with decreasing "a" and one might expect a transition from a solution near A to one near D with a resulting value of φ_0 given by Eq. (20). However, even if there is only one surface state per hundred surface atoms, the slope of the line σ_s is so great that the solution still lies near point A even when a is reduced to atomic distances, say 3A. This may be verified by making a rough calculation based on Fig. 4. For the value of φ_0 to be largely determined by the semi-conductor, the value of φ_0 for the solution B must lie closer to A than to D. The necessary and sufficient condition for this is that the slope of the line σ_s be much greater, in absolute value, than the slope of "L." We have

$$\text{slope of } \sigma_s = m_s = en/\epsilon_0,$$

$$\text{slope of } L = -m_L = -1/4\pi ea. \tag{21}$$

The condition that m_s/m_L be large is

$$m_s/m_L = 4\pi e^2 an/\epsilon_0 \gg 1, \tag{22}$$

or

$$n \gg \epsilon_0/4\pi e^2 a. \tag{23}$$

Setting for example, $\epsilon_0 \sim 10^{-12}$ erg and $a \sim 3 \times 10^{-8}$ cm, this condition requires that

$$n \gg 10^{13}. \tag{24}$$

Thus if there is appreciably more than about one surface state per hundred surface atoms, the metal work function will have little effect on φ_0. This is about an order of magnitude larger than the surface density required for the existence of an appreciable boundary layer at the free surface.[14]

The theory is worked out in detail for the special case of a uniform Schottky exhaustion layer[1] in the appendix.

Conclusions

If the density of surface levels with energies in the "forbidden" band is sufficiently high ($> \sim 10^{12}/cm^2$), there will be a double layer at the free surface of a semi-conductor formed from a surface states charge and a space charge of opposite sign. The space charge region is similar to that which exists at a rectifying contact. This double layer tends to make the work function independent of the height of the Fermi level in the interior, and so independent of the impurity content.

The total strength of the double layer at a rectifying junction between a metal and semi-conductor is fixed by the difference in chemical potentials, and so depends on the body properties of the metal and semi-conductor, and is independent of the work functions of the surfaces before they are brought into contact. The double layer consists of the following parts:

(1) A double layer of atomic dimensions at the metal surface.

(2) A double layer of atomic dimensions at the semi-conductor surface.

(3) A double layer formed from surface charges on the metal and semi-conductor, both of atomic dimensions.

[14] S. Benzer, *Phys. Rev.* **71**, 141 (1947), has recently reported on the current–voltage characteristic observed when contact is made between two pieces of the same (homogeneous) germanium crystal. He states that "the characteristic observed for both polarities is more the order of the back resistance observed when either piece of the crystal is contacted with a metal; in both directions the negative resistance at high voltage appears, which is typical of the back characteristics of metal–Ge contacts using these alloys." The presence of a space charge layer at the surface of each piece which is little modified by contact would result in a characteristic similar to that of two rectifiers in series opposition. Such boundary layers are to be expected if the density of surface states is the order of that given by Eq. (24) and if the contact is not too intimate. Benzer's results are thus indirect evidence for surface states on germanium crystals.

(4) A double layer formed from a surface charge of atomic dimensions and a space charge extending to a depth of 10^{-6} to 10^{-4} cm into the semi-conductor.

The strengths of the double layers may be estimated in different cases as follows:

(a) If the density of surface levels is sufficiently high ($> \sim 10^{13}/$ cm^2) the double layer (4) will be independent of the metal, and will be the same as that for the free surface of the semi-conductor. The rectification properties will then be largely independent of the work function of the metal. The difference in contact potentials is compensated by (3).

(b) If the density of surface levels is small ($< \sim 10^{13}/$cm^2), the double layer (3) will be small, and (4) will be determined approximately by the difference in work functions.

(c) If the contact between the metal and semi-conductor is very intimate, it may not be possible to distinguish between the double layers (1), (2), and (3). The metal will tend to broaden the surface levels, but if the broadening is small compared with the energy gap, conclusion (a) will still be valid.

(d) If the broadening of the surface levels by the metal is large, no conclusions about the space charge can be drawn from measurements of contact potential differences.

It is believed that all of these cases may be realized.

The author is indebted to various members of the technical staff of the Bell Telephone Laboratories, particularly to W. Shockley, C. Herring, and W. H. Brattain, for the benefit of numerous discussions concerning the subject matter of this paper, and for helpful comments on the preparation of the manuscript.

APPENDIX

Theory for Schottky Exhaustion Layer

The detailed calculation of φ_0 requires a knowledge of the distribution of space charge in the semi-conductor and its dependence on φ_0. The dependence of surface charge on φ_0 is also required. We will carry through the calculation explicitly only for the case of a Schottky exhaustion layer[1] with a uniform density of charge. This case is particularly simple and brings out the essential features of the problem. For simplicity we also assume that the surface states are uniformly distributed in energy.

Let eN be the positive charge density in the barrier region, assumed constant. Let l be the thickness of the charged layer. Let $nd\epsilon/\epsilon_0$ be the number of surface levels per unit area with energies in the range $d\epsilon$. We assume that n is a constant, independent of energy. For other notation see Fig. 3.

We have the following relations:

(a) The total space charge per unit area is:

$$\sigma_i = Nel. \tag{12}$$

(b) The potential energy at the surface of the semi-conductor is

$$\varphi_0 = \frac{2\pi e^2 N}{\kappa} l^2, \tag{13}$$

where κ is the dielectric constant.

(c) The surface states charge is

$$\sigma_s = -en(\epsilon_0 - \varphi_0 - \zeta)/\epsilon_0. \tag{15}$$

(d) The total surface charge is

$$\sigma_i + \sigma_s = Nel - en(\epsilon_0 - \varphi_0 - \zeta)/\epsilon_0. \tag{25}$$

(e) The work function of the semi-conductor is:

$$\chi_2 = \varphi_s + \zeta + \frac{2\pi e^2 N}{\kappa} l^2. \tag{26}$$

Equating $\sigma_i + \sigma_s$ with $(\chi_1 - \chi_2)/4\pi ea$, we get Eq. (17) from which ϕ_0 or the thickness of the barrier layer, l, can be determined. With the notation:

$$l_0 = \frac{n}{N}(1 - \zeta/\epsilon_0), \tag{27a}$$

$$l_1 = \kappa\epsilon_0/2\pi e^2 n, \tag{27b}$$

$$l_2{}^2 = \kappa(\chi_1 - \varphi_s - \zeta)/2\pi e^2 N, \tag{27c}$$

Eq. (17) reduces to:

$$l^2/l_1 + l - l_0 = (l_2^2 - l^2)/2\kappa a, \tag{28}$$

which is a simple quadratic equation for l.

Whether the semi-conductor or the metal predominates in determining l, and thus the barrier height, depends on the relative magnitudes of the terms on the left and right sides of Eq. (28). The terms on the right side will be negligible if

$$l_1 \ll 2\kappa a \tag{29}$$

and

$$l_0 \gg l_2^2/2\kappa a. \tag{30}$$

The first condition requires that

$$n \gg \epsilon_0/2\pi e^2 a, \tag{31}$$

and the second that

$$n \gg (\epsilon_0/4\pi e^2 a)\,(\chi_1 - \varphi_s - \zeta)/(\epsilon_0 - \zeta). \tag{31a}$$

These conditions are essentially equivalent to that given by Eq. (23), and lead to the conclusion that $n \gg 10^{13}$ in order that the metal have little influence on the space charge region. In this case of high density of surface states, the equation for the layer thickness reduces to that for the free surface of the semi-conductor:

$$l^2/l_1 + l - l_0 = 0. \tag{32}$$

Equation (32) may, of course, be used to estimate the thickness of the space charge region at the free surface of the semi-conductor regardless of the density of surface states. The limiting case of high density corresponds to

$$l_0 \gg l_1, \tag{33a}$$

or

$$n^2 \gg N\kappa\epsilon_0^2/2\pi e^2(\epsilon_0 - \zeta). \tag{33b}$$

This is essentially the requirement, stated above Eq. (15), that n be large compared with Nl. The approximate solution of Eq. (32) is then

$$l^2 \approx l_0 l_1.$$

The product $l_0 l_1$ is independent of n, and is just the square of the thickness of the Schottky layer for a barrier height

$$\varphi_0 = \epsilon_0 - \zeta. \tag{34}$$

This is the condition that the Fermi level cross the surface near the energy corresponding to zero surface states charge.

In the limiting case of a vanishingly small density of surface states, the thickness of the barrier layer is determined by setting the right-hand side of Eq. (28) to zero. This gives

$$\varphi_0 = \chi_1 - \varphi_s - \zeta. \tag{35}$$

The height of the barrier is equal to the difference in work functions.

Equation (28) may be used for intermediate cases.

PAPER 3

The Transistor, a Semi-conductor Triode†

J. BARDEEN and W. H. BRATTAIN

Bell Telephone Laboratories, Murray Hill, New Jersey

June 25, 1948

A THREE-ELEMENT electronic device which utilizes a newly discovered principle involving a semi-conductor as the basic element
is described. It may be employed as an amplifier, oscillator, and
for other purposes for which vacuum tubes are ordinarily used.
The device consists of three electrodes placed on a block of germanium[1] as shown schematically in Fig. 1. Two, called the

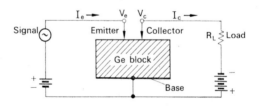

FIG. 1. Schematic of semi-conductor triode.

emitter and collector, are of the point-contact rectifier type and are
placed in close proximity (separation $\sim$.005 to .025 cm) on the
upper surface. The third is a large area low resistance contact on
the base.

† *The Physical Review*, **74**, 230 (1948).
[1] While the effect has been found with both silicon and germanium, we
describe only the use of the latter.

The germanium is prepared in the same way as that used for high back-voltage rectifiers.[2] In this form it is an N-type or excess semi-conductor with a resistivity of the order of 10 ohm cm. In the original studies, the upper surface was subjected to an additional anodic oxidation in a glycol borate soltuion[3] after it had been ground and etched in the usual way. The oxide is washed off and plays no direct role. It has since been found that other surface treatments are equally effective.[†] Both tungsten and phosphor bronze points have been used. The collector point may be electrically formed[‡] by passing large currents in the reverse direction.

Each point, when connected separately with the base electrode, has characteristics similar to those of the high back-voltage rectifier. Of critical importance for the operation of the device is the nature of the current in the forward direction. We believe, for reasons discussed in detail in the accompanying letter,[4] that there is a thin layer next to the surface of P-type (defect) conductivity. As a result, the current in the forward direction with respect to the block is composed in large part of holes, i.e., of carriers of sign opposite to those normally in excess in the body of the block.

When the two point contacts are placed close together on the surface and d.c. bias potentials are applied, there is a mutual influence which makes it possible to use the device to amplify a.c. signals. A circuit by which this may be accomplished is shown in Fig. 1. There is a small forward (positive) bias on the emitter, which causes a current of a few milliamperes to flow into the surface. A reverse (negative) bias is applied to the collector, large enough to make the collector current of the same order or greater

† Note the empirical approach to what has become an important aspect of modern transistors.

‡ The importance of electrical forming is not even implied here.

[2] The germanium was furnished by J. H. Scaff and H. C. Theuerer. For methods of preparation and information on the rectifier, see H. C. Torrey and C. A. Whitmer, *Crystal Rectifiers* (McGraw-Hill Book Company, Inc., New York, New York, 1948), Chap. 12.

[3] This surface treatment is due to R. B. Gibney, formerly of Bell Telephone Laboratories, now at Los Alamos Scientific Laboratory.

[4] W. H. Brattain and J. Bardeen, *Phys. Rev.*, this issue.

than the emitter current. The sign of the collector bias is such as to attract the holes which flow from the emitter so that a large part of the emitter current flows to and enters the collector. While the

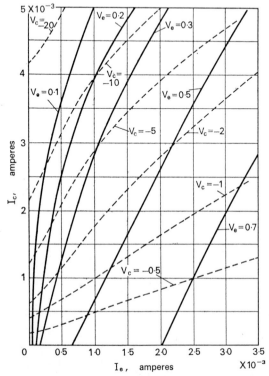

FIG. 2. D.C. characteristics of an experimental semi-conductor triode. The currents and voltages are as indicated in Fig. 1.

collector has a high impedance for flow of electrons into the semi-conductor, there is little impediment to the flow of holes into the point. If now the emitter current is varied by a signal voltage, there will be a corresponding variation in collector current. It has been found that the flow of holes from the emitter into the collector may alter the normal current flow from the base to the collector in such a way that the change in collector current is larger than the change in emitter current. Furthermore, the collector, being operated in the reverse direction as a rectifier, has a high impedance (10^4 to 10^5 ohms) and may be matched to a high impedance load. A large ratio of output to input voltage, of the same order as the ratio of the reverse to the forward impedance of the point, is obtained. There is a corresponding power amplification of the input signal.

The d.c. characteristics of a typical experimental unit are shown in Fig. 2. There are four variables, two currents and two voltages, with a functional relation between them. If two are specified the other two are determined. In the plot of Fig. 2 the emitter and collector currents I_e and I_c are taken as the independent variables and the corresponding voltages, V_e and V_c, measured relative to the base electrode, as the dependent variables. The conventional directions for the currents are as shown in Fig. 1. In normal operation, I_e, I_c, and V_e are positive, and V_c is negative.

The emitter current, I_e, is simply related to V_e and I_c. To a close approximation:

$$I_e = f(V_e + R_F I_c), \tag{1}$$

where R_F is a constant independent of bias. The interpretation is that the collector current lowers the potential of the surface in the vicinity of the emitter by $R_F I_c$, and thus increases the effective bias voltage on the emitter by an equivalent amount. The term $R_F I_c$ represents a positive feedback, which under some operating conditions is sufficient to cause instability.

The current amplification factor a is defined as

$$a = (\partial I_c / \partial I_e)_{V_c=\text{const.}}$$

This factor depends on the operating biases. For the unit shown in Fig. 2, a lies between one and two if $V_c < -2$.

Using the circuit of Fig. 1, power gains of over 20 db have been obtained. Units have been operated as amplifiers at frequencies up to 10 megacycles.

We wish to acknowledge our debt to W. Shockley for initiating and directing the research program that led to the discovery on which this development is based. We are also indebted to many other of our colleagues at these Laboratories for material assistance and valuable suggestions.

Nature of the Forward
Current in Germanium Point Contacts†

W. H. BRATTAIN and J. BARDEEN

Bell Telephone Laboratories, Murray Hill, New Jersey

June 25, 1948

THE forward current in germanium high back-voltage rectifiers[1] is much larger than that estimated from the formula for the spreading resistance, R_s, in a medium of uniform resistivity, ρ. For a contact of diamater d,

$$R_s = \rho/2d.$$

Taking as typical values $\rho = 10$ ohm cm and $d = .0025$ cm, the formula gives $R_s = 2000$ ohms. Actually the forward current at one volt may be as large as 5 to 10 mA, and the differential resistance is not more than a few hundred ohms. Bray[2] has attempted to account for this discrepancy by assuming that the resistivity decreases with increasing field, and has made tests to observe such an effect.

In connection with the development of the semi-conductor triode discussed in the preceding letter,[3] the nature of the excess conductivity has been investigated by means of probe measurements of the potential in the vicinity of the point.[4] Measurements

† *The Physical Review*, **74**, 231 (1948).

[1] H. C. Torrey and C. A. Whitmer, *Crystal Rectifiers*, McGraw-Hill Book Company, Inc., New York, New York, 1948, Chap. 12.

[2] R. Bray, *Bull. Am. Phys. Soc.* **23**, 21 (1948), Abstract 63 of Washington Meeting, April 29–30, 1948.

[3] J. Bardeen and W. H. Brattain, *Phys. Rev.*, this issue.

[4] The micromanipulator used for this work was designed by W. L. Bond.

were made on the plane surface of a thick block. Various surface treatments, such as anodizing, oxidizing, and sand blasting were used in different tests, in addition to the etch customarily employed in the preparation of rectifiers.

The potential, $V(r)$, at a distance r from a point carrying a current, I, is measured relative to a large area low resistance contact at the base. In Fig. 1 we have plotted some typical data for a surface prepared by grinding and etching, and then oxidizing in air at 500°C for one hour. The ordinate is $2\pi r V(r)/I$ which for a

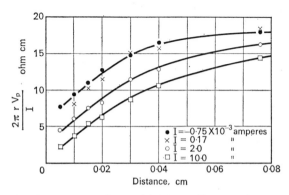

FIG. 1. Measurements of potential, V_p at a distance r from a point contact throughout which a current I is flowing into a germanium surface.

body of uniform resistivity, ρ, should be a constant equal in magnitude to ρ. Actually it is found that the ratio is much less than ρ at small distances from the point, and increases with r, approaching the value ρ asymptotically at large distances. The departure from the constant value indicates an excess conductivity in the neighborhood of the point.

The manner in which the excess conductivity varies with current indicates that two components are involved. One is ohmic and is represented by the upper curve of Fig. 1 which applies for reverse (negative) currents and for small forward currents. This component is attributed to a thin conducting layer on the surface which is believed to be *P*-type (i.e. of opposite type to that of the block). A layer with a surface conductivity of .002 mhos is sufficient to account for the departure of the upper curve from a constant value. The second component of the excess conductivity increases with increasing forward current, and is attributed to an increase in the concentration of carriers (holes and electrons) in the vicinity of the point with increasing forward bias. The relative

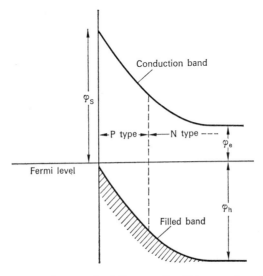

Fig. 2. Schematic energy level diagram of an N-type semi-conductor with a thin layer of P-type conductivity next to the surface.

as well as the absolute magnitudes of these two components vary with surface treatment. Two different crystal faces on the same block may have different charactersitics.

The thin *P*-type conducting layer may result from an excess of acceptor impurities near the surface or from a space charge barrier layer which is sufficient to raise the filled band to a position close to the Fermi level. The latter situation is shown in the energy level diagram of Fig. 2. It is assumed that there is a uniform excess of donor impurities in the interior. The surface states are such as to require the Fermi level to cross the surface near the top of the filled band.[5] The conductivity in the layer right next to the surface is then *P*-type, and this layer is separated from the normal *N*-type region in the interior by the *P–N* rectifying barrier.† The energy gap in germanium is about 0.75 eV. Approximate values for the other energies shown on the diagram are: $\varphi_e = 0.25$ eV, $\varphi_h = 0.50$ eV, $\varphi_s = 0.70$ eV. The thickness of the space charge layer is about 10^{-4} cm.

Benzer[6] has found that the activation energy of the saturation component of the reverse current in a germanium rectifier is almost equal to the energy gap (0.67 eV as compared with 0.75 eV). This is in confirmation of the picture of *P*-type conductivity at the surface.

A large part of the current in both the forward and reverse directions flows *via* the *P*-type conducting layer at the surface. The conditions in the *immediate* vicinity (< .01 cm) of the point are complicated by the requirement of conservation of both hole current and electron current. The voltage drop is determined principally by that part of the current (in this case electrons) which encounters the highest resistance. This accounts for the high resistances found for reverse biases and for small foward biases, in spite of the relatively high conductivity of the surface layer.

† Essentially *p–n* junction rectification.
[5] J. Bardeen, *Phys. Rev.* **71**, 717 (1947).
[6] S. Benzer, *Temperature Dependence of High Voltage Germanium Rectifier D-C Characteristics*, NDRC 14–579, Purdue University, October 31, 1945.

PAPER 5

Physical Principles
Involved in Transistor Action †

J. Bardeen and W. H. Brattain

Bell Telephone Laboratories, Murray Hill, New Jersey

(Received December 27, 1948)

Summary

The transistor in the form described herein consists of two point-contact electrodes, called emitter and collector, placed in close proximity on the upper face of a small block of germanium. The base electrode, the third element of the triode, is a large area, low resistance contact on the lower face. Each point contact has characteristics similar to those of the high back-voltage rectifier. When suitable d.c. bias potentials are applied, the device may be used to amplify a.c. signals. A signal introduced between the emitter and base appears in amplified form between collector and base. The emitter is biased in the positive direction, which is that of easy flow. A larger negative or reverse voltage is applied to the collector. Transistor action depends on the fact that electrons in semiconductors can carry current in two different ways: by excess or conduction electrons and by defect "electrons" or holes. The germanium used is n-type, i.e., the carriers are conduction electrons. Current from the emitter is composed in large part of holes, i.e., of carriers of opposite sign to those normally in excess in the body of the block. The holes are attracted by the field of the collector current, so that a large part of the emitter current, introduced at low impedance, flows into the collector circuit and through a high impedance load. There is a voltage gain and a power gain of an input signal. There may be current amplification as well.

The influence of the emitter current, I_e, on collector current, I_c, is expressed in terms of a current multiplication factor, α, which gives the rate of change of I_c with respect to I_e at constant collector voltage. Values of α in typical units range from about 1 to 3. It is shown in a general way how α depends on bias voltages, frequency, temperature, and electrode spacing. There is an influence of collector current on emitter current in the nature of a positive feedback which under some operating conditions may lead to instability.

† *The Physical Review* **75**, (8) 1208 (1949).

The way the concentrations and mobilities of electrons and holes in germanium depend on impurities and on temperature is described briefly. The theory of germanium point contact rectifiers is discussed in terms of the Mott–Schottky theory. The barrier layer is such as to raise the levels of the filled band to a position close to the Fermi level at the surface, giving an inversion layer of *p*-type or defect conductivity. There is considerable evidence that the barrier layer is intrinsic and occurs at the free surface, independent of a metal contact. Potential probe tests on some surfaces indicate considerable surface conductivity which is attributed to the *p*-type layer. All surfaces tested show an excess conductivity in the vicinity of the point contact which increases with forward current and is attributed to a flow of holes into the body of the germanium, the space charge of the holes being compensated by electrons. It is shown why such a flow is to be expected for the type of barrier layer which exists in germanium, and that this flow accounts for the large currents observed in the forward direction. In the transistor, holes may flow from the emitter to the collector either in the surface layer or through the body of the germanium. Estimates are made of the field produced by the collector current, of the transit time for holes, of the space charge produced by holes flowing into the collector, and of the feedback resistance which gives the influence of collector current on emitter current. These calculations confirm the general picture given of transistor action.

I. Introduction

THE transistor, a semiconductor triode which in its present form uses a small block of germanium as the basic element, has been described briefly in the Letters to the Editor columns of the *Physical Review*.[1] Accompanying this letter were two further communications on related subjects.[2, 3] Since these initial publications a number of talks describing the characteristics of the device and the theory of its operation have been given by the authors and by other members of the Bell Telephone Laboratories staff.[4]

[1] J. Bardeen and W. H. Brattain, *Phys. Rev.* **74**, 230 (1948).

[2] W. H. Brattain and J. Bardeen, *Phys. Rev.* **74**, 231 (1948).

[3] W. Shockley and G. L. Pearson, *Phys. Rev.* **74**, 232 (1948).

[4] This paper was presented in part at the Chicago meeting of the American Physical Society, Nov. 26, 27, 1948. W. Shockley and the authors presented a paper on "The Electronic Theory of the Transistor" at the Berkeley meeting of the National Academy of Sciences, Nov. 15–17, 1948. A talk was given by one of the authors (W. H. B.) at the National Electronics Conference at Chicago, Nov. 4, 1948. A number of talks have been given at local meetings by J. A. Becker and other members of the Bell Telephone Laboratories Staff, as well as by the authors.

Several articles have appeared in the technical literature.[5] We plan to give here an outline of the history of the development, to give some further data on the characteristics and to discuss the physical principles involved. Included is a review of the nature of electrical conduction in germanium and of the theory of the germanium point-contact rectifier.

A schematic diagram of one form of transistor is shown in Fig. 1. Two point contacts, similar to those used in point-contact

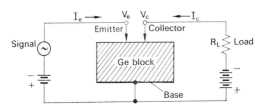

FIG. 1. Schematic of transistor showing circuit for amplification of an a.c. signal and conventional direction for currents. Note bias currents I_e and V_e are normally positive, I_c and V_c negative.

rectifiers, are placed in close proximity ($\sim$0.005–0.025 cm) on the upper surface of a small block of germanium. One of these, biased in the forward direction, is called the emitter. The second, biased in the reverse direction, is called the collector. A large area, low resistance contact on the lower surface, called the base electrode, is the third element of the triode. The transistor can be used for many functions now performed by vacuum tubes.

During the war, a large amount of research on the properties of germanium and silicon was carried out by a number of university, government, and industrial laboratories in connection with the development of point-contact rectifiers for radar. This work is

[5] Properties and characteristics of the transistor are given by J. A. Becker and J. N. Shive in *Elec. Eng.* **68**, 215 (1949). A coaxial form of transistor is described by W. E. Kock and R. L. Wallace, Jr. in *Elec. Eng.* **68**, 222 (1949). See also "The Transistor, A Crystal Triode," D. G. F. and F. H. R. *Electronics*, September (1948) and a series of articles by S. Young White in *Audio Eng.*, August through December (1948).

summarized in the book of Torrey and Whitmer.[6] The properties of germanium as a semiconductor and as a rectifier have been investigated by a group working under the direction of K. Lark-Horovitz at Purdue University. Work at the Bell Laboratories[7] was initiated by R. S. Ohl before the war in connection with the development of silicon rectifiers for use as detectors at microwave frequencies. Research and development on both germanium and silicon rectifiers during and since the war has been done in large part by a group under J. H. Scaff. The background of information obtained in these various investigations has been invaluable.

The general research program leading to the transistor was initiated and directed by W. Shockley. Work on germanium and silicon was emphasized because they are simpler to understand than most other semiconductors. *One of the investigations undertaken was the study of the modulation of conductance of a thin film of semiconductor by an electric field applied by an electrode insulated from the film.*[3]† If, for example, the film is made one plate of a parallel plate condenser, a charge is induced on the surface. If the individual charges which make up the induced charge are mobile, the conductance of the film will depend on the voltage applied to the condenser. The first experiments performed to measure this effect indicated that most of the induced charge was not mobile. This result, taken along with other unexplained phenomena such as the small contact potential difference between n- and p-type silicon[8] and the independence of the rectifying properties of the point-contact rectifier on the work function of the metal point led one of the authors to an explanation in terms of surface states.[9] This work led to the concept that space-charge barrier layers may be present at the free surfaces of semiconductors such as germanium and silicon, independent of a metal contact. Two experiments immediately suggested were to measure the dependence of

---

† Italics mine (E.J.M.K.).

[6] H. C. Torrey and C. A. Whitmer, *Crystal Rectifiers*, McGraw-Hill Book Company, Inc., New York, 1948.

[7] J. H. Scaff and R. S. Ohl, *Bell Sys. Tech. J.* **26,** 1 (1947).

[8] Walter E. Meyerhof, *Phys. Rev.* **71,** 727 (1947).

[9] John Bardeen, *Phys. Rev.* **71,** 717 (1947).

contact potential on impurity concentration[10] and to measure the change of contact potential on illuminating the surface with light.[11] Both of these experiments were successful and confirmed the theory. It was while studying the latter effect with a silicon surface immersed in a liquid that it was found that the density of surface charges and the field in the space-charge region could be varied by applying a potential across an electrolyte in contact with the silicon surface.[12] While studying the effect of field applied by an electrolyte on the current voltage characteristic of a high back-voltage germanium rectifier, the authors were led to the concept that a portion of the current was being carried by holes flowing near the surface. Upon replacing the electrolyte with a metal contact transistor action was discovered.

The germanium used in the transistor is an n-type or excess semiconductor with a resistivity of the order of 10 ohm cm and is the same as the material used in high back-voltage germanium rectifiers.[13] All of the material we have used was prepared by J. C. Scaff and H. C. Theuerer of the metallurgical group of the Laboratories.

While different metals may be used for the contact points, most work has been done with phosphor bronze points. The spring contacts are made with wire from 0.002 to 0.005″ in diameter. The ends are cut in the form of a wedge so that the two contacts can be placed close together. The actual contact area is probably no more than about 10^{-6} cm^2.

The treatment of the germanium surface is similar to that used in making high back-voltage rectifiers.[14] The surface is ground flat and then etched. In some cases special additional treatments such as anodizing the surface or oxidation at 500°C have been used. The

[10] W. H. Brattain and W. Shockley, *Phys. Rev.* **72**, 345(L) (1947).

[11] Walter H. Brattain, *Phys. Rev.* **72**, 345(L) (1947).

[12] R. B. Gibney, formerly of Bell Telephone Laboratories, now at Los Alamos Scientific Laboratory, worked on chemical problems for the semi-conductor group, and the authors are grateful to him for a number of valuable ideas and for considerable assistance.

[13] J. H. Scaff and H. C. Theuerer, *Preparation of High Back Voltage Germanium Rectifiers*, NDRC 14–155, Oct. 24, 1945. See reference 6, Chap. 12.

[14] The surface treatment is described in reference 6, p. 369.

oxide films formed in these processes wash off easily and contact is made to the germanium surface.

The circuit of Fig. 1 shows how the transistor may be used to amplify a small a.c. signal. The emitter is biased in the forward (positive) direction so that a small d.c. current, of the order of 1 mA, flows into the germanium block. The collector is biased in the reverse (negative) direction with a higher voltage so that a d.c. current of a few milliamperes flows out through the collector point and through the load circuit. It is found that the current in the collector circuit is sensitive to and may be controlled by changes of current from the emitter. In fact, when the emitter current is varied by changing the emitter voltage, keeping the collector voltage constant, the change in collector current may be larger than the change in emitter current. As the emitter is biased in the direction of easy flow, a small a.c. voltage, and thus a small power input, is sufficient to vary the emitter current. The collector is biased in the direction of high resistance and may be matched to a high resistance load. The a.c. voltage and power in the load circuit are much larger than those in the input. An over-all power gain of a factor of 100 (or 20 db) can be obtained in favorable cases.

Terminal characteristics of an experimental transistor[15] are illustrated in Fig. 2, which shows how the current–voltage characteristic of the collector is changed by the current flowing from the emitter. Transistor characteristics, and the way they change with separation between the points, with temperature, and with frequency, are discussed in Section II.

The explanation of the action of the transistor depends on the nature of the current flowing from the emitter. It is well known that in semiconductors there are two ways by which the electrons can carry electricity which differ in the signs of the effective mobile charges.[16] The negative carriers are excess electrons which

[15] The transistor whose characteristics are given in Fig. 2 is one of an experimented pilot production which is under the general direction of J. A. Morton.

[16] See, for example, A. H. Wilson, *Semi-Conductors and Metals*, Cambridge University Press, London, 1939, or F. Seitz, *The Modern Theory of Solids*, McGraw-Hill Book Company, Inc., New York, 1940, Sec. 68.

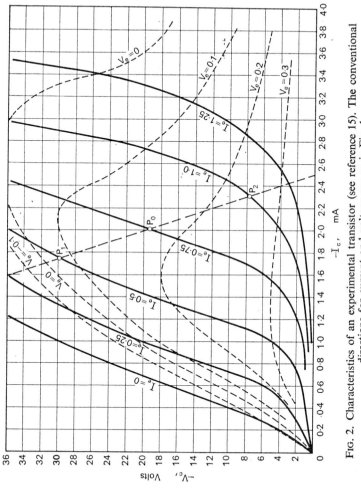

FIG. 2. Characteristics of an experimental transistor (see reference 15). The conventional directions for current and voltage are as in Fig. 1.

are free to move and are denoted by the term conduction electrons or simply electrons. They have energies in the conduction band of the crystal. The positive carriers are missing or defect "electrons" and are denoted by the term "holes." They represent unoccupied energy states in the uppermost normally filled band of the crystal. The conductivity is called n- or p-type depending on whether the mobile charges normally in excess in the material under equilibrium conditions are electrons (negative carriers) or holes (positive carriers). The germanium used in the transistor is n-type with about 5×10^{14} conduction electrons per cc; or about one electron per 10^8 atoms. Transistor action depends on the fact that the current from the emitter is composed in large part of *holes*; that is, of carriers of opposite sign to those normally in excess in the body of the semiconductor.

The collector is biased in the reverse, or negative direction. Current flowing in the germanium toward the collector point provides an electric field which is in such a direction as to attract the holes flowing from the emitter. When the emitter and collector are placed in close proximity, a large part of the hole current from the emitter will flow to the collector and into the collector circuit. The nature of the collector contact is such as to provide a high resistance barrier to the flow of electrons from the metal to the semiconductor, but there is little impediment to the flow of holes into the contact. This theory explains how the change in collector current might be as large as but not how it can be larger than the change in emitter current. The fact that the collector current may actually change more than the emitter current is believed to result from an alteration of the space charge in the barrier layer at the collector by the hole current flowing into the junction. The increase in density of space charge and in field strength make it easier for electrons to flow out from the collector, so that there is an increase in electron current. It is better to think of the hole current from the emitter as modifying the current–voltage characteristic of the collector, rather than as simply adding to the current flowing to the collector.

In Section III we discuss the nature of the conductivity of germanium, and in Section IV the theory of the current–voltage characteristic of a germanium-point contact. In the latter section we attempt to show why the emitter current is composed of carriers of opposite sign to those normally in excess in the body of germanium. Section V is concerned with some aspects of the theory of transistor action. A complete quantitative theory is not yet available.

There is evidence that the rectifying barrier in germanium is internal and occurs at the free surface, independent of the metal contact.[9, 17] The barrier contains what Schottky and Spenke[18] call an inversion region; that is, a change of conductivity type. The outermost part of the barrier next to the surface is p-type. The p-type region is very thin, of the order of 10^{-5} cm in thickness. An important question is whether there is a sufficient density of holes in this region to provide appreciable lateral conductivity along the surface. Some evidence bearing on this point is described below.

Transistor action was first discovered on a germanium surface which was subjected to an anodic oxidation treatment in a glycol borate solution after it had been ground and etched in the usual way for diodes. Much of the early work was done on surfaces which were oxidized by heating in air. In both cases the oxide is washed off and plays no direct role. Some of these surfaces were tested for surface conductivity by potential probe tests. Surface conductivities, on a unit area basis, of the order of 0.0005 to 0.002 mhos were found.[2] The value of 0.0005 represents about the lower limit of detection possible by the method used. It is inferred that the observed surface conductivity is that of the p-type layer, although there has been no direct proof of this. In later work it was found that the oxidation treatment is not essential for transistor action. Good transistors can be made with surfaces prepared in the usual way for high back-voltage rectifiers provided that the collector point is electrically formed. Such surfaces exhibit no measurable surface conductivity.

One question that may be asked is whether the holes flow from

[17] The nature of the barrier is discussed in Section IV.
[18] W. Schottky and E. Spenke, *Wiss. Veroff. Siemens Werken*, **18,** 225 (1939).

the emitter to the collector mainly in the surface layer or whether they flow through the body of the germanium. The early experiments suggested flow along the surface. W. Shockley proposed a modified arrangement in which in effect the emitter and collector are on opposite sides of a thin slab, so that the holes flow directly across through the semiconductor. Independently, J. N. Shive made, by grinding and etching, a piece of germanium in the form of a thin flat wedge.[19] Point contacts were placed directly opposite each other on the two opposite faces where the thickness of the wedge was about 0.01 cm. A third large area contact was made to the base of the wedge. When the two points were connected as emitter and collector, and the collector was electrically formed, transistor action was obtained which was comparable to that found with the original arrangement. There is no doubt that in this case the holes are flowing directly through the n-type germanium from the emitter to the collector. With two points close together on a plane surface holes may flow either through the surface layer or through the body of the semi-conductor.

Still later, at the suggestion of W. Shockley, J. R. Haynes[20] further established that holes flow into the body of the germanium. A block of germanium was made in the form of a thin slab and large area electrodes were placed at the two ends. Emitter and collector electrodes were placed at variable separations on one face of the slab. The field acting between these electrodes could be varied by passing currents along the length of the slab. The collector was biased in the reverse direction so that a small d.c. current was drawn into the collector. A signal introduced at the emitter in the form of a pulse was detected at a slightly later time in the collector circuit. From the way the time interval, of the order of a few microseconds, depends on the field, the mobility and sign of the carriers were determined. It was found that the carriers are positively charged, and that the mobility is the same as that of holes in bulk germanium (1000 cm²/volt sec.).

These experiments clarify the nature of the excess conductivity

[19] John N. Shive, *Phys. Rev.* **75,** 689 (1949).
[20] J. R. Haynes and W. Shockley, *Phys. Rev.* **75,** 691 (1949).

observed in the forward direction in high back-voltage germanium rectifiers which has been investigated by R. Bray, K. Lark-Horovitz, and R. N. Smith[21] and by Bray.[22] These authors attributed the excess conductivity to the strong electric field which exists in the vicinity of the point contact. Bray has made direct experimental tests to observe the relation between conductivity and field strength. We believe that the excess conductivity arises from holes injected into the germanium at the contact. Holes are introduced because of the nature of the barrier layer rather than as a direct result of the electric field. This has been demonstrated by an experiment of E. J. Ryder and W. Shockley.[23] A thin slab of germanium was cut in the form of a pie-shaped wedge and electrodes placed at the narrow and wide boundaries of the wedge. When a current is passed between the electrodes, the field strength is large at the narrow end of the wedge and small near the opposite electrode. An excess conductivity was observed when the narrow end was made positive; none when the wide end was positive. The magnitude of the current flow was the same in both cases. Holes injected at the narrow end lower the resistivity in the region which contributes most to the over-all resistance. When the current is in the opposite direction, any holes injected enter in a region of low field and do not have sufficient lifetime to be drawn down to the narrow end and so do not alter the resistance very much. With some surface treatments, the excess conductivity resulting from hole injection may be enhanced by a surface conductivity as discussed above.

The experimental procedure used during the present investigation is of interest. Current–voltage characteristics of a given point contact were displayed on a d.c. oscilloscope.[24] The change or modulation of this characteristic produced by a signal impressed on a neighboring electrode or point contact could be easily observed. Since the input impedance of the scope was 10 megohms,

[21] R. Bray, K. Lark-Horovitz, and R. N. Smith, *Phys. Rev.* **72**, 530 (1947).

[22] R. Bray, *Phys. Rev.* **74**, 1218 (1948).

[23] E. J. Ryder and W. Shockley, *Phys. Rev.* **75**, 310 (1949).

[24] This instrument was designed and built by H. R. Moore, who aided the authors a great deal in connection with instrumentation and circuit problems.

and the gain of the amplifiers such that the lower limit of sensitivity was of the order of a millivolt, the oscilloscope was also used as a very high impedance voltmeter for probe measurements. Means were included for matching the potential to be measured with an adjustable d.c. potential the value of which could be read on a meter. A micromanipulator designed by W. L. Bond was used to adjust the positions of the contact points.

II. Some Transistor Characteristics

The static characteristics of the transistor are completely specified by four variables which may be taken as the emitter and collector currents, I_e and I_c, and the corresponding voltages, V_e and V_c. As shown in the schematic diagram of Fig. 1, the conventional directions for current flow are taken as positive into the germanium and the terminal voltages are relative to the base electrode. Thus I_e and V_e are normally positive, I_c and V_c negative.

There is a functional relation between the four variables such that if two are specified the other two are determined. Any pair may be taken as the independent variables. As the transistor is essentially a current-operated device, it is more in accord with the physics involved to choose the currents rather than the voltages. All fields in the semiconductor outside of the space charge regions immediately surrounding the point contacts are determined by the currents, and it is the current flowing from the emitter which controls the current–voltage characteristic of the collector. The voltages are single-valued functions of the currents, but, because of inherent feedback, the currents may be double-valued functions of the voltages. In reference 1, the characteristics of an experimental transistor were shown by giving the constant voltage contours on a plot in which the independent variables I_e and I_c are plotted along the coordinate axes.

In the following we give further characteristics, and show in a general way how they depend on the spacing between the points, on the temperature, and on the frequency. The data were taken mainly on experimental set-ups on a laboratory bench, and are not to be taken as necessarily typical of the characteristics of finished units. They do indicate in a general way the type of results which can be obtained. Characteristics of units made in pilot production have been given elsewhere.[5]

The data plotted in reference 1 were taken on a transistor made with phosphor bronze points on a surface which was oxidized and on which potential probe tests gave evidence for considerable surface conductivity. The collector resistance is small in units prepared in this way. In Fig. 2 are shown the characteristics of a unit[15] in which the surface was prepared in a different manner. The surface was ground and etched in the usual way,[14] but was not subjected to the oxidation treatment. Phosphor bronze contact points made from 5-mil wire were used. The collector was electrically formed by passing large currents in the reverse direction. This reduced the resistance of the collector in the reverse direction, improving the transistor action. However, it remained considerably higher than that of the collector on the oxidized surface.

While there are many ways of plotting the data, we have chosen to give the collector voltage, V_c, as a function of the collector current, I_c, with the emitter current, I_e, taken as a parameter. This plot shows in a direct manner the influence of the emitter current on the current–voltage characteristic of the collector. The curve corresponding to $I_e = 0$ is just the normal reverse characteristic of the collector as a rectifier. The other curves show how the characteristic shifts to the right, corresponding to larger collector currents, with increase in emitter current. It may be noted that the change in collector current for fixed collector voltage is larger than the change in emitter current. The current amplification factor, α, defined by

$$a = -(\partial I_c / \partial I_e) v_{c=\text{const}}, \qquad (\text{II}.1)$$

is between 2 and 3 throughout most of the plot.

The dotted lines on Fig. 2 correspond to constant values of the emitter voltage, V_e. By interpolating between the contours, all four variables corresponding to a given operating point may be obtained. The V_e contours reach a maximum for I_e about 0.7 mA and have a negative slope beyond. To the left of the maximum, V_e increases with I_e as one follows along a line corresponding to $V_c = $ const. To the right, V_e decreases as I_e increases, corresponding to a negative input admittance. For given values of V_e and V_c, there are two possible operating points. Thus for $V_e = 0.1$ and $V_c = -20$ one may have $I_e = 0.3$ mA, $I_c = -1.1$ mA or $I_e = 1.0$, $I_c = -2.7$.

The negative resistance and instability result from the effect of the collector current on the emitter current.[1] The collector current lowers the potential of the surface in the vicinity of the emitter and increases the effective bias on the emitter by an equivalent amount. This potential drop is $R_F I_c$, where R_F is a feed-back resistance which may depend on the currents flowing. The effective bias on the emitter is then $V_e - R_F I_c$, and we may write

$$I_e = f(V_e - R_F I_c), \tag{II.2}$$

where the function gives the forward characteristic of the emitter point. In some cases R_F is approximately constant over the operating range; in other cases R_F decreases with increasing I_e as the conductivity of the germanium in the vicinity of the points increases with forward current. Increase of I_e by a change of V_e increases the magnitude of I_c, which by the feedback still further increases I_e. Instability may result. Some consequences will be discussed further in connection with the a.c. characteristics.

Also shown in Fig. 2 is a load line corresponding to a battery voltage of -100 in the output circuit and a load, R_L, of 40,000 ohms, the equation of the line being

$$V_e = -100 - 40 \times 10^3 I_c. \tag{II.3}$$

The load is an approximate match to the collector resistance, as given by the slope of the solid lines. If operated between the points P_1 and P_2, the output voltage is 8.0 volts r.m.s. and the output current is 0.20 mA. The corresponding values at the input are 0.07 and 0.18, so that the over-all power gain is

$$\text{Gain} \sim 8 \times 0.20/(0.07 \times 0.18) \sim 125, \tag{II.4}$$

which is about 21 db. This is the available gain for a generator with an impedance of 400 ohms, which is an approximate match for the input impedance.

We turn next to the equations for the a.c. characteristics. For small deviations from an operating point, we may write

$$\Delta V_e = R_{11}\Delta I_e + R_{12}\Delta I_c, \tag{II.5}$$

$$\Delta V_c = R_{21}\Delta I_e + R_{22}\Delta I_c, \tag{II.6}$$

in which we have taken the currents as the independent variables and the directions of currents and voltages as in Fig. 1. The differentials represent small changes from the operating point, and may be small a.c. signals. The coefficients are defined by:

$$R_{11} = (\partial V_e/\partial I_e)_{I_c=\text{const}}, \tag{II.7}$$

$$R_{12} = (\partial V_e/\partial I_c)_{I_e=\text{const}}, \tag{II.8}$$

$$R_{21} = (\partial V_c/\partial I_e)_{I_c=\text{const}}, \tag{II.9}$$

$$R_{22} = (\partial V_c/\partial I_c)_{I_e=\text{const}}. \tag{II.10}$$

These coefficients are all positive and have the dimensions of resistances. They are functions of the d.c. bias currents, I_e and I_c which define the operating point. For $I_e = 0.75$ mA and $I_c = -2$ mA the coefficients of the unit of Fig. 2 have the following approximate values:

$$\begin{aligned}
R_{11} &= 800 \text{ ohms}, \\
R_{12} &= 300, \\
R_{21} &= 100,000, \\
R_{22} &= 40,000.
\end{aligned} \tag{II.11}$$

Equation (II.5) gives the emitter characteristic. The coefficient R_{11} is the input resistance for a fixed collector current (open circuit for a.c.). To a close approximation, R_{11} is independent of I_c, and is just the forward resistance of the emitter point when a current I_e is flowing. The coefficient R_{12} is the feedback or base resistance, and is equal to R_F as defined by Eq. (II.2) in case R_F is a constant. Both R_{11} and R_{12} are of the order of a few hundred ohms, R_{12} usually being smaller than R_{11}.

Equation (II.6) depends mainly on the collector and on the flow of holes from the emitter to the collector. The ratio R_{21}/R_{22} is just the current amplification factor α as defined by Eq. (II.1). Thus we may write

$$\Delta V_c = R_{22}(\alpha \Delta I_e + \Delta I_c). \tag{II.12}$$

The coefficient R_{22} is the collector resistance for fixed emitter current (open circuit for a.c.), and is the order of 10,000–50,000 ohms. Except in the range of large I_e and small I_c, the value of R_{22} is relatively independent of I_e. The factor α generally is small when I_c is small compared with I_e, and increases with I_c, approaching a constant value the order of 1 to 4 when I_c is several times I_e.

The a.c. power gain with the circuit of Fig. 1 depends on the operating point (the d.c. bias currents) and on the load impedance. The positive feedback represented by R_{12} increases the available gain, and it is possible to get very large power gains by operating near a point of instability. In giving the gain under such conditions, the impedance of the input generator should be specified. Alternatively, one can give the gain which would exist with no feedback. The maximum available gain neglecting feedback, obtained when the load R_L is equal to the collector resistance R_{22} and the impedance of the generator is equal to the emitter resistance, R_{11}, is:

$$\text{Gain} = \alpha^2 R_{22}/4R_{11}, \tag{II.13}$$

which is the ratio of the collector to the emitter resistance multiplied by $\frac{1}{4}$ the square of the current amplification factor. This gives the a.c. power delivered to the load divided by the a.c. power fed into the transistor. Substituting the values listed above (Eqs. (II.11)) for the unit whose characteristics are shown in Fig. 2 gives a gain of about 80 times (or 19 db) for the operating point P_0. This is to be compared with the gain of 21 db estimated above for operation between P_1 and P_2. The difference of 2 db represents the increase in gain by feedback, which was omitted in Eq. (II.13).

Equations (II.5) and (II.6) may be solved to express the currents as functions of the voltages, giving

$$\Delta I_e = Y_{11}\Delta V_e + Y_{12}\Delta V_c, \tag{II.14}$$

$$\Delta I_c = Y_{21}\Delta V_e + Y_{22}\Delta V_c, \tag{II.15}$$

where

$$Y_{11} = R_{22}/D, \qquad Y_{12} = -R_{12}/D, \tag{II.16}$$
$$Y_{21} = -R_{21}/D, \qquad Y_{22} = R_{11}/D,$$

and D is the determinant of the coefficients

$$D = R_{11}R_{22} - R_{12}R_{21}. \tag{II.17}$$

The admittances, Y_{11} and Y_{22} are negative if D is negative, and the transistor is then unstable if the terminals are short-circuited for a.c. currents. Stability can be attained if there is sufficient impedance in the input and output circuits exterior to the transistor. Feedback and instability are increased by adding resistance in series with the base electrode. Further discussion of this subject would carry us too far into circuit theory and applications. From the standpoint of transistor design, it is desirable to keep the feedback resistance, R_{12}, as small as possible.

Variation with Spacing

One of the important parameters affecting the operation of the transistor is the spacing between the point electrodes. Measurements to investigate this effect have been made on a number of germanium surfaces. Tests were made with use of a micromanipulator to adjust the positions of the points. The germanium was generally in the form of a slab from 0.05 to 0.20 cm thick, the lower surface of which was rhodium plated to form a low resistant contact, and the upper plane surface ground and etched, or otherwise treated to give a surface suitable for transistor action. The collector point was usually kept fixed, since it is more critical, and the emitter point moved. Measurements were made with formed collector points. Most of the data have been obtained on surfaces oxidized as described below.

As expected, the emitter current has less and less influence on the collector as the separation, s,[25] is increased. This is shown by a decrease in R_{21}, or α, with s. The effect of the collector current on the emitter, represented by the feed-back resistance R_{12}, also decreases with increase in s. The other coefficients, R_{11} and R_{22}, are but little influenced by spacing. Figures 3, 4, and 5 illustrate the variation of R_{12} and α with the separation. Shown are results

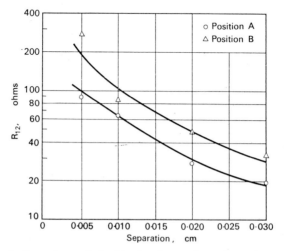

FIG. 3. Dependence of a feed-back resistance R_{12} on electrode separation for two different parts A and B of the same germanium surface. The surface has been oxidized by heating in air.

for two different collector points A and B on different parts of the same germanium surface.[26] In making the measurements, the bias currents were kept fixed as the spacing was varied. For collector A, $I_e = 1.0$ mA and $I_c = 3.8$ mA; for collector B, $I_e = 1.0$ mA and $I_c = 4.0$ mA. The values of R_{11} and R_{22} were about 300 and 10,000, respectively, in both cases.

[25] Measured between centers of the contact areas.

[26] The surface had been oxidized, and potential probe measurements (reference 2) gave evidence for considerable surface conductivity.

Figure 4 shows that α decreases approximately exponentially with *s* for separations from 0.005 cm to 0.030 cm, the rate of decrease being about the same in all cases. Extrapolating down to *s* = 0 indicates that a further increase of only about 25 percent in α could be obtained by decreasing the spacing below 0.005 cm.

Figure 5 shows that the decrease of α with distance is dependent on the germanium sample used. Curve 1 is similar to the results in Fig. 4. Curve 2 is for a germanium slice with the same surface treatment but from a different melt.

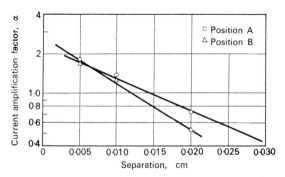

FIG. 4. Dependence of current amplification factor α on electrode separation for formed and unformed collector points. Positions *A* and *B* as in Fig. 3.

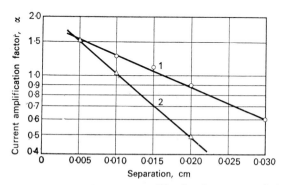

FIG. 5. Dependence of current amplification factor α on electrode separation for germanium surfaces from two different melts, 1 and 2.

Figure 4 shows the corresponding results for R_{12}. There is an approximate inverse relationship between R_{12} and s.

Another way to illustrate the decreased influence of the emitter on the collector with increase in spacing is to plot the collector characteristic for fixed emitter current at different spacings.

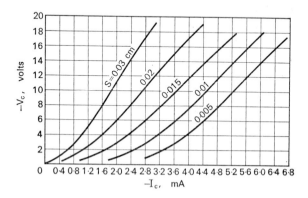

FIG. 6. Collector characteristic V_c vs. I_c for fixed I_e but variable difference of separation.

Figure 6 is such a plot for a different surface which was ground flat, etched, and then oxidized at 500°C in moist air for 1 hour. The resultant oxide film was washed off.[27] The emitter current, I_e, was kept constant at 1.0 mA.

Data taken on the same surface have been plotted in other ways. As the spacing increases, more emitter current is required to produce the same change in collector current. The fraction of the emitter current which is effective at the collector decreases with spacing. It is of interest to keep V_c and I_c fixed by varying I_e as s is changed and to plot the values of I_e so obtained as a function of s. Such a plot is shown in Fig. 7. The collector voltage, V_c, is fixed at −15 volts. Curves are shown for $I_c = -3, -4, -6,$ and −8 mA.

[27] Potential probe measurements on the same surface, given in reference 2, gave evidence of surface conductivity.

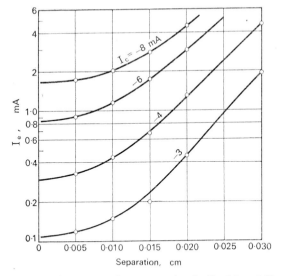

FIG. 7. Emitter current I_e vs. separation for fixed I_c and V_c.

We may define a geometrical factor, g, as the ratio of I_e extrapolated to zero spacing to the value of g at the separation s:

$$g(s) = (I_e(0)/I_e(s))_{V_{c'}\ I_c=\text{const}} \qquad \text{(II.18)}$$

It is to be expected that $g(s)$ will depend on I_c, as it is the collector current which provides the field which draws the holes into the collector. For the same reason, it is expected that $g(s)$ will be relatively independent of V_c. This was indeed found to be true in this particular case and values $V_c = -5$, -10, and -15 were used in Fig. 8 which gives a plot of g versus s for several values of I_c. The dotted lines give the extrapolation to $s = 0$. As expected, g increases with I_c for a fixed s. The different curves can be brought into approximate agreement by taking $s/I_c^{\frac{1}{3}}$ as the independent variable, and this is done in Fig. 9. As will be discussed in Section V, such a relation is to be expected if g depends on the transit time for the holes.

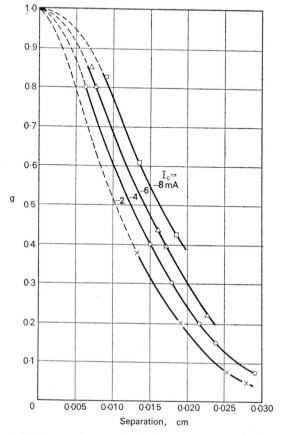

FIG. 8. The factor g is the ratio of the emitter current extrapolated to $s = 0$ to that at electrode separation s required to give the same collector currents, I_c and voltage V_c. Plot shows variation of g with s for different I_c. The factors independent of V_c over the range plotted.

Variation with Temperature

Only a limited amount of data has been obtained on the variation of transistor characteristics with temperature.[5] It is known that the reverse characteristic of the germanium diode varies

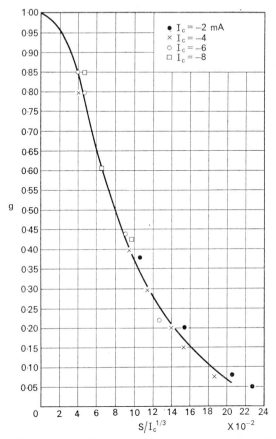

FIG. 9. The factor g (Fig. 8) plotted as a function of $s/I_c^{\frac{1}{3}}$ with s in cm and I_c in amp.

rapidly with temperature, particularly in the case of units with high reverse resistance. In the transistor, the collector is electrically formed in such a way as to have relatively low reverse resistance, and its characteristic is much less dependent on temperature. Both R_{22} and R_{11} decrease with increase in T, R_{22} usually decreasing more rapidly than R_{11}. The feed-back resistance, R_{12}, is relatively independent of temperature. The current multiplication factor, α, increases with temperature, but the change is not extremely rapid. Figure 10 gives a plot of α *versus* T for two experimental units. The d.c. bias currents are kept fixed as the temperature is varied. The over-all change in α from $-50°C$ to $+50°C$ is only about 50 percent. The increase in α with T results in an increase in power gain with temperature. This may be nullified by a decrease in the ratio R_{22}/R_{11}, so that the over-all gain at fixed bias current may have a negative temperature coefficient.

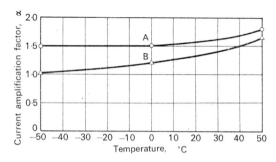

FIG. 10. Current amplification factor α vs. temperature for two experimental units A and B.

Variation with Frequency

Equations (II.5) and (II.6) may be used to describe the a.c. characteristics at high frequencies if the coefficients are replaced by general impedances. Thus if we use the small letters i_e, v_e, i_c, v_c, to denote the amplitude and phase of small a.c. signals about a given operating point, we may write

$$v_e = Z_{11}i_e + Z_{12}i_c, \tag{II.19}$$

$$v_c = Z_{21}i_e + Z_{22}i_c. \tag{II.20}$$

Measurements of A. J. Rack and others[28] show that the over-all power gain drops off between 1 and 10 mc/sec. and few units have

[28] Unpublished data.

positive gain above 10 mc/sec. The measurements showed further that the frequency variation is confined almost entirely to Z_{21} or α. The other coefficients, Z_{11}, Z_{12}, and Z_{22} are real and independent of frequency, at least up to 10 mc/sec. Figure 11 gives a plot of α *versus* frequency for an experimental unit. Associated with the drop in amplitude is a phase shift which varies approximately

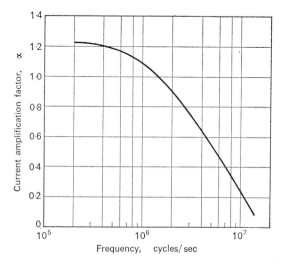

FIG. 11. Current amplification factor α vs. frequency.

linearly with the frequency. A phase shift in Z_{21} of 90° occurs at a frequency of about 4 mc/sec, corresponding to a delay of about 5×10^{-8} second. Estimates of transit time for the holes to flow from the emitter to the collector, to be made in Section V, are of the same order. These results suggest that the frequency limitation is associated with transit time rather than electrode capacities. Because of the difference in transit times for holes following different paths, there is a drop in amplitude rather than simply a phase shift.

III. Electrical Conductivity of Germanium

Germanium, like carbon and silicon, is an element of the fourth group of the periodic table, with the same crystal structure as diamond. Each germanium atom has four near neighbors in a tetrahedral configuration with which it forms covalent bonds. The specific gravity is about 5.35 and the melting point 958°C.

The conductivity at room temperature may be either n- or p-type, depending on the nature and concentration of impurities.

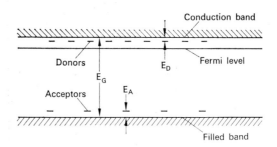

FIG. 12. Schematic energy level diagram for germanium showing filled and conduction bands and donor and acceptor levels.

Scaff, Theuerer, and Schumacher[29] have shown that group III elements with one less valence electron, give p-type conductivity, group V elements, with one more valence electron, give n-type conductivity. This applies to both germanium and silicon. There is evidence that both acceptor (p-type) and donor (n-type) impurities are substitutional.[30]

A schematic energy level diagram[31] which shows the allowed energy levels for the valence electrons in a semiconductor like germanium is given in Fig. 12. There is a continuous band of levels, the filled band, normally occupied by the electrons in the

[29] J. H. Scaff, H. C. Theuerer, and E. E. Schumacher, "P-type and N-type Silicon and the Formation of the Photovoltaic Barrier in Silicon" (in publication).

[30] G. L. Pearson and J. Bardeen, *Phys. Rev.* **75,** 865 (1949).

[31] See, for example, reference 6, Chap. 3.

valence bonds, an energy gap, E_G, in which there are no levels of the ideal crystal, and then another continuous band of levels, the conduction band, normally unoccupied. There are just sufficient levels in the filled band to accommodate the four valence electrons per atom. The acceptor impurity levels, which lie just above the filled band, and the donor levels, just below the conduction band, correspond to electrons localized about the impurity atoms. Donors are normally neutral, but become positively charged by excitation of an electron to the conduction band, an energy E_D being acquired. Acceptors, normally neutral, are negatively ionized by excitation of an electron from the filled band, an energy E_A being required. Both E_D and E_A are so small in germanium that practically all donors and acceptors are ionized at room temperature. If only donors are present, the concentration of conduction electrons is equal to the concentration of donors, and the conductivity is n-type. If only acceptors are present, the concentration of missing electrons, or holes, is equal to that of the acceptors, and the conductivity is p-type.

It is possible to have both donor and acceptor type impurities present in the same crystal. In this case, electrons will be transferred from the donor levels to the lower lying acceptor levels. The conductivity type then depends on which is in excess, and the concentration of carriers is equal to the difference between the concentrations of donors and acceptors. It is probable that impurities of both types are present in high back-voltage germanium. The relative numbers in solid solution can be changed by heat treatment, thus changing the conductivity and even the conductivity type.[13]

The conductivity depends on the concentrations and mobilities of the carriers: Let μ_e and μ_h be the mobilities, expressed in cm²/volt sec., and n_e and n_h the concentrations (number/cm³) of the electrons and holes, respectively. If both types of carriers are present, the conductivity, in mhos/cm, is

$$\sigma = n_e e \mu_e + n_h e \mu_h, \qquad (III.1)$$

where e is the electronic charge in coulombs (1.6×10^{-19}).

Except for relatively high concentrations ($\sim 10^{17}$/cm^3 or larger), or at low temperatures, the mobilities in germanium are determined mainly by lattice scattering and so should be approximately the same in different samples. Approximate values, estimated from Hall and resistivity data obtained at Purdue University[32] and at the Bell Telephone Laboratories[33] are:

$$\mu_h = 5 \times 10^6 T^{-\frac{3}{2}}, \tag{III.2}$$

$$\mu_e = 6.5 \times 10^6 T^{-\frac{3}{2}} (\text{cm}^2/\text{volt sec.}), \tag{III.3}$$

in which T is the absolute temperature. There is a considerable spread among the different measurements, possibly arising from inhomogeneity of the samples. The temperature variation is as indicated by theory. These equations give $\mu_h \sim 1000$ and $\mu_e \sim 1300$ cm^2/volt sec. at room temperature. The resistivity of the germanium used varies from about 1 to 30 ohm cm, corresponding to values of n_e between 1.5×10^{14} and 4×10^{15}/cm^3.

At high temperatures, electrons may be thermally excited from the filled band to the conduction band, an energy E_G being required. Both the excited electron and the hole left behind contribute to the conductivity. The conductivities of all samples approach the same limiting values, regardless of impurity concentration, given by an equation of the form

$$\sigma = \sigma_\infty \exp\left(-E_G/2kT\right), \tag{III.4}$$

[32] Lark-Horovitz, Middleton, Miller, and Walerstein, *Phys. Rev.* **69**, 258 (1946).

[33] Hall and resistivity data at the Bell Laboratories were obtained by G. L. Pearson on samples furnished by J. H. Scaff and H. C. Theuerer. *Added in proof:* Recent Hall measurements of G. L. Pearson on single crystals of *n*- and *p*-type germanium give values of 2700 and 1600 cm^2/volt sec. for electrons and holes, respectively, at room temperature. The latter value has been confirmed by J. R. Haynes by measurements of the drift velocity of holes injected into *n*-type germanium. These values are higher, particularly for electrons, than earlier measurements on polycrystalline samples. Use of the new values will modify some of the numerical estimates made herein, but the orders of magnitude, which are all that are significant, will not be affected. W. Ringer and H. Welker, *Zeits. f. Naturforschung* **1**, 20 (1948), give a value of 2000 cm^2/volt sec. for high resistivity *n*-type germanium.

where k is Boltzmann's constant. For germanium, σ_∞ is about 3.3×10^4 mhos/cm and E_G about 0.75 eV.

The exponential factor comes from the variation of concentration with temperature. Statistical theory[34] indicates that n_e and n_h depend on temperature as

$$n_e = C_e T^{\frac{3}{2}} \exp\left(-\varphi_e/kT\right), \qquad \text{(III.5a)}$$

$$n_h = C_h T^{\frac{3}{2}} \exp\left(-\varphi_h/kT\right), \qquad \text{(III.5b)}$$

where φ_e is the energy difference between the bottom of the conduction band and the Fermi level and φ_h is the difference between the Fermi level and the top of the filled band. The position of the Fermi level depends on the impurity concentration and on temperature. The theory gives

$$C_e \sim C_h \sim 2(2\pi mk/h^2)^{\frac{3}{2}} \sim 5 \times 10^{15}, \qquad \text{(III.6)}$$

where m is an effective mass for the electrons (or holes) and h is Plank's constant. The numerical value is obtained by using the ordinary electron mass for m.

The product $n_e n_h$ is independent of the position of the Fermi level, and thus of impurity concentration, and depends only on the temperature. From Eqs. (III.5a) and (III.5b)

$$n_e n_h = C_e C_h T^3 \exp(-E_G/kT). \qquad \text{(III.7)}$$

In the intrinsic range, we may set $n_e = n_h = n$, and find, using (III.1), (III.2), and (III.3), an expression of the form (III.4) for σ with

$$\sigma_\infty = 11.5 \times 10^6 e(C_e C_h)^{\frac{1}{2}}. \qquad \text{(III.8)}$$

Using the theoretical value (III.6) for $(C_e C_h)^{\frac{1}{2}}$, we find

$$\sigma_\infty = 0.9 \times 10^4 \text{ mhos/cm},$$

as compared with the empirical value of 3.3×10^4, a difference of a factor of 3.6. A similar discrepancy for silicon appears to be

[34] See R. H. Fowler, *Statistical Mechanics*, Cambridge University Press, London, 1936, 2nd edition.

related to a variation of E_G with temperature. With an empirical value of

$$C_e C_h = 25 \times 10^{30} \times 3.6^2 \sim 3 \times 10^{32}, \qquad \text{(III.9)}$$

Eq. (III.7) gives

$$n_e n_h \sim 10^{27}/\text{cm}^6 \qquad \text{(III.10)}$$

when evaluated for room temperature. Thus for $n_e \sim 10^{15}/\text{cm}^3$, n_h is the order of 10^{12}. The equilibrium concentration of holes is small.

Below the intrinsic temperature range, n_e is approximately constant and n_h varies as

$$n_h = (C_e C_h T^3/n_e) \exp(-E_G/kT). \qquad \text{(III.11)}$$

IV. Theory of the Diode Characteristic

Characteristics of metal point-germanium contacts include high forward currents, as large as 5 to 10 mA at 1 volt, small reverse currents, corresponding to resistances as high as one megohm or more at reverse voltages up to 30 volts, and the ability to withstand large voltages in the reverse direction without breakdown. A considerable variation of rectifier characteristics is found with changes in preparation and impurity content of the germanium, surface treatment, electrical power or forming treatment of the contacts, and other factors.

A typical d.c. characteristic of a germanium rectifier[35] is illustrated in Fig. 13. The forward voltages are indicated on an expanded scale. The forward current at 1-volt bias is about 3.5 mA and the differential resistance is about 200 ohms. The reverse current at 30 volts is about 0.02 ma and the differential resistance about 5×10^5 ohms. The ratio of the forward to the reverse current at 1-volt bias is about 500. At a reverse voltage of about 160 the differential resistance drops to zero, and with further increase in current the voltage across the unit drops. The nature of

[35] From unpublished data of K. M. Olsen.

this negative resistance portion of the curve is not completely understood, but it is believed to be associated with thermal effects. Successive points along the curve correspond to increasingly higher temperatures of the contact. The peak value of the reverse voltage varies among different units. Values of more than 100 volts are not difficult to obtain.

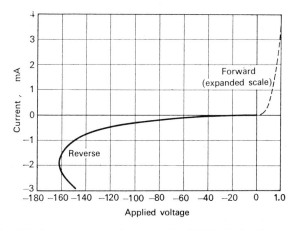

FIG. 13. Current–voltage characteristic of high back-voltage germanium rectifier. Note that the voltage scale in the forward direction has been expandeed by a factor of 20.

Theories of rectification as developed by Mott,[36] Schottky,[37] and others[38] have not been successful in explaining the high back-voltage characteristic in a quantitative way. In the following we give an outline of the theory and its application to germanium. It is believed that the high forward currents can now be explained in terms of a flow of holes. The type of barrier which gives a flow of carriers of conductivity type opposite to that of the base material

[36] N. F. Mott, *Proc. Roy. Soc.* **A171**, 27 (1939).

[37] W. Schottky, *Zeits. f. Physik* **113**, 367 (1939); *Physik. Zeits.* **41**, 570 (1940); *Zeits. f. Physik.* **118**, 539 (1942). Also see reference 18.

[38] See reference 6, Chap. 4.

is discussed. It is possible that a hole current also plays an important role in the reverse direction.

The Space-charge Layer

According to the Mott–Schottky theory, rectification results from a potential barrier at the contact which impedes the flow of electrons between the metal and the semiconductor. A schematic energy level diagram of the barrier region, drawn roughly to scale for germanium, is given in Fig. 14. There is a rise in the electrostatic potential energy of an electron at the surface relative to the interior which results from a space-charge layer in the semiconductor next to the metal contact. The space charge arises from positively ionized donors, that is from the same impurity centers which give the conduction electrons in the body of the semiconductor. In the interior, the space charge of the donors is neutralized by the space charge of the conduction electrons, which

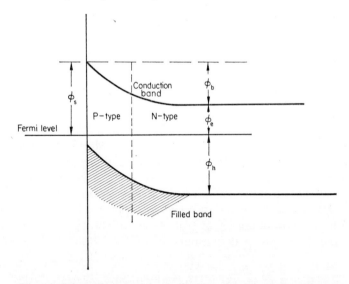

Fig. 14. Schematic energy level diagram of barrier layer at germanium surface showing inversion layer of *p*-type conductivity.

are present in equal numbers. Electrons are drained out of the space-charge layer near the surface, leaving the immobile donor ions.

The space-charge layer may be a result of the metal–semiconductor contact, in which case the positive charge in the layer is compensated by an induced charge of opposite sign on the metal surface. Alternatively, the charge in the layer may be compensated by a surface charge density of electrons trapped in surface states on the semiconductor.[9] It is believed, for reasons to be discussed below, that the latter situation applies to high back-voltage germanium, and that a space-charge layer exists at the free surface, independent of the metal contact. The height of the conduction band above the Fermi level at the surface, φ_s, is then determined by the distribution in energy of the surface states.

That the space-charge layer which gives the rectifying barrier in germanium arises from surface states is indicated by the following:

(1) Characteristics of germanium-point contacts do not depend on the work function of the metal, as would be expected if the space-charge layer were determined by the metal contact.

(2) There is little difference in contact potential between different samples of germanium with varying impurity concentration. Benzer[39] found less than 0.1-volt difference between samples ranging from n-type with 2.6×10^{18} carriers/cm^3 to p-type with 6.4×10^{18} carriers/cm^3. This is much less than the difference of the order of the energy gap, 0.75 volt, which would exist if there were no surface effects.

(3) Benzer[40] has observed the characteristics of contacts formed from two crystals of germanium. He finds that in both directions the characteristic is similar to the reverse

[39] S. Benzer, *Progress Report*, Contract No. W-36-039-SC-32020, Purdue University (Sept. 1–Nov. 30, 1946).
[40] S. Benzer, *Phys. Rev.* **71**, 141 (1947).

characteristic of one of the crystals in contact with a highly conducting metal-like germanium crystal.

(4) One of the authors[11] has observed a change in contact potential with light similar to that expected for a barrier layer at the free surface.

Prior to Benzer's experiments, Meyerhof[8] had shown that the contact potential difference measured between different metals and silicon showed little correlation with rectification, and that the contact potential difference between n- and p-type silicon surfaces was small. There is thus evidence that the barrier layers in both germanium and silicon are internal and occur at the free surface.[41]

In the development of the mathematical theory of the space-charge layer at a rectifier contact, Schottky and Spenke[18] point out the possibility of a change in conductivity type between the surface and the interior if the potential rise is sufficiently large. The conductivity is p-type if the Fermi level is closest to the filled band, n-type if it is closest to the conduction band. In the illustration (Fig. 14), the potential rise is so large that the filled band is raised up to a position close to the Fermi level at the surface. This situation is believed to apply to germanium. There is then a thin layer near the surface whose conductivity is p-type, superimposed on the n-type conductivity in the interior. Schottky and Spenke call the layer of opposite conductivity type an inversion region.

Referring to Eqs. (III.5a) and (III.5b) for the concentrations, it can be seen that since C_e and C_h are of the same order of magnitude, the conductivity type depends on whether φ_e is larger or smaller than φ_h. The conductivity is n-type when

$$\varphi_e < \tfrac{1}{2}E_G, \quad \varphi_h > \tfrac{1}{2}E_G, \tag{IV.1}$$

---

[41] Further evidence that the barrier is internal comes from some unpublished experiments of J. R. Haynes with the transistor. Using a fixed collector point, and keeping a fixed distance between emitter and collector, he varied the material used for the emitter point. He used semiconductors as well as metals for the emitter point. While the impedance of the emitter point varied, it was found that equivalent emitter currents give changes in current at the collector of the same order for all materials used. It is believed that in all cases a large part of the forward current consists of holes.

and is p-type when the reverse situation applies. The maximum resistivity occurs at the position where the conductivity type changes and

$$\varphi_e \sim \varphi_h \sim \tfrac{1}{2}E_G. \qquad \text{(IV.2)}$$

The change from n- to p-type will occur if

$$\varphi_s > \tfrac{1}{2}E_G, \qquad \text{(IV.3)}$$

or if the over-all potential rise, φ_b, is greater than

$$\tfrac{1}{2}E_G - \varphi_{e0}, \qquad \text{(IV.4)}$$

where φ_{e0} is the value of φ_e in the interior. Since for high back-voltage germanium, $E_G \sim 0.75$ eV and $\varphi_{e0} \sim 0.25$ eV, a rise of more than 0.12 eV is sufficient for a change of conductivity type to occur. A rise of 0.50 eV will bring the filled band close to the Fermi level at the surface.

Schottky[37] relates the thickness of the space-charge layer with a potential rise as follows. Let ρ be the average change density, assumed constant for simplicity, in the space-charge layer. In the interior ρ is compensated by the space charge of the conduction electrons. Thus, if n_0 is the normal concentration of electrons,[42]

$$\rho = en_0. \qquad \text{(IV.5)}$$

Integration of the space-charge equations gives a parabolic variation of potential with distance, and the potential rise, φ_b, is given in terms of the thickness of the space-charge layer, l, by the equation

$$\varphi_b = 2\pi e\rho l^2/\kappa = 2\pi e^2 n_0 l^2/\kappa. \qquad \text{(IV.6)}$$

For

$$\varphi_b = \varphi_s - \varphi_{e0} \sim 0.5 \text{ eV} \sim 8 \times 10^{-13} \text{ erg},$$

and

$$n_0 \sim 10^{15}/\text{cm}^3,$$

the barrier thickness, l, is about 10^{-4} cm. The dielectric constant, κ, is about 18 in germanium.

When a voltage V_a is applied to a rectifying contact, there will

---

[42] The space charge of the holes in the inversion region of the barrier layer is neglected for simplicity.

be a drop V_b across the space-charge layer itself and an additional drop, IR_s, in the body of the germanium which results from the spreading resistance, R_s, so that

$$V_a = V_b + IR_s. \qquad (IV.7)$$

The potential energy drop, $-eV_b$, is superimposed on the drop φ_b which exists under equilibrium conditions. For this case Eq. (IV.6) becomes

$$\varphi_b - eV_b = 2\pi e^2 n_0 l^2 / \kappa. \qquad (IV.8)$$

The potential V_b is positive in the forward direction, negative in the reverse. A reverse voltage increases the thickness of the layer, a forward voltage decreases the thickness of the layer. The barrier disappears when $eV_b = \varphi_b$, and the current is then limited entirely by the spreading resistance in the body of the semiconductor.

The electrostatic field at the contact is

$$F = 4\pi e n_0 l / \kappa = (8\pi n_0 (\varphi_b - eV_b) / \kappa)^{\frac{1}{2}}. \qquad (IV.9)$$

For $n_0 \sim 10^{15}$, $l \sim 10^{-4}$, and $\kappa \sim 18$, the field F is about 30 e.s.u. or 10,000 volts/cm. The field increases the current flow in much the way the current from a thermionic emitter is enhanced by an external field.

Previous theories of rectification have been based on the flow of only one type of carrier, i.e., electrons in an n-type or holes in a p-type semiconductor. If the barrier layer has an inversion region, it is necessary to consider the flow of both types of carriers. Some of the hitherto puzzling features of the germanium diode characteristic can be explained by the hole current. While a complete theoretical treatment has not been carried out, we will give an outline of the factors involved and then give separate discussions for the reverse and forward directions.

The current of holes may be expected to be important if the concentration of holes at the semiconductor boundary of the space-charge layer is as large as the concentration of electrons at the metal–semiconductor interface. In equilibrium, with no current flow, the former is just the hole concentration in the interior, n_{h0}, which is given by

$$n_{h0} = C_h T^{\frac{3}{2}} \exp(-\varphi_{h0}/kT), \qquad \text{(IV.10)}$$

where φ_{h0} is the energy difference between the Fermi level in the interior and the top of the filled band. The concentration of electrons at the interface is given by:

$$n_{cm} = C_e T^{\frac{3}{2}} \exp(-\varphi_s/kT). \qquad \text{(IV.11)}$$

Since C_h and C_e are of the same order, n_{h0} will be larger than n_{em} if φ_s is larger than φ_{h0}. This latter condition is met if the hole concentration at the metal interface is larger than the electron concentration in the interior. The concentrations will, of course, be modified when a current is flowing, but the criterion just given is nevertheless a useful guide. The criterion applies to an inversion barrier layer regardless of whether it is formed by the metal contact or is of the surface states type. In the latter case, as discussed in the Introduction, a lateral flow of holes along the surface layer into the contact may contribute to the current.

Two general theories have been developed for the current in a rectifying junction which apply in different limiting cases. The diffusion theory applies if the current is limited by the resistance of the space-charge layer. This will be the case if the mean free path is small compared with the thickness of the layer, or, more exactly, small compared with the distance required for the potential energy to drop kT below the value at the contact. The diode theory applies if the current is limited by the thermionic emission current over the barrier. In germanium, the mean free path (10^{-5} cm) is of the same order as the barrier thickness. Analysis shows, however, that scattering in the barrier is unimportant and that it is the diode theory which should be used.[43]

Reverse Current

Different parts of the d.c. current–voltage characteristics require separate discussion. We deal first with the reverse direction. The

[43] Reference 6, Chapter 4.

applied voltages are assumed large compared with kT/e (0.025 volt at room temperature), but small compared with the peak reverse voltage, so that thermal effects are unimportant. Electrons flow from the metal point contact to the germanium, and holes flow in the opposite direction.

Benzer[44] has made a study of the variation of the reverse characteristic with temperature. He divides the current into three components whose relative magnitudes vary among different crystals and which vary in different ways with temperature. These are:

(1) A saturation current which rises very rapidly with applied voltage, approaching a constant value at a fraction of a volt.
(2) A component which increases linearly with the voltage.
(3) A component which increases more rapidly than linearly with the voltage.

The first two increase rapidly with increasing temperature, while the third component is more or less independent of ambient temperature. It is the saturation current, and perhaps also the linear component, which are to be identified with the theoretical diode current.

The third component is the largest in units with low reverse resistance. It is probable that in these units the barrier is not uniform. The largest part of the current, composed of electrons, flows through patches in which the height of the barrier is small. The electrically formed collector in the transistor may have a barrier of this sort.

Benzer finds that the saturation current predominates in units with high reverse resistance, and that this component varies with temperature as

$$I_s = -I_0 e^{\epsilon/kT}, \tag{IV.12}$$

[44] S. Benzer, *Temperature Dependence of High Voltage Germanium Rectifier D.C. Characteristics*, NDRC 14–579, Purdue University, October 31, 1945. See reference 6, p. 376.

with ϵ nearly 0.7 eV. The negative sign indicates a reverse current. According to the diode theory,[43] one would expect it to vary as

$$I_s = -BT^2 e^{\epsilon/kT}. \tag{IV.13}$$

Since ϵ is large, the observed current can be fitted just about as well with the factor T^2 as without. The value of ϵ obtained using (IV.13) is about 0.6 eV. The saturation current[43] at room temperature varies from 10^{-7} to 10^{-6} amp., which corresponds to values of B in the range of 0.01 to 0.1 amp./deg.[2].

The theoretical value of B is 120 times the contact area, A_c. Taking $A_c \sim 10^{-6}$ cm[2] as a typical value for the area of a point contact gives $B \sim 10^{-4}$ amp./deg.[2] which is only about 1/100 to 1/1000 of the observed. It is difficult to reconcile the magnitude of the observed current with the large temperature coefficient, and it is possible that an important part of the total flow is a current of holes into the contact. Such a current particularly is to be expected on surfaces which exhibit an appreciable surface conductivity.

Neglecting surface effects for the moment, an estimate of the saturation hole current might be obtained as follows. The number of holes entering the space-charge region per second is[45]

$$n_{hb} v_a A_c / 4,$$

where n_{hb} is the hole concentration at the semiconductor boundary of the space-charge layer and v_a is an average thermal velocity ($\sim 10^7$ cm/sec.). The hole current, I_h, is obtained by multiplying by the electronic charge, giving

$$I_h = -n_{bh} e v_a A_c / 4. \tag{IV.14}$$

If we set n_{nb} equal to the equilibrium value for the interior, say 10^{12}/cm[3], we get a current $I_h \sim 4 \times 10^{-7}$ amp., which is of the observed order of magnitude of the saturation current at room temperature. With this interpretation, the temperature variation of I_s is attributed to that of n_h, which, according to Eq. (III.11)

[45] See, for example, E. H. Kennard, *Kinetic Theory of Gases*, McGraw-Hill Book Company, Inc., New York, 1938, p. 63.

varies as $\exp(-E_G/kT)$. The observed value of ϵ is indeed almost equal to the energy gap.

The difficulty with this picture is to see how n_{hb} can be as large as n_{h0} when a current is flowing. Holes must move toward the contact area primarily by diffusion, and the hole current will be limited by a diffusion gradient. The saturation current depends on how rapidly holes are generated, and reasonable estimates based on the mean lifetime, τ, yield currents which are several orders of magnitude too small. A diffusion velocity, v_D, of the order

$$v_D \sim (D/\tau)^{\frac{1}{2}}, \qquad (IV.15)$$

replaces $v_a/4$ in Eq. (IV.14). Setting $D \sim 25$ cm²/sec. and $\tau \sim 10^{-6}$ sec. gives $v_D \sim 5 \times 10^3$, which would give a current much smaller than the observed. What is needed, then, is some other mechanism which will help maintain the equilibrium concentration near the barrier. Surface effects may be important in this regard.

Forward Current

The forward characteristic is much less dependent on such factors as surface treatment than the reverse. In the range from 0 to 0.4 volt in the forward direction, the current can be fitted quite closely by a semi-empirical expression[46] of the form:

$$I = I_0(e^{\beta V_b} - 1), \qquad (IV.16)$$

where V_b is the drop across the barrier resulting from the applied voltage, as defined by Eq. (IV.7). Equation (IV.16) is of the general form to be expected from theory, but the measured value of β is generally less than the theoretical value e/kT (40 volts⁻¹ at room temperature). Observed values of β may be as low as 10, and in other units are nearly as high as the theoretical value of 40. The factor I_0 also varies among different units and is of the order 10^{-7} to 10^{-6} ampere. While both experiment and theory indicate that the forward current at large forward voltages is largely composed of holes, the composition of the current at very small forward

[46] Reference 6, p. 377.

voltages is uncertain. Small areas of low φ_s, unimportant at large forward voltages, may give most of the current at very small voltages. Currents flowing in these areas will consist largely of electrons.

Above about 0.5 volt in the forward direction, most of the drop occurs across the spreading resistance, R_s, rather than across the barrier. The theoretical expression for R_s for a circular contact of diameter d on the surface of a block of uniform resistivity ρ is:

$$R_s = \rho/2d. \qquad \text{(IV.17)}$$

Taking as typical values for a point contact on high back-voltage germanium, $\rho = 10$ ohm cm and $d = 0.0025$ cm, we obtain $R_s = 2000$ ohms, which is the order of ten times the observed.

As discussed in the Introduction, Bray and others[21, 22] have attempted to account for this discrepancy by assuming that the resistivity decreases with increasing field, and Bray has made tests to observe such an effect. The authors have investigated the nature of the forward current by making potential probe measurements in the vicinity of a point contact.[2] These measurements indicate that there may be two components involved in the excess conductivity. Some surfaces, prepared by oxidation at high temperatures, give evidence for excess conductivity in the vicinity of the point in the reverse as well as in the forward direction. This ohmic component has been attributed to a thin p-type layer on the surface. All surfaces investigated exhibit an excess conductivity in the forward direction which increases with increasing forward current. This second component is attributed to an increase in the concentration of carriers, holes and electrons, in the vicinity of the point with increase in forward current. Holes flow from the point into the germanium and their space charge is compensated by electrons.

The ohmic component is small, if it exists at all, on surfaces treated in the normal way for high back-voltage rectifiers (i.e., ground and etched). The nature of the second component on such surfaces has been shown by more recent work of Shockley, Haynes,[20] and Ryder[23] who have investigated the flow of holes under the influence of electric fields. These measurements prove that the forward current consists at least in large part of holes flowing into the germanium from the contact.

It is of interest to consider the way the concentrations of holes and electrons vary in the vicinity of the point. An exact calculation, including the effect of recombination, leads to a non-linear differential equation which must be solved by numerical methods. A simple solution can be obtained, however, if it is assumed that all of the forward current consists of holes and if recombination is neglected.

The electron current then vanishes everywhere, and the electric field is such as to produce a conduction current of electrons which just cancels the current from diffusion, giving

$$n_e F = -(kT/e) \text{ grad } n_e. \qquad (IV.18)$$

This equation may be integrated to give the relation between the electrostatic potential, V, and n_e,

$$V = (kT/e) \log (n_e/n_{e0}). \qquad (IV.19)$$

The constant of integration has been chosen so that $V = 0$ when n_e is equal to the normal electron concentration n_{e0}. The equation may be solved for n_e to give:

$$n_e = n_{e0} \exp(eV/kT). \qquad (IV.20)$$

If trapping is neglected, electrical neutrality requires that

$$n_e = n_h + n_{e0}. \qquad (IV.21)$$

Using this relation, and taking n_{e0} a constant, we can express the field F in terms of n_h

$$F = -(kT/e(n_h + n_{e0})) \text{ grad } n_h. \qquad (IV.22)$$

The hole current density, i_h, is the sum of a conduction current resulting from the field F and a diffusion current:

$$i_h = n_h e \mu_h F - kT \mu_h \text{ grad } n_h. \qquad (IV.23)$$

Using Eq. (IV. 22), we may write this in the form

$$i_h = -kT \mu_h ((2n_h + n_{e0})/(n_h + n_{e0})) \text{ grad } n_h. \qquad (IV.24)$$

The current density can be written

$$i_h = -\text{grad } \psi, \qquad (\text{IV.25})$$

where

$$\psi = kT\mu_h(2n_h - n_{e0} \log((n_h + n_{e0})/n_{e0})). \qquad (\text{IV.26})$$

Since i_h satisfies a conservation equation,

$$\text{div } i_h = 0, \qquad (\text{IV.27})$$

ψ satisfies Laplace's equation.

If surface effects are neglected and it is assumed that holes flow radially in all directions from the point contact, ψ may be expressed simply in terms of the total hole current, I_h, flowing from the contact:

$$\psi = -I_h/2\pi r. \qquad (\text{IV.28})$$

Using (IV.26), we may obtain the variation of n_h with r. We are interested in the limiting case in which n_h is large compared with the normal electron concentration, n_{e0}. The logarithmic term in (IV.26) can then be neglected, and we have

$$n_h = I_h/4\pi r\mu_h kT. \qquad (\text{IV.29})$$

For example, if $I_h = 10^{-3}$ amp., $\mu_h = 10^3$ cm²/volt sec., and $kT/e = 0.025$ volt, we get, approximately,

$$n_h = 2 \times 10^{13}/r. \qquad (\text{IV.30})$$

For $r \sim 0.0005$ cm, the approximate radius of a point contact,

$$n_h \sim 4 \times 10^{16}/\text{cm}^3, \qquad (\text{IV.31})$$

which is about 40 times the normal electron concentration in high back-voltage germanium. Thus the assumption that n_h is large compared with n_{e0} is valid, and remains valid up to a distance of the order of 0.005 cm, the approximate distance the points are separated in the transistor.

To the same approximation, the field is

$$F = kT/er, \qquad (\text{IV.32})$$

independent of the magnitude of I_h.

The voltage drop outside of the space-charge region can be obtained by setting n_e in (IV.19) equal to the value at the semiconductor boundary of the space-charge layer. This result holds generally, and does not depend on the particular geometry we have assumed. It depends only on the assumption that the electron current i_e is everywhere zero. Actually i_h will decrease and i_e increase by recombination, and there will be an additional spreading resistance for the electron current.

If it is assumed that the concentration of holes at the metal–semiconductor interface is independent of applied voltage and that the resistive drop in the barrier layer itself is negligible, that part of the applied voltage which appears across the barrier layer itself is:

$$V_b = (kT/e) \log(n_{hb}/n_{h0}), \qquad \text{(IV.33)}$$

where n_{hb} is the hole concentration at the semiconductor boundary of the space-charge layer and n_{h0} is the normal concentration. For $n_{hb} \sim 5 \times 10^{16}$ and $n_{h0} \sim 10^{12}$, V_b is about 0.30 volt.

The increased conductivity caused by hole emission accounts not only for the large forward currents, but also for the relatively small dependence of spreading resistance on contact area. At a small distance from the contact, the concentrations and voltages are independent of contact area. The voltage drop within this small distance is a small part of the total and does not vary rapidly with current.

We have assumed that the electron current, I_e, at the contact is negligible compared with the hole current, I_h. An estimate of the electron current can be obtained as follows. From the diode theory,

$$I_e = (e n_{eb} v_a A_c / 4) \exp(-(\varphi_b - eV_b)/kT), \qquad \text{(IV.34)}$$

since the electron concentration at the semiconductor boundary of the space-charge layer is n_{eb} and the height of the barrier with the voltage applied is $\varphi_b - eV_b$. For simplicity we assume that both n_{eb} and n_{hb} are large compared with n_{e0} so that we may replace

n_{eb} by n_{hb} without appreciable error. The latter can be obtained from the value of ψ at the contact:

$$\psi = I_h/4a. \tag{IV.35}$$

Expressing ψ in terms of n_{hb}, we find

$$n_{hb} = I_h/8kT\mu_h a. \tag{IV.36}$$

Using (IV.33) for V_b, and (III.5b) for n_{h0} we find after some reduction,

$$I_e = I_h^2/I_{\text{crit}}, \tag{IV.37}$$

where

$$I_{\text{crit}} = \frac{256 C_h (kT\mu_h)^2 T^{\frac{3}{2}}}{\pi e v_a} \exp(-\varphi_{hm}/kT). \tag{IV.38}$$

The energy difference φ_{hm} is the difference between the Fermi level and the filled band at the metal-semiconductor interface. Evaluated for germanium at room temperature, (IV.38) gives

$$I_{\text{crit}} = 0.07 \exp(-\varphi_{hm}/kT)\,\text{amp}. \tag{IV.39}$$

which is a fairly large current if φ_{hm} is not too large compared with kT. If I_h is small compared with I_{crit}, the electron current will be negligible.

V. Theoretical Considerations on Transistor Action

In this section we discuss some of the problems connected with transistor action, such as:

(1) fields produced by the collector current,
(2) transit times for the holes to flow from emitter to collector,
(3) current multiplication in collector,
(4) feed-back resistance.

We do no more than estimate orders of magnitude. An exact calculation, taking into account the change of conductivity introduced by the emitter current, loss of holes by recombination, and effect of surface conductivity is difficult and is not attempted.

To estimate the field produced by the collector, we assume that the collector current is composed mainly of conduction electrons, and that the electrons flow radially away from the collector. This assumption should be most nearly valid when the collector current is large compared with the emitter current. The field at a distance r from the collector is,

$$F = \rho I_c / 2\pi r^2. \tag{V.1}$$

For example, if, $\rho = 10$ ohm cm, $I_c = 0.001$ amp., and $r = 0.005$ cm, F is about 100 volts/cm.

The drift velocity of a hole in the field F is $\mu_h F$. The transit time is

$$T = \int \frac{dr}{\mu_h F} = \frac{2\pi}{\mu_h \rho I_c} \int_0^s r^2 dr, \tag{V.2}$$

where s is the separation between the emitter and collector. Integration gives,

$$T = 2\pi s^3 / 3\mu_{h0} I_c. \tag{V.3}$$

For $s = 0.005$ cm, $\mu_h = 1000$ cm²/volt sec., $\rho = 10$ ohm cm, and $I_c = 0.001$ amp. T is about 0.25×10^{-7} sec. This is of the order of magnitude of the transit times estimated from the phase shift in α or Z_{21}.

The hole current, I_h, is attenuated by recombination in going from the emitter to the collector. If τ is the average lifetime of a hole, I_h will be decreased by a factor, $e^{-T/\tau}$. In Section II it was found that the geometrical factor, g, which gives the influence of separation on the interaction between emitter and collector depends on the variable $s/I_c^{\frac{1}{3}}$. This suggests that the transit time is the most important factor in determining g. An estimate[47] of τ, obtained from the data of Fig. 9, is 2×10^{-7} sec.

---

[47] Obtained by plotting $\log g$ *versus* S^3/I_c. This plot is not a straight line, but has an upward curvature corresponding to an increase in τ with separation. The value given is a rough average, corresponding to S^3/I_c the order of 10^{-3} cm³/amp.

Because of the effect of holes in increasing the conductivity of the germanium in the vicinity of the emitter and collector, it can be expected that the field, the lifetime, and the geometrical factor will depend on the emitter current. The effective value of ρ to be used in Eqs. (V.1) and (V.2) will decrease with increase in emitter current. This effect is apparently not serious with the surface used in obtaining the data for Figs. 7 to 9.

Next to be considered is the effect of the space charge of the holes on the barrier layer of the collector. An estimate of the hole concentration can be obtained as follows. The field in the barrier layer is of the order of 10^4 volts/cm. Multiplying by the mobility gives a drift velocity, v_d of 10^7 cm/sec., which is approximately thermal velocity.[48] The hole current is

$$I_h = n_h e v_d A_c, \qquad (V.4)$$

where A_c is the area of the collector contact, and n_h the concentration of holes in the barrier. Solving for the latter, we get

$$n_h = I_h / e v_d A_c. \qquad (V.5)$$

For $I_h = 0.001$ amp., $v_d = 10^7$ cm/sec. and $A_c = 10^{-6}$ cm², n_h is about 0.6×10^{15}, which is of the same order as the concentration of donors. Thus the hole current can be expected to alter the space charge in the barrier by a significant amount, and correspondingly alter the flow of electrons from the collector. It is believed that current multiplication (values of $\alpha > 1$) can be accounted for along these lines.

As discussed in Section II, there is an influence of collector current on emitter current of the nature of a positive feedback. The collector current lowers the potential of the surface in the vicinity of the emitter by an amount

$$V = \rho I_c / 2\pi s. \qquad (V.6)$$

[48] One may expect that the mobility will depend on field strength when the drift velocity is as large as or is larger than thermal velocity. Since ours is a borderline case, the calculation using the low field mobility should be correct at least as to order of magnitude.

The feed-back resistance R_F as used in Eq. (II.2) is

$$R_F = \rho/2\pi s. \tag{V.7}$$

For $\rho = 10$ ohm cm and $s = 0.005$ cm, the value of R_F is about 300 ohms, which is of the observed order of magnitude. It may be expected that R_F will decrease as ρ decreases with increase in emitter current.

The calculations made in this section confirm the general picture which has been given of the way the transistor operates.

VI. Conclusions

Our discussion has been confined to the transistor in which two point contacts are placed in close proximity on one face of a germanium block. It is apparent that the principles can be applied to other geometrical designs and to other semiconductors. Some preliminary work has shown that transistor action can be obtained with silicon and undoubtedly other semiconductors can be used.

Since the initial discovery, many groups in the Bell Laboratories have contributed to the progress that has been made. This work includes investigation of the physical phenomena involved and the properties of the materials used, transistor design, and measurements of characteristics and circuit applications. A number of transistors have been made for experimental use in a pilot production. Obviously no attempt has been made to describe all of this work, some of which has been reported on in other publications.[5, 19, 20, 23]

In a device as new as the transistor, various problems remain to be solved. A reduction in noise and an increase in the frequency limit are desirable. While much progress has been made toward making units with reproducible characteristics, further improvement in this regard is also desirable.

It is apparent from reading this article that we have received a large amount of aid and assistance from other members of the Laboratories staff, for which we are grateful. We particularly wish to acknowledge our debt to Ralph Bown, Director of Research, who has given us a great deal of encouragement and aid from the inception of the work and to William Shockley, who has made numerous suggestions which have aided in clarifying the phenomena involved.

The Double-surface Transistor†

JOHN N. SHIVE

Bell Telephone Laboratories, Murray Hill, New Jersey

December 28, 1948

IN a series of Letters to the Editor[1] appearing in a recent issue of this journal, there are described the physical construction and proposed theory of operation of a solid state semiconductor triode. This device, which is now called the type A transistor, comprises a block of high back-voltage germanium on one of the faces of which are two contacts, side by side with each other and close together. These contacts are called the emitter and collector, respectively. A large area contact to the opposite face of the semiconductor block is called the base contact.

The present communication describes another semiconductor triode, the double-surface transistor, in which the emitter and collector contacts bear on the two opposite faces of a thin wedge or slab of semiconductor. This slab is prepared from an ingot of high back-voltage germanium of N-type.[2] After being ground approximately to the desired shape, the slab is etched and provided with a suitable large-area base contact. For good gain characteristics it is advantageous that the thickness of the slab be no greater

† *The Physical Review*, **75**, 689 (1949).

[1] J. Bardeen and W. H. Brattain, *Phys. Rev.* **74**, 230 (1948); W. H. Brattain and J. Bardeen, *ibid.* **74**, 231 (1948); W. Shockley and G. L. Pearson, *ibid.* **74**, 232 (1948).

[2] The ingot was prepared by J. H. Scaff and H. T. Theuerer according to the method generally described in H. C. Torrey and C. A. Whitmer's *Crystal Rectifiers* (McGraw-Hill Book Company, Inc., Chapter 12, New York).

than about 0.01 cm at the place where the contacts bear upon it. These contacts should be within about the same distance of coming exactly opposite each other on the two faces of the slab. Tungsten, copper, and phosphor bronze have been used successfully as contact materials. This device, together with its electrical connections for use as a grounded-base amplifier, is illustrated schematically in Fig. 1. In operation a comparatively large d.c. reverse bias (-50 to -100 volts) is applied to the collector, while a

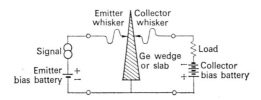

FIG. 1. Electrode geometry and circuit connections for a double-surface transistor.

comparatively small d.c. forward bias (a few tenths of a volt) is applied to the emitter. Because of positive feed-back effects in the base contact and semiconductor body, the emitter bias voltage-to-base may in some cases be zero or even negative.

The static characteristics of a double-surface transistor are presented in Fig. 2. Families of collector voltage *vs.* collector current curves are given, with constant emitter current as parameter for the solid lines, and with constant emitter voltage as parameter for the dashed lines. Such a plot allows one to make judicious choice of d.c. operating point. It furnishes in addition complete information from which can be obtained, almost by inspection, the dynamic input and output impedances and the forward and backward transfer impedances of the device about any operating point selected.

In the double-surface transistor the emitter and collector points can be separated by surface paths many times longer than those in the type *A* transistor. It appears that double-surface transistor action takes place through the body of the slab rather than along its surface layers. A tentative explanation of the transfer mechanism in this case is illustrated in the energy level diagram of Fig. 3. An important part of the picture is the bending up of the energy bands of the semiconductor from D to C, either as a result of the contact potential difference between metal and semiconductor,[3] or because of the presence of partly filled surface states on the surface of the semiconductor.[4] It is postulated that the

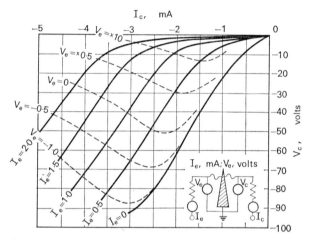

FIG. 2. Static characteristics of a double-surface transistor.

bending up is sufficient to make the topmost levels of the filled band in the germanium accessible for the entry of positive holes from the conduction levels of the emitter metal. The potential of the interior of the semiconductor slab in the neighborhood of D is held at or near the base potential by the low resistance electrical path to the base. Application to the emitter of a positive bias with respect to the base decreases the depth of the barrier from C to D and increases the flow of holes past D into the interior of the slab, whence they are swept away by the collector field. Modulation of

[3] N. F. Mott, *Proc. Camb. Phil. Soc.* **34**, 568 (1938); W. Schottky, *Zeits. f. Physik.* **113**, 367 (1939); see also Reference 2, Chapters 3 and 4.

[4] John Bardeen, *Phys. Rev.* **71**, 717 (1947).

the hole current to the collector is thus secure by modulation of the emitter voltage.

A large part of the useful gain of the device is voltage gain resulting from the introduction of current from the emitter at comparatively low impedance and its subsequent withdrawal by the collector at comparatively high impedance. In some regions of the characteristic there is observed also a current amplification

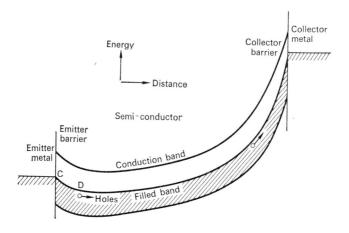

FIG. 3. Energy level diagram illustrating theory of double-surface transistor operation.

$\partial I_c / \partial I_e | V_c$ of magnitude greater than unity. For the example of the unit described in Fig. 2 this current amplification is about 1.5 throughout the useful operating region. Some of this multiplication may be caused by ionizing collisions by holes in transit through the field at the collector barrier, and some by the alteration of this barrier field by the positive hole space charge in such a way as to increase the field emission of electrons from the collector.

The impetus for this development was supplied by the transistor discoveries by J. Bardeen, W. H. Brattain, and W. Shockley. To these men, and to J. A. Becker, the author is indebted for stimulating associations and discussions.

Investigation of
Hole Injection in Transistor Action†

J. R. HAYNES and W. SHOCKLEY

Bell Telephone Laboratories, Murray Hill, New Jersey

December 28, 1948

THE experiments to be described here were undertaken to furnish direct experimental evidence concerning the nature of the carriers responsible for the impedance decrease which is produced at a collector point by passing current in the forward direction through an emitter point of a transistor.[1]

The sample of germanium used in the experiment was a block of *n*-type high back voltage material having dimensions of 9 × 3 × 0.5 mm and provided with plated electrodes at either end. The circuit used is shown in Fig. 1. Current is passed through five emitter points and into the germanium crystal on closing a relay which is actuated sixty times a second. A battery and a key are connected in series across the electrodes so that the electric field in the crystal may be altered.

In series with a collector point is placed a resistance of 5000 ohms and a battery. The collector is negative with respect to the germanium so that the impedance at the contact point is high (order of 0.1 megohm). The current through the 5000-ohm resistance is accordingly closely proportional to the collector point conductance. The voltage across this resistance is connected to the vertical plates of a cathode-ray oscilloscope so that the collector point conductance can be examined as a function of time.

† *The Physical Review*, **75**, 691 (1949).
[1] J. Bardeen and W. H. Brattain, *Phys. Rev.* **74**, 250 (1948).

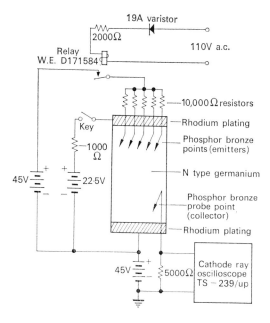

FIG. 1. Circuit arrangement for the investigation of hole injection.

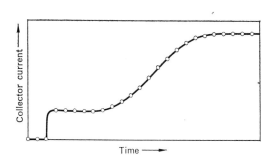

FIG. 2. Oscilloscope trace showing the delay of holes in reaching connector.

A sketch of the oscilloscope trace obtained when the collector point is placed 1 millimeter from the emitter point is shown in Fig. 2. The dots represent 1-microsecond marker intervals obtained on the oscilloscope trace. An initial short rise in signal voltage is obtained when the relay is closed. This initial rise is primarily due to the potential drop produced by the normal current flow in the germanium.

After this initial rise the current into the collector point remains constant for about five microseconds when a second rise begins. This time delay between the injection of current from the emitter points and the start of current increase in the collector point is found to vanish as the collector point approaches the emitter points. It is evident, therefore, that the delay in this second increase in current through the collector point is due to the finite velocity of some kind of carrier which increases the conductance of the collector point on arrival.

The sign of the charge borne by the carriers was found by closing the key. This decreases the transit time of the carriers when the battery is connected as shown in Fig. 1 and increases it when the battery is reversed. Quantitative investigation of the relationship between electric field, delay, and distance shows that the effect is transmitted as expected for positive particles with a mobility of about 1.2×10^3 cm²/volt sec. in agreement within experimental error with the behavior of holes as established by Hall effect in p-type germanium. Further experiments with the collector placed on the opposite side of the block from the emitter points show that the holes are distributed through the interior. These results are consistent with J. N. Shive's observation[2] that transistor action can be obtained with points on the opposite sides of a thin piece of germanium and with those of E. J. Ryder and W. Shockley[3] on resistance in high electric fields.

An estimate of the mean life of positive holes in this sample of germanium has been made by measuring the signal voltage increase produced on hole arrival as a function of time delay.

---

[2] J. N. Shive, *Phys. Rev.*, this issue.
[3] E. J. Ryder and W. Shockley, *Phys. Rev.* **75**, 310 (1949).

Analysis of the data shows that this voltage decreases exponentially at the rate of $1/e$ in 10 microseconds. This value is evidently also the mean life of the positive holes if it is assumed that the collector conductance is an approximately linear function of hole density.

We are indebted to A. H. White and C. Herring for suggestions regarding the interpretation of the mobility data.

Effects of Electrical Forming on the Rectifying Barriers of *n*- and *p*-Germanium Transistors†

J. BARDEEN and W. G. PFANN

Bell Telephone Laboratories, Murray Hill, New Jersey

December 12, 1949

THE amplifying properties of transistors made with *n*- or *p*-germanium can be improved by an electrical forming or power treatment of one of the point electrodes. W. H. Brattain[1] discovered that transistor action in *n*-type germanium having a resistivity of the order of one to ten ohm-centimeters can generally be improved by passing large reverse currents through the collector. Later, it was discovered that transistor action in *p*-type germanium could be greatly enhanced by passing a large forward current through the emitter.[2] Since this initial work, other members of the Bell Telephone Laboratories' staff have contributed to our knowledge of the effects of various forming treatments. The purpose of the present note is to present some qualitative data on forming and to give a tentative interpretation of the results in terms of modifications of the rectifying barrier layer at the contact.

The forming treatments which we shall describe involve applications of direct current in either the forward or reverse direction for times of the order of seconds or less. The extent of the changes

† *The Physical Review*, **77**, 401 (1949).
[1] J. H. Bardeen and W. H. Brattain, *Phys. Rev.* **75**, 1208 (1949).
[2] W. G. Pfann and J. H. Scaff, *Phys. Rev.* **76**, 459 (1949).

caused by forming depends in part on the surface treatment of the germanium and in part on the material used for the point contact. We have used phosphor bronze points on surfaces which were ground and etched.

Transistor action depends on the presence of an inversion layer or change of conductivity type in the barrier layer of the emitter contact. In the case of n-germanium, there is evidence that such a barrier layer exists at the free surface, independent of the

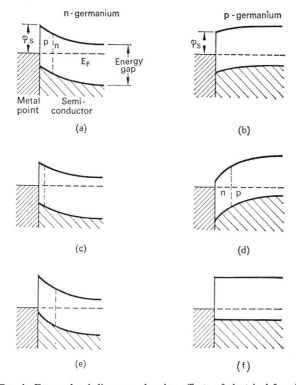

FIG. 1. Energy level diagrams showing effects of electrical forming on the rectifying barriers at contacts with n- and p-germanium: (a,b) —unformed; (c,d)—formed by negative current; (e,f)—formed by positive current.

contact, and hence effective emitter action is obtained without electrical forming. Such a barrier layer is shown schematically in the energy level diagram of Fig. 1a. The position of the Fermi level at the surface, closer to the filled band than to the conduction band, is determined by the energy levels of electrons in surface states.

Since the same surface treatment has been used for both n- and p-germanium, the surface states and position of the Fermi level at the free surface of p-germanium are expected to be similar to those for n-germanium, as shown in Fig. 1b. Unless a barrier layer is formed by the metal contact, little or no rectification to p-germanium is to be expected. It is, indeed, found that a metal point contact to p-germanium makes a poor rectifier unless there is some electrical forming or power treatment.

Forming may affect the surface layers, and thus the height of the barrier layer, ϕ_s, as well as the distribution of donor and acceptor ions in depth in the vicinity of the contact. While it is believed that both effects occur, we shall be concerned with forming methods in which the principal results can be interpreted in terms of changes in ϕ_s. Changes in ion concentrations may predominate with heavy forming such as may be produced by large current pulses. That the germanium and its surface layers are affected is indicated by the fact that a formed point may be replaced by another point, with little change of characteristics.[3]

The observed changes in characteristics produced by forming are given in Table 1 for both n- and p-germanium. The conventional direction of current is positive for flow of positive charge from point to germanium. This is the forward rectifying direction for n-type semiconductors and the reverse for p-type. These qualitative changes can be interpreted in terms of changes in ϕ_s if we assume that a *positive* forming current *increases* ϕ_s and that a *negative* forming current *decreases* ϕ_s. These changes are in the directions which would result from the movement of donor or acceptor ions from the interior of the germanium to the surface under the influence of the field of the forming current.

[3] Experimental results of W. H. Brattain and G. R. Price.

TABLE 1. CHANGES IN CHARACTERISTICS OF RECTIFYING JUNCTIONS
PRODUCED BY FORMING

| Forming current | n-Germanium | | p-Germanium | |
	Forward current	Reverse current	Forward current	Reverse current
Unformed	Large; mostly holes; good emitter of holes	Small; good rectifier	Small; mostly holes; poor emitter of electrons	Large; poor rectifier
Negative	Hole current smaller	Greater; collector formed	Electron current increased, emitter formed	Little change
Positive	Little change	Smaller	Little change	Greater

As illustrated in Figs. 1a and 1b, which represent unformed points, there is a good rectifying junction with n-germanium and a poor one with p-germanium. Because of the inversion layer, the forward current in the former case consists largely of holes, although conduction electrons are normally in excess in the interior. A decrease in ϕ_s, caused by a negative forming current, as shown in Fig. 1c, enhances the electron current in the reverse direction in n-germanium and improves the point as a collector. This is accompanied by a decrease in hole current in the forward direction. For p-germanium, as shown in Fig. 1d, a negative forming current may produce an inversion layer of n-type conductivity, and thus increase the emission of electrons. The reverse characteristic, while altered in shape, is not changed greatly in magnitude. A positive forming current decreases ϕ_s, as shown in Figs. 1e and 1f, making the reverse current in n-germanium smaller and impairing the rectification in p-germanium.

Actually, there are probably large variations in ϕ_s over the contact area, and the changes of ϕ_s indicated in Fig. 1 should be interpreted merely as giving the trends in a qualitative way. For example, it is necessary to have only a few "low spots" in the barrier to give a relatively large reverse current through a point contact to n-germanium, and a few spots with an inversion layer may be sufficient to make a reasonably good emitter function in p-germanium.

p-n Junctions in Semiconductors†

W. SHOCKLEY

5. Internal Contact Potentials‡

The theory of *p–n* junctions presented above has interesting consequences when applied to the distribution of potential between two semiconductors under conditions of hole or electron injection. In Fig. 9 we illustrate an X-shaped structure. A forward current flows across the junction P_1 and out of branch N_1. If the distance across the intersection is comparable with or small compared to the diffusion length for holes, a potential difference should be measured between P_2 and N_2. The reason for this is that holes flow easily into P_2 since the potential distribution there favors their entrance. Since, however, P_2 is open-circuited this hole flow biases J_2 in the forward direction; since J_2 is high resistance, an appreciable bias is developed before the counter current equals the inward hole flow and a steady state is reached. No similar effect occurs in the branch N_2; consequently P_2 will be found to be floating (open-circuited) at a more positive potential than N_2.

Parts (b) to (e) describe this reasoning in more complete terms. We suppose that the *p*-regions are more highly conducting than the *n*-regions so that the current across J_1, shown in (b), is mainly holes. The potentials φ_p and φ_n along the *x*-axis will be similar to

† *The Bell System Technical Journal* **28,** 435 (1949).

‡ These sections 5 and 6 are only the particularly pertinent portions of a classic paper by Shockley (1949) on *p–n* junctions. The reader is advised to read the complete paper in order to appreciate the magnitude of the contribution the paper makes to transistor theory. (N.B. c.g.s. units are used.)

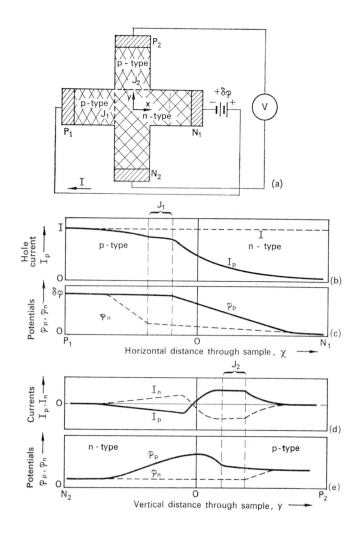

FIG. 9. Potential showing how presence of injected holes produces a contact potential J_2.

those of Figs. 5 and 6;† (c) shows this situation and indicates that the diffusion length for electrons in the *p*-region is less than for holes in the *n*-region. Along the *y* axis φ_p and φ_n vary as shown in (e), the reasoning being as follows: At the origin of coordinates φ_p and φ_n have the same values as for (c). The transverse hole current (d) has a small positive component at $y = 0$ since, as mentioned above, P_2 tends to absorb holes and thus increase diffusion along the plus *y*-axis. Since the net transverse current is zero, $I_n = I_p$ in (d). The φ curves of (e) have been drawn to conform to the currents in (d); φ_n is nearly constant in the *n*-region and φ_p is nearly constant in the *p*-region. As concluded in connection with Figs. 5 and 6,† φ_n and φ_p are also nearly constant across the transition region. These conclusions lead to the shape of φ_n and φ_p for $y > 0$ in (e). For $y < 0$, the reasoning is the same as that used in Sections 3 and 4 and we conclude that φ_n is essentially constant. Hence, a difference in the Fermi levels at P_2 and N_2 will result.

In Fig. 10 we show a structure for which we can make quantitative calculations of the variations of φ_p and φ_n. We assume for this case that the forward current from P_1 to N does not produce an appreciable voltage drop, i.e. change in ψ and φ_n, in region N. This will be a good approximation if the dimensions are suitably proportioned. We shall next solve for the steady-state distribution of *p* subject to the indicated boundary conditions assuming that *p* is a function of *x* only. As we have discussed in Section 4.1, when *p* is small compared to *n* in the *n*-region, we can write

$$p = p_n e^{q(\varphi_p - \varphi_n)/kT} \tag{5.1}$$

In keeping with the treatment in the next section of this structure as a transistor, the terminals are designated emitter, collector and base, the potentials with respect to the base being φ_ϵ and φ_c. The contact to *N* or the base is such that $\varphi_b = \varphi_n$ in this region. Hence, the boundary conditions at J_1 and J_2 are

$$p_1 = p_n e^{q\varphi_\epsilon/kT} \qquad x = -w \tag{5.2}$$

$$p_2 = p_n e^{q\varphi_c/kT} \qquad x = +w \tag{5.3}$$

† Not shown here.

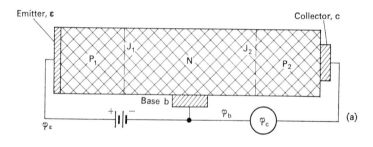

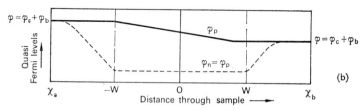

FIG. 10. Model used for calculation of internal contact potential and to illustrate *p–n–p* transistor. (a) Semi-conductor with two *p–n* junctions and ohmic metal contacts. (b) Quasi Fermi levels showing internal contact potential between b and c.

The function $p(x)$ which satisfies these boundary conditions and the equation

$$D \frac{d^2 p}{dx^2} - \frac{p - p_n}{\tau_p} = 0 \qquad (5.4)$$

is

$$p(x) = p_n + \frac{p_1 + p_2 - 2p_n}{2 \cosh (w/L_p)} \cosh (x/L_p) + \frac{p_2 - p_1}{2 \sinh (w/L_p)} \sinh (x/L_p) \qquad (5.5)$$

which gives rise to a hole current across J_2 into P_2 of amount

$$I_p = -qD \frac{dp}{dx}\bigg|_{x=w}$$

$$= \frac{qD}{2L_p} \left[(p_1 - p_2) \coth \frac{w}{L_p} + (2p_n - p_1 - p_2) \tanh \frac{w}{L_p} \right]$$

$$= \frac{qD}{2L_p} \left[(p_1 - p_n) \left(\coth \frac{w}{L_p} - \tanh \frac{w}{L_p} \right) \right. \tag{5.6}$$

$$\left. - (p_2 - p_n) \left(\coth \frac{w}{L_p} + \tanh \frac{w}{L_p} \right) \right]$$

$$= + \frac{p_n qD}{L_p} \left[\frac{[e^{q\varphi/kT} - 1]}{\sinh (2w/L_p)} - \frac{(e^{q\varphi_c/rT} - 1)}{\tanh (2w/L_p)} \right]$$

$$= \operatorname{csch} (2w/L_p) I_{p0}(\varphi_\epsilon) - \coth (2wL_p) I_{p0}(\varphi_c)$$

where, by $I_{p0}(\varphi)$, we mean the hole current which would flow in the forward direction across either J_1 or J_2 if uninfluenced by the other (i.e. the function of (4.11) or (4.18) and (4.20).) The equation shows that a fraction csch $(2w/L_p)$ of the current $I_{p0}(\varphi_\epsilon)$, which would be injected by φ_ϵ on P_1 in the absence of J_2, flows into P_2. The conductance of P_2 across J_2 is increased by the factor coth $(2w/L_p)$.

The current *into* P_2 carried by electrons will be unaffected by J_1 and can be denoted by $-I_{n0}(\varphi_c)$ the minus sign resulting from the fact that currents *into* P_2 are in the reverse direction. The total current flowing *into* P_2 contains the $-I_{n0}(\varphi_c)$ and $-I_{p0}(\varphi_c)$ terms and must cancel the $+I_{p0}(\varphi_\epsilon)$ term for equilibrium. Hence:

$$I_{n0}(\varphi_c) + \coth (2w/L_p) I_{p0}(\varphi_c) = \operatorname{csch} (2w/L_p) I_{p0}(\varphi_\epsilon). \tag{5.7}$$

If $p_n \gg n_p$, the I_{n0} term can be neglected compared to coth $(2w/L_p)$ I_{n0}. Hence the value of φ_c must satisfy

$$I_{p0}(\varphi_c) = \operatorname{sech} (2w/L_p) I_{p0}(\varphi_\epsilon). \tag{5.8}$$

For $\varphi_\epsilon > kT/q$, the exponential approximation may be used for I_{p0} in both terms:

$$\varphi_c = \varphi_\epsilon - (kT/q) \ln \cosh (2w/L_p), \tag{5.9}$$

so that, if $(2w/L_p)$ is the order of unity, φ_c should be only about (kT/q) less than φ_ϵ. For $(2w/L_p)$ large, we get

$$\varphi_c = \varphi_\epsilon - (kT/q)(2w/L_p) \tag{5.10}$$

corresponding to the linear drop of φ_p, discussed in connection with equation (4.9), across the distance $2w$.

When φ_ϵ is negative, so that we have to deal with reverse current, φ_c will not decrease indefinitely but will reach a minimum value given by

$$[\exp q\varphi_c/kT] - 1 = -\text{sech } (2w/L_p) \qquad (5.11)$$

and corresponding to saturation reverse current across J_1, so that

$$\varphi_c = -(kT/q) \ln [1 + (1/2) \text{ csch}^2(w/L_p)]. \qquad (5.12)$$

The floating potentials of p-type contacts to n-type material into which holes have been injected (or n-type contacts to p-type material with injected electrons) are reminiscent of probes in gas discharges which tend to become charged negative in respect to the space around them because they catch electrons more easily than positive ions. The situation may also be compared with that producing thermal e.m.f.'s; in fact a "concentration temperature" of the semiconductor with injected holes can be defined by finding the temperature for which $np = n_i^2(T)$. We conclude that, in the absence of thermal equilibrium, different potentials depending on the nature of the contact are, in general, the rule rather than the exception.

The bias developed on P_2 or c will change its conductance. If we suppose that φ_ϵ and φ_b are held constant, then the current flowing into c is obtained by the same reasoning that led to (5.7) and is

$$I_c(\varphi_c,\varphi_\epsilon) = I_{n0}(\varphi_c) + \coth \frac{2w}{L_p} I_{p0}(\varphi_c) - \text{csch} \frac{2w}{L_p} I_{p0}(\varphi_\epsilon).$$

$$(5.13)$$

For an infinitesimal change in φ_c from the value which makes $I_c(\varphi_c, \varphi_\epsilon)$ vanish, the admittance to c is readily found from (4.18) and (4.19) to be

$$\left(\frac{\partial I_c}{\partial \varphi_c}\right)_{\varphi_\epsilon} = I'_{n0}(\varphi_c) + \coth \frac{2w}{L_p} I'_{p0}(\varphi_c)$$

$$= \left[G_{n0} + \coth \frac{2w}{L_p} G_{p0} \right] e^{q\varphi_c/kT}$$

$$(5.14)$$

which shows that pronounced variations in admittance should be associated with variations in hole density in N in Fig. 10.[1]

6. *p–n–p* Transistors

The structure shown in Fig. 10 is a transistor with power gain provided the distance w is not too great. As a first approximation, we shall neglect the drop due to currents in the N region. If we use P_2 as the collector and call the collector current, I_c, positive when it flows into P_2 from outside, we shall have from (5.13)

$$I_c = -\operatorname{csch} \frac{2w}{L_p} I_{p0}(\varphi_\epsilon) + \coth \frac{2w}{L_p} I_{p0}(\varphi_c) + I_{n0}(\varphi_c). \quad (6.1)$$

The emitter current is similarly

$$I_\epsilon = -\coth \frac{2w}{L_p} I_{p0}(\varphi_\epsilon) - \operatorname{csch} \frac{2w}{L_p} I_{p0}(\varphi_c) + I_{n0}(\varphi_\epsilon). \quad (6.2)$$

If $p_n \gg n_p$, then the I_{n0} terms can be neglected. However, the base current will not vanish but will be

$$I_b = -I_\epsilon - I_c = \left[\operatorname{csch} \frac{2w}{L_p} - \coth \frac{2w}{L_p}\right] [I_{p0}(\varphi_\epsilon) + I_{p0}(\varphi_c)]$$

$$= \frac{2 \sinh^2 w/L_p}{\sinh 2w/L_p} [I_{p0}(\varphi_\epsilon) + I_{p0}(\varphi_c)]. \quad (6.3)$$

For w/L_p large, the junctions do not interact and the hyperbolic coefficient becomes unity and $I_b = -[I_{p0}(\varphi_\epsilon) + I_{p0}(\varphi_c)]$.

If φ_c is several volts negative, so that $I_{p0}(\varphi_c)$ has its saturation value I_{ps} (see (4.11) and (4.20)), then the ratio $-\delta I_c/\delta I_e \equiv a$ has the value

$$a = -\frac{\delta I_c}{\delta I_\epsilon} = \frac{\operatorname{csch} \dfrac{2w}{L_p}}{\coth \dfrac{2w}{L_p}} = \operatorname{sech} \frac{2w}{L_p}. \quad (6.4)$$

---

[1] The variations in admittance discussed in connection with metal point contacts in an accompanying paper in this issue (W. Shockley, G. L. Pearson and J. R. Haynes, *Bell Sys. Tech. Jl.*, July 1949), arise from this cause; however, the nature of the contact is not as simple as here.

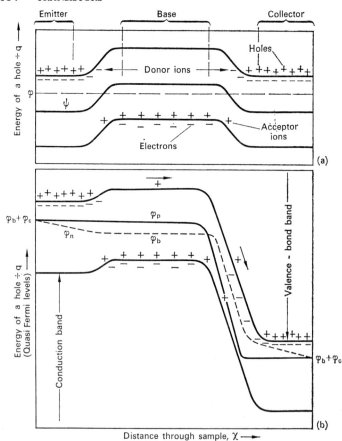

FIG. 11. p–n–p transistor. (a) Thermal equilibrium. (b) Operating
condition.

For $(2w/L_p) = 0.5, 1, 2$ respectively, $a = 0.89, 0.65, 0.27$. Since the
output impedance R_{22} will be very high when φ_c is in the reverse
direction, and the input impedance will be low, the power gain
formula[2] $a^2 R_{22}/R_{11}$ will yield power gain even when a is less than
unity.

[2] J. Bardeen and W. H. Brattain, Physical principles involved in transistor
action, *Phys. Rev.* **75,** 1208 (1949).

In certain ways the structure of Fig. 10 resembles a vacuum tube. In Fig. 11, we show the energy band diagram, with energies of holes plotted upwards so as to be in accord with the convention for voltages. (a) shows the thermal equilibrium distribution and (b) the distribution under operating conditions. It is seen that the potential hill, which holes must climb in reaching the collector, has been reduced by φ_e. The *n*-region represents in a sense the grid region in a vacuum tube, in which the potential and hence plate current, is varied by the charge on the grid wires. Here the potential in the *n*-region is varied by the voltage applied between base and emitter. In both cases one current is controlled by another. In the vacuum tube the current which charges the grid wires controls the space current. Because the grid is negative to the cathode, the electrons involved in the space current are kept away from the grid while at the same time the electrons in the grid are kept out of the space by the work function of the grid (provided that the grid does not become overheated.) In Fig. 11, the electrons flowing into the base control the hole current from emitter to collector. In this case the controlled and controlling currents flow in the same space but in different directions because of the opposite signs of their charges.

As this discussion suggests, it may be advantageous to operate the *p–n–p* transistor like a grounded cathode vacuum tube, with the emitter grounded and the input applied to the base.

The *p–n–p* transistor has the interesting feature of being calculable to a high degree. One can consider such questions as the relative ratios of width to length of the *n*-region and the effect of altering impurity contents and scaling the structure to operate in different frequency ranges. However, we shall not pursue these questions of possible applications further here.

PAPER 10

p-n Junction Transistors †

W. Shockley, M. Sparks, and G. K. Teal

Bell Telephone Laboratories, Inc., Murray Hill, New Jersey

(Received May 24, 1951)

Summary

The effects of diffusion of electrons through a thin *p*-type layer of germanium have been studied in specimens consisting of two *n*-type regions with the *p*-type region interposed. It is found that potentials applied to one *n*-type region are transmitted by diffusing electrons through the *p*-type layer although the latter is grounded through an ohmic contact. When one of the *p–n* junctions is biased to saturation, power gain can be obtained through the device. Used as "*n–p–n* transistors" these units will operate on currents as low as 10 microamperes and voltages as low as 0.1 volt, have power gains of 50 db, and noise figures of about 10 db at 1000 cps. Their current–voltage characteristics are in good agreement with the diffusion theory.

I. Introduction

In this article we shall consider the phenomena which occur when voltages are applied to a semiconductor consisting of several regions of different conductivity types. Structures of this sort, consisting in particular of two regions of one conductivity type separated by another region of the opposite type, are of great practical interest in transistor electronics. Such structures can also be used to exhibit the behavior of hole and electron diffusion in rather impressive ways. In particular, the phenomenon of "internal contact potentials" can be strikingly demonstrated with such structures.

† *Physical Review*, **83**, 151 (1951).

Transistors in which the nonlinear effects originate within the germanium as a result of the relationships of *p*-type and *n*-type regions are called "*p-n* junction transistors" to distinguish them from point-contact types, in which the metal semiconductor contact often plays an essential role. There are a number of possible *p-n* junction transistor structures: The *p-n-p* transistor has been discussed previously from a theoretical viewpoint.[1, 2] In this article we shall consider chiefly the *n-p-n* transistor,[3] the *n*-type phototransistor with a *p-n* hook collector and a *p-n-p-n* transistor with *p*-type emitter and *p-n* hook collector.

In the following sections we shall describe first in simple terms the basic phenomena and effects with which we are concerned. We shall next describe the actual physical structure of several of the *n-p-n* transistors and their electrical characteristics. The theoretical principles will then be put in quantitative form and the current–voltage relationships derived for certain particular models. Finally a direct comparison between theory and experiment will be presented.

II. The *n-p-n* Structure as a Transistor and as a "Hook Multiplier"

In Fig. 1 we represent an *n-p-n* structure and indicate how it may be used as a transistor. Like the type-A transistor, the current paths between emitter terminal and base and between collector terminal and base have rectifying junctions. Unlike the type-A transistor, however, the rectification arises in the interior of the germanium and not at the contacts between metal leads and the germanium, which are substantially ohmic. There are other important differences between the *n-p-n* and the type-A: In the

[1] W. Shockley, *Bell System Tech. J.* **28**, 435–489 (1949).

[2] W. Shockley, *Electrons and Holes in Semiconductors*, D. van Nostrand Company, Inc., New York, 1950.

[3] R. L. Wallace and W. J. Pietenpol, *Bell System Tech. J.*, July 1951. (This article, to which we shall refer a number of times, deals with a number of practical features which we do not consider here.) It is also scheduled for the *Proc. Inst. Radio Engrs.*, July 1951.

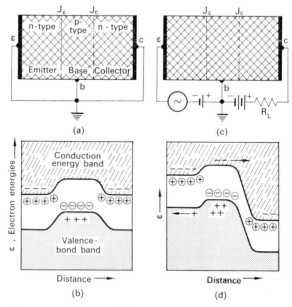

FIG. 1. *p–n–p* structure and the energy level scheme. (a) and (b) Thermal equilibrium. (c) and (d) Biased as an amplifier.

n–p–n the flow of injected carriers takes place chiefly by diffusion rather than by drift in an electric field; the current multiplication at the collector, which makes possible the positive feed-back instability of the type-A transistor, is lacking in the *n–p–n* transistor.

In this section we shall give a brief resumé of the theory of the operation of the transistor. Additional details will be found in the cited references. In Secs. V *et seq.*, some aspects of the theory will be treated analytically. The analysis is simplified by the use of the following assumptions:[4]

(1) The donors and acceptors are fully ionized (this is a good assumption for germanium at room temperature).

[4] These assumptions are discussed further in references 1 and 2.

(2) The density of minority carriers is much smaller than the density of majority carriers in each region.

(3) The net rate of recombination in any region is linear in the deviation of the minority carrier density from its thermal equilibrium value. (Assumptions (2) and (3) permit us to use linear equations in dealing with the currents arising from carrier injection.)

(4) Space charge is negligible except at the space-charge regions in the *p–n* junctions themselves.

In Fig. 1 we show the energy band diagram for the structure under consideration for zero bias and for biases applied in such a way that the unit becomes an amplifying transistor. Under the latter condition the junction J_c on the right of the figure is biased in the reverse direction. This direction is such that electrons in the *n*-type collector region have low potential energy and cannot climb the potential energy hill to the base region; similarly holes are held in the base region. Electrons in the emitter region, however, may climb the small potential hill into the base region and once in this region may diffuse so that some of them will arrive at the right-hand junction. The flow over the hill depends on the height of the hill and this height may be varied by applying a variable potential to the emitter while maintaining the base at constant potential. If the base region is very thin, few of the electrons will recombine with holes in it and, as a result, efficient transmission of electron current through the layer will occur. Furthermore, if the emitter region is more highly conducting than the base region, there will be many more electrons available to climb the hill than there are holes to climb the corresponding hill in the opposite direction. As a result, most of the current across the left junction will consist of electrons. Under these conditions the behavior of this device is closely analogous to that of a vacuum tube: the emitter region corresponds to the cathode, the base to the region around the grid wires, and the collector region corresponds to the plate. In favorably designed units the controlled electron current flowing through the base region may be very much larger than the current furnished the base region for control purposes so that the transistor has a current amplification factor that is very high. It may, therefore, be operated like a grounded cathode triode with the emitter region grounded and the signal applied to the base. In Sec. IV some current–voltage characteristics for transistors are shown and for them it may be seen that the current transmission is nearly perfect.

It is interesting to note that both for the vacuum tube and for the transistor, control is accomplished by the interaction of two forms of electron flow. In the vacuum tube, metallic flow in the grid wire controls the flow of thermionic electrons in the space between grid wires. In the transistor, hole flow in the base changes the base–emitter voltage and controls electron flow through the base layer.

The structure shown in Fig. 1 with the same operating biases may be used as a collector with high multiplication in a transistor.[5] It may also be used as a phototransistor.[6] We shall consider the application as a collector in a transistor later and shall describe here how multiplication of photocurrents can occur. For this purpose there need be no electrode connected to the base layer. If light shines on the germanium near the junctions, then the hole electron pairs generated will be separated by the field of the junctions and consequently a current of holes will flow into the base layer. These holes will accumulate in the layer and will charge it positively and thus reduce its potential energy for electrons. As a result more electrons will be able to climb the hill and flow to the collector. The effect of the added holes will die away after the light is removed due to the diffusion of holes into the left region where they combine with electrons and also due to recombination with electrons which diffuse into the base layer. If the layer is very thin, however, and the density of electrons in the left region is very high, then a very large number of electrons will be able to climb over the hill for each hole that is able to enter the emitter region and

[5] W. Shockley, *Phys. Rev.* **78,** 294 (1950).

[6] J. N. Shive who has developed the phototransistor [*Phys. Rev.* **76,** 575 (1949)] has proposed this use of the *p–n* hook.

recombine. In Sec. VII we shall show that the current amplification obtained in this way is proportional to the ratio of the conductivities of the two layers and is inversely proportional to the thickness of the base layer.

An interesting consequence of the diffusion of electrons through the base layer is the occurrence of "internal contact potentials."[7] In order to illustrate these we shall suppose that the base layer is grounded and that a potential is applied to the emitter. If an additional ohmic contact is also made to the base region, it will of course show ground potential. If the contact is rectifying, however, and in particular if it carries most of its current in the form of electrons, its potential will be determined by the electron density in the base layer rather than by the potential established by the grounding contact. The *n*-region on the right represents such a contact. It is found both theoretically and experimentally that if the base layer is grounded, then potentials applied to the region on the left are transmitted through the base layer, although its electrostatic potential is practically unaltered, and exhibit themselves in the region to the right, which tends to "float" (when no current is drawn from it) at a potential approximately equal to that of the left region—at least over a certain range of voltages. Theory and experiment related to this phenomenon are given in Secs. VII and VIII.

III. Description of Experimental Units

The experimental units were made of a piece of single crystal germanium in which a thin *p*-type layer is interposed between two *n*-type sections. Units of a variety of conductivity values have been prepared. Typical values for an *n–p–n* structure as shown in Fig. 1 are: emitter, 100 (ohm-cm)$^{-1}$; base, 1 (ohm-cm)$^{-1}$; and collector, 0.1 (ohm-cm)$^{-1}$. Typical values of lifetime of the minority carrier

[7] These were first discussed in reference 1. Internal contact potentials for point contacts have been measured by G. L. Pearson and analyzed by J. Bardeen [*Bell System Tech. J.* **29**, 469–495 (1950)].

in the collector section are 300–400 microseconds. The experimental evidence is that lifetimes in the other sections, in which direct measurement of lifetimes is more difficult, do not differ greatly from this. The leads to the three sections being mechanically strong and ohmic in character. The structure thus operates through conditions arising within the interior of the single crystal and not because of phenomena arising at the contacts between the leads and the germanium.

IV. Performance Characteristics

The performance characteristics of n–p–n transistors will be considered briefly.[8] Since these devices operate uniformly over the surfaces of p–n junctions they may be greatly altered as to the size of the active area, in contrast to point-contact devices. Thus it is possible to increase power output without corresponding increases in current density. One of the larger n–p–n transistors[9] studies as an amplifier had a junction area of 0.3 sq cm, a base layer thickness of about 0.07 cm, and delivered 2.0 watts of undistorted output in class A operation. Its frequency cutoff was about 10,000 cps, this limit being in general agreement with the effect of diffusion through the p-layer as discussed in Sec. IX.

The low power potentialities of these structures have been more thoroughly investigated. A junction area of about 0.01 sq cm and a base layer thickness of about 1.5×10^{-3} cm are typical dimensions for these units. They have operated with gains of 50 db and noise figures of about 10 db to 15 db at 1000 cycles per second. Each of these quantities is an improvement of several orders of magnitude over point-contact transistors. For low signal levels they give essentially full gain with collector voltages higher than 0.1 volt and are, therefore, exceptionally good very low power amplifiers. At some sacrifice in gain they may be operated at efficiencies of 48 to 49 percent out of a theoretical maximum of 50

[8] An extensive presentation of circuit properties is given in reference 3.

[9] The performance of this transistor was discussed at the June 1950 Inst. Radio Engrs. Conference on Electron Devices at the University of Michigan, and also at the July 1950 Conference on Semiconductors at Reading.

percent for class A. An oscillator has been constructed by R. L. Wallace, Jr., and D. E. Thomas of this laboratory which operates on 0.6-microwatt input. The same small transistors will also operate as amplifiers with maximum output powers of several hundred milliwatts. A set of operating curves is given in Fig. 2. The frequency cutoff of these units in high gain circuits is determined chiefly by the capacitance of the collector junction and is much lower than the limit set by diffusion through the base layer. A discussion of the capacitative effect will be found in the article by Wallace and Pietenpol.

V. Theoretical Principles and Boundary Conditions

In this and following sections we shall give analytic form to the ideas discussed in Sec. II. The principal symbols used in dealing with the theory are shown in the accompanying table of notation. In this section and the next we shall deal with the *n–p–n* structure in general terms and for this reason shall use subscripts "*l*" and "*r*" standing for "left" and "right" for the two *n*-type regions. This permits us to consider impartially cases in which either region may be biased as a collector or as an emitter.

We shall first discuss the boundary conditions at the junctions when potentials are applied across them.[10] The electrostatic potential ψ in the interior of the semiconductor may have its zero chosen arbitrarily. For our purpose the zero is so chosen that $-q\psi$ is approximately the energy of an electron at a level of energy midway in the energy gap. The exact value of ψ is such that

$$n = n_i \exp q(\psi - \varphi)kT \tag{5.1}$$

$$p = n_i \exp q(\varphi - \psi)/kT \tag{5.2}$$

under equilibrium conditions. Under nonequilibrium conditions,

---

[10] The notation used here is similar to that of references 1 and 2 and the analysis is substantially an abbreviation of that of reference 1.

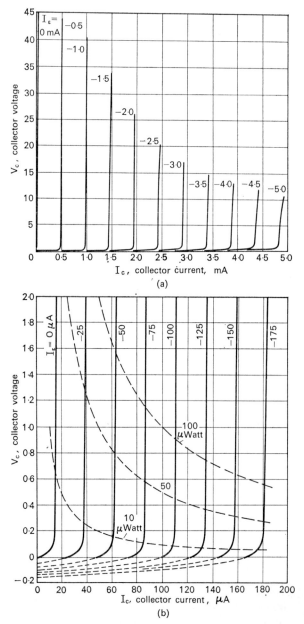

FIG. 2. Current–voltage relationships for an *n–p–n* transistor.

similar equations determine the "imrefs"[11] φ_n and φ_p in terms of ψ, n, and p as follows:

$$n = n_i \exp q(\psi - \varphi_n)/kT \tag{5.3}$$

$$p = n_i \exp q(\varphi_p - \psi)/kT. \tag{5.4}$$

Notation

A = cross-sectional area of unit;
$b = \mu_n/\mu_p = 2.1$;
$B_l = (kT/q)[1 - \exp(-q\varphi_l/kT)]$;
$B_r = (kT/q)[1 - \exp(-q\varphi_r/kT)]$;
e = base of naperian logarithms;
D_n, D_p = diffusion constants for electrons and holes;
G_{ll}, G_{lr}, etc. = conductances at zero voltage;
n = density of electrons;
$n_b = n$ in the base layer;
$n_i = n$ in an intrinsic specimen;
n_1 = deviation of n from its thermal equilibrium value;
N_d, N_a = density of donors, acceptors;
p = density of holes;
q = charge of a hole = $-$ charge of an electron;
V, v = dc and ac components of voltage;
W = thickness of base layer;
μ_n, μ_p = mobilities of electrons, holes = 3600, 1700 cm²/ volt sec;
σ_i = intrinsic conductivity;
$\tau_{pl}, \tau_{pr}, \tau_{nb}$ = lifetimes of minority carriers;
φ = (Fermi level)/$(-q)$;
φ_n = imref for electrons;
φ_p = imref for holes;
$\varphi_l, \varphi_b, \varphi_r$ = voltages of the three regions; and
ψ = electrostatic potential.

[11] We are indebted to the most appropriate authority for suggesting this modified name for the quasi-Fermi levels.

The imrefs or "quasi-Fermi levels" are introduced for convenience in discussing boundary conditions at the junctions and the meaning of applied voltages. In terms of the imrefs the current densities assume a particularly simple form:

$$I_n = qD_n\nabla n + q\mu_n nE = -q\mu_n n\nabla\varphi_n \qquad (5.5)$$

$$I_p = -qD_n\nabla p + q\mu_n pE = -q\mu_p p\nabla\varphi_p. \qquad (5.6)$$

These equations show that the current densities are those corresponding to materials with the conductivity appropriate for the electron and hole densities, respectively, and to electric fields derived from the imrefs as potentials. From these relationships it is evident that a given electron current will produce much bigger changes of the imrefs when it flows in a p-type region, where the electron density is small, than it will in an n-type region. In fact the ratio of conductivity by electrons is so great between the two regions that the imref for electrons can be regarded as substantially constant in the n-type region. In accordance with the assumption that the minority carrier density is small compared to the majority density and the assumption that the space charge is negligible, it follows that the potential ψ is substantially uniform in the interior of each region also. If the contacts on regions l and r are so far from the junctions that no injected carriers reach them and are substantially ohmic, then it also follows that the imrefs for electrons in these regions are simply the voltage applied to the two contacts. In accordance with the assumption that current to the base contact is carried by holes, it also follows that the imref for holes in this region is equal to φ_b.

We shall now apply the aforementioned conclusions to the boundary condition at J_l. For simplicity we shall assume that the base is grounded so that we shall consider in general cases in which

$$\varphi_l \neq 0, \quad \varphi_b = 0, \quad \varphi_r \neq 0. \qquad (5.7)$$

By the reasoning of the preceding paragraph, the imref for electrons is continuous across the junction J_l and in fact has its largest gradient only after the interior of the base region is reached.

Consequently we may take φ_n in the base region near J_l as substantially equal to φ_l. The electron density in the base region near J_l is thus given by

$$n(\text{in } b \text{ near } J_l) = n_b \exp(-q\varphi_l/kT), \qquad (5.8)$$

where n_b is the thermal equilibrium concentration of electrons at the corresponding point. (This equation follows directly from (5.3) together with the conclusion previously reached that ψ and φ_p in the base layer are unaffected by the applied potentials of (5.7).)

We shall be chiefly concerned with deviations of the densities from their equilibrium values and shall use the subscript 1 to indicate such densities. The deviation corresponding to (5.8) is

$$n_1 = n_b[\exp(-q\varphi_l/kT) - 1] \equiv -n_b q B_l/kT. \qquad (5.9)$$

In this expression we have introduced the quantity B_l defined as

$$B_l \equiv (kT/q)[1 - \exp(-q\varphi_l/kT)]. \qquad (5.10)$$

This symbol is introduced since all the currents with which we shall be concerned depend functionally upon the voltages in the form (5.10). The coefficient kT/q is introduced so that B_l has the dimensions of a voltage and for small values of φ_l, B_l is in fact approximately equal to φ_l.

Entirely similar reasoning leads to corresponding relationships for the hole density in the l region:

$$p(\text{in } l \text{ near } J_l) = p_l \exp(-q\varphi_l/kT) \qquad (5.11)$$

$$p_1 = p_l[\exp(-q\varphi_l/kT) - 1] \equiv -p_l q B_l/kT. \qquad (5.12)$$

VI. The Current–Voltage Relationships

The analysis of the last section indicates that near J_l the deviations of both hole and electron densities are proportional to B_l. These deviations lead to diffusion currents, which would vanish for the case of thermal equilibrium with $B_l = 0$. As a result of the linear approximations discussed in Sec. II, these currents will be

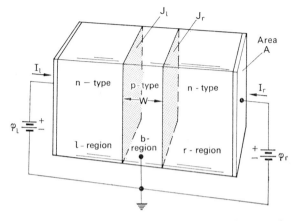

FIG. 3. Dimensions and conventions for voltage and current for an
n–p–n structure.

proportional to B_l. In Fig. 3 the conventions selected for signs of
current are shown. We shall accordingly denote the current into
region b due to hole flow across J_l as follows:

$$I_{lp} = G_{llp}B_l. \qquad (6.1)$$

For the case of a uniform cross section of area A and material of
uniform conductivity and uniform lifetime τ_{pl}, the value of the
coefficient may be easily derived:[12]

$$G_{nlp} = q\mu_p p_{nl}A/L_{pl} = \sigma_i^2 bA/(1 + b)^2\sigma_l L_{pl} \qquad (6.2)$$

in which the diffusion length is given by the equation,

$$L_{pl} = (D_p\tau_{pl})^{\frac{1}{2}}. \qquad (6.3)$$

The last form of (6.2) expresses the conductance G_{llp} in terms of
the conductivity σ_i of an intrinsic sample and the actual con-

[12] Reference 1, Eqs. (4.20) and (4.21), or reference 2, p. 316. In a specimen
of finite cross section, the recombination must be described in terms of a set of
normal modes. For the cross sections of the small transistors, the lowest mode
dominates and its lifetime may be used in the formulas derived for the one-
dimensional case. See reference 1, Appendix V.

ductivity of the n-type region. The quantity b occurring in the equation is the ratio of mobilities:

$$b = \mu_n/\mu_p. \tag{6.4}$$

The electron current flowing across J_l can also be directly evaluated for the case of $B_r = 0$. Even if no potential is applied across J_r, some of the electrons injected across J_l will arrive in the r-region. This is a consequence of the fact that the deviation n_1 is required to be zero at J_r when φ_r is zero. The electron currents across the two junctions are found to be[13]

$$I_{ln} = [(q\mu_n n_b A/L_n)\coth(W/L_n)]B_l \equiv G_{lln}B_l \tag{6.5}$$

$$I_{rn} = -[(q\mu_n n_b A/L_n)\operatorname{csch}(W/L_n)]B_l \equiv G_{rln}B_l. \tag{6.6}$$

The conductance G_{lln} may be expressed in terms of the properties of the base layer as follows:

$$G_{lln} = [\sigma_i{}^2 bA/(1 + b^2)\sigma_b L_n]\coth(W/L_n). \tag{6.7}$$

A similar treatment for J_r leads to a corresponding set of equations. In terms of the G's and the B's the current–voltage relationship may be written as follows:

$$I_l = G_{ll}B_l + G_{lr}B_r \tag{6.8}$$

$$I_r = G_{rl}B_l + G_{rr}B_r \tag{6.9}$$

$$G_{ll} = G_{lln} + G_{llp}, \quad G_{lr} = G_{lrn} \tag{6.10}$$

$$G_{rl} = G_{rln}, \quad G_{rr} = G_{rrn} + G_{rrp}. \tag{6.11}$$

For low voltages we have the approximate relationship,

$$B_l \doteq \varphi_l, \quad B_r \doteq \varphi_r \quad \text{for} \quad |\varphi_{l,\,r}| \ll kT/q, \tag{6.12}$$

so that the coefficients in Eqs. (6.8) and (6.9) are simply the low voltage conductance components. If the potentials consist of a bias plus a small ac component so that we may write

$$\varphi_l = V_l + v_l, \quad \varphi_r = V_r + v_r, \tag{6.13}$$

---

[13] Reference 1, Eq. (5.6), modified for electron diffusion.

then the small signal equations become

$$i_l = g_{ll}v_l + g_{lr}v_r \qquad (6.14)$$

$$i_r = g_{rl}v_l + g_{rr}v_r, \qquad (6.15)$$

where the relationship between the small g's and the large G's is

$$g_{ll}/G_{ll} = g_{rl}/G_{rl} = \exp(-qV_l/kT) \qquad (6.16)$$

while a similar equation applies for the other two coefficients.

From these relationships one can also derive the result that each g is proportional to the deviation of its corresponding GB term from its saturation value corresponding to $B = (kT/q)$. This may be expressed symbolically as follows:

$$g = (\text{deviation of } GB \text{ from saturation}) \cdot (q/kT). \qquad (6.17)$$

For the model discussed in connection with Eqs. (6.5) and (6.6), it is evident that symmetry leads to the equation,

$$G_{lr} = G_{rl}. \qquad (6.18)$$

If the conductivity varies in an unsymmetrical way, however, in the middle layer or if the lifetime is greater at one side of the layer than the other, then we cannot reach the conclusion that the two G's are equal from symmetry arguments. It can be shown, however, that it is a consequence of the linear assumptions described in Sec. II that the symmetry relationship holds no matter what the geometry of the middle layer. The proof of this result is given in an appendix.[14] This leads us to the conclusion that for the idealized sort of model in which all of the currents are linear in the injected carrier

---

[14] This symmetry result may be derived in a more general way from the reciprocity principle of electrical conduction provided no magnetic field is present. The necessary theorem is proved in section 5 of H. B. G. Casimir [*Revs. Modern Phys.* **17,** 343 (1945)]. The proof there shows that in the linear range of conductivity, G_{lr} must equal G_{rl}. Since we have shown that the currents are linear functions of the B's by an independent argument, it follows that we may take $G_{lr} = G_{rl}$ in general. The method used by Casimir is based on Onsager's principle of microscopic reversibility and has an unnecessarily abstract flavor so far as the needs of this article are concerned. The desired theorem can be proved by straightforward analytical methods as is shown in the Appendix.

density, the behavior of the transistor is described by three parameters, at least so far as low frequencies are concerned. These parameters are the four coefficients in Eqs. (6.8) and (6.9) with the relationship (6.18) between two of them.

In terms of these coefficients we may define the "alpha" of the unit using either junction as an emitter. The two α's need not be equal and the α for the left junction is given by the relationship,

$$\alpha_l \equiv -(\partial I_r/\partial I_l) \quad [\text{for} \quad \varphi_r \text{ const}] = -G_{rl}/G_{ll}$$
$$= -G_{rln}/(G_{lln} + G_{llp})$$
$$= (-G_{rln}/G_{lln})[G_{lln}/(G_{lln} + G_{llp})] = \gamma_l\beta_l. \tag{6.19}$$

The definition of γ in transistor terminology is the fraction of the current at the emitter junction produced by emitter voltage that is carried by minority carriers in the base; evidently

$$\gamma_l = G_{lln}/(G_{lln} + G_{llp}). \tag{6.20}$$

The fraction of these injected carriers that reaches the collector is defined as β:

$$\beta_l = -G_{rln}/G_{lln} = \text{sech}(W/L_n). \tag{6.21}$$

The "intrinsic α" or α^* of the collector junction is defined as the ratio of change in total current per unit minority carrier current arriving at it. For a simple $p–n$ junction collector, α^* is unity. For a "hook collector," which we treat in the next section, the arrival of injected current provokes a flow of carriers and α^* may be 100 or more.

If the middle layer is thin so that the hyperbolic functions of (6.5) and (6.6) may be approximated by their first terms, we may write

$$\beta_l \doteq 1 - \tfrac{1}{2}(W/L_n)^2 \doteq 1 \tag{6.22}$$

$$\gamma_l \doteq 1/[1 + (\sigma_b W/\sigma_l L_{pl})] \tag{6.23}$$

$$\alpha_l \doteq 1/[1 + (\sigma_b W/\sigma_l L_{pl})] \tag{6.24}$$

$$G_{lln} \doteq \sigma_1^2 bA/(1 + b)^2 \sigma_b W. \tag{6.25}$$

Entirely similar expressions may be written for J_r simply by interchanging r and l.

VII. Special Operating Conditions

We shall next consider the consequences of the equations derived in the previous section for several limiting cases of voltages and currents.

A. Operating as an Amplifier

In order to get into the range of linear behavior it is necessary to apply a sufficiently large reverse bias to the collector so that its current saturates. This condition corresponds to the straight parts of the characteristics shown in Fig. 2. The voltage required to get into this range must exceed about $4kT/q$. After this point is reached the emitter current and collector current may be approximated by

$$I_\iota = G_{\iota\iota}B_\iota - a_\iota G_{rr}kT/q \tag{7.1a}$$

$$I_r = -a_\iota G_{\iota\iota}B_\iota + G_{\iota\iota}kT/q$$
$$= -a_\iota I_\iota + (G_{rr} + a_\iota^2 G_{\iota\iota})(kT/q). \tag{7.1b}$$

Equation (7.1b) accounts for the parallel lines with currents increasing linearly in I_ι shown in Fig. 2 for high collector voltages.

For applications in circuit theory, it is important to know the emitter admittance $g_{\iota\iota}$. To the approximation emphasized in this paper in which series ohmic resistances are neglected, this admittance is $1/r_\epsilon$ of the equivalent circuit.[3] The range of interest is usually such that $-\varphi_\iota > 4kT/q$ so that the application of the reasoning of (6.17) leads to

$$1/r_\epsilon = g_{\iota\iota} = \partial I_\iota / \partial \varphi_\iota = G_{\iota\iota} \exp(-q\varphi_\iota/kT)$$
$$\doteq I_\iota q/kT \doteq 40 I_\iota \text{ mho.} \tag{7.2}$$

If the unit is operated with grounded emitter and with the collector current saturated, then the input admittance is

$$dI_b/d\varphi_b = d(-I_\iota - I_r)/d(-\varphi_b)$$
$$= (1 - a_\iota)G_{\iota\iota} \exp(-q\varphi_\iota/kT) \tag{7.3}$$

while the transconductance is $1/(1 - a_\iota)$ larger. Thus if $a_\iota = 0.99$, there will be a current gain of 100-fold, if the collector current is saturated. The theoretical power gain would be infinite if the collector impedance were infinite corresponding to the ideal saturation of (7.1b). Actually collector resistances of 10^7 to 10^8 ohms are observed. For currents large compared to saturation currents, (7.3) leads to an admittance of $(1 - a_l)I_r q/kT = 10^{-2} \times 10^{-4} \times 40 = 4 \times 10^{-5}$ mhos for $I_r = 10^{-4}$ amp, a typical value for high gain performance. The power gain will be roughly the ratio of output to input impedances times the square of the current gain and will thus be about $10^7 \times 4 \times 10^{-5} \times 10^4 \doteq 66$ db for a matched load. As discussed in Sec. IV, gains as high as 50 db have been obtained in practical circuits.

B. Hook Collector in p–n–p–n Transistor

Point contact transistors are frequently observed to have current multiplication in the sense that at a fixed collector bias, changes in emitter current produce changes in collector current several fold larger. One explanation is that a "*p–n* hook" is formed at the collector junction so that the "intrinsic a" or a^* of the collector is high. We shall illustrate this theory for the case of an *n*-type transistor in which holes are injected by a *p–n* junction emitter and the collector consists of *n* and *p* layers.

This structure is represented in Fig. 4 and is shown for bias conditions similar to those discussed for Fig. 1 except for the added emitter region and the absence of a contact to the *b* layer. Regarded as a transistor, the emitter, base, and collector are ϵ', b', and c'. The operating biases put reverse voltage across J_r and forward across J_l. The base layer *b* will float at a potential such that the net current to it is zero:

$$I_r + I_l = G_{ll}(1 - a_l)B_l + G_{rr}(1 - a_r)B_r = 0. \qquad (7.4)$$

For large reverse biases B_r will be positive and B_l negative and

$$\varphi_l - \varphi_r = V_{c'}, \qquad (7.5)$$

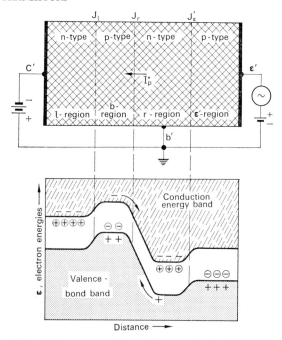

FIG. 4. A p–n–p transistor with a p–n hook collector.

where $V_{c'}$ is the voltage on the collector. For large $V_{c'}$, B_r will saturate and φ_l will be determined by

$$B_l = -G_{rr}(1 - a_r)(kT/q)/G_{ll}(1 - a_l) \qquad (7.6)$$

so that the saturation current is

$$I_r(\text{sat.}) = (1 - a_r a_l)G_{rr}kT/q(1 - a_l). \qquad (7.7)$$

If holes are injected by ϵ' so that a hole current I_p* arrives at J_r, then the condition,

$$I_r + I_l + I_p* = 0 \qquad (7.8)$$

leads to a change

$$\Delta B_l = -I_p*/G_{ll}(1 - a_l) \qquad (7.9)$$

and this produces an increased electron current across J_r which leads to

$$\Delta I_{nr} = G_{rl}\Delta B_l = a_l I_p^*/(1 - a_l). \tag{7.10}$$

The "intrinsic a" or a^* of the composite structure is

$$a^* = (\Delta I_{nr} + I_p^*)/I_p^* = 1/(1 - a_l). \tag{7.11}$$

For the thin layer approximation we see that

$$a^* \doteq 1 + (\sigma_l L_{pl}/\sigma_b W). \tag{7.12}$$

Thus for thin layers and for highly conducting l regions, a^* may be made very large.

The reason for calling the structure a "*p–n* hook" is illustrated in Fig. 4b. The high energy potential for electrons in layer b is low potential for holes. Holes injected by ϵ' become caught in this hook and bias J_l forward so as to provoke the enhanced electron flow.

C. *Phototransistor*

The structure in Fig. 4 can act as a phototransistor if the hole injection by the emitter junction is simply replaced by hole electron pair generation by light. For this application, the structure has only two terminals, b' and c' of Fig. 4, the region ϵ' being absent. If the hole electron pairs are generated in the neighborhood of J_r, then they will be separated by the field in the junction with a current equivalent to the passage of one hole across J_r for each pair so separated. The hole current across the junction will under these conditions be multiplied just as for the case of the *p–n–p–n* transistor so that the apparent quantum efficiency for hole electron pairs generated at J_r is

apparent quantum efficiency

$$= a^* \doteq 1 + (\sigma_l L_{pl}/\sigma_b W) \tag{7.13}$$

by the reasoning that leads to Eq. (7.12). In the following section we shall discuss some values of a^* determined by measurements of photocurrents.

D. Internal Contact Potentials

In order to discuss internal contact potentials we return to a consideration of the three region device of Fig. 3. If b is grounded and region r is allowed to seek its own potential, then potentials applied to region l will produce potentials on region r although the potential measured with an ohmic contact to b would everywhere be zero. The floating potential of region r is determined by setting the total current equal to zero so that we have

$$0 = I_r = G_{rl}B_l + G_{rr}B_r \qquad (7.14)$$

$$B_r = (-G_{rl}/G_{rr})B_l = (-G_{lr}/G_{rr})B_i = a_r B_l \qquad (7.15)$$

$$\exp(-q\varphi_r/kT) = 1 - a_r + a_r \exp(-q\varphi_l/kT). \qquad (7.16)$$

Equation (7.16) expresses φ_r as a function of φ_l and a_r. It takes simple limiting form for extreme bias conditions:

Forward bias:

$$-q\varphi_l/kT \gg 1$$

$$\varphi_r = \varphi_l - (kT/q)\ln a_r \qquad (7.17a)$$

$$a_r = \exp q(\varphi_l - \varphi_r)/kT. \qquad (7.17b)$$

Zero bias:

$$|q\varphi_l/kT| \ll 1$$

$$\varphi_r = a_r \varphi_l. \qquad (7.18)$$

Reverse bias:

$$q_l\varphi/kT \gg 1$$

$$\varphi_r = -(kT/q)\ln(1 - a_r) \qquad (7.19a)$$

$$a_r = 1 - \exp(-q\varphi_r/kT). \qquad (7.19b)$$

In the following section, we shall show that these expressions are approximately satisfied.

VIII. Comparison with Experiment

In this section we shall be chiefly concerned with an analysis of data on an *n-p-n* transistor and with showing that it may be interpreted on the basis of the theory discussed above. The data were taken under two sets of conditions: In the first the voltages were small compared to (kT/q) and from these the G's were determined using the approximation (6.12). In the second set, a wide range of voltages were used; for all conditions, however, one of the two B's was taken as independent and the other B was either constant or else proportional to the independent B. Consequently, each current is of the form

$$I = c + mB = I_s + m[B - (kT/q)]$$
$$= I_s - I_v \exp(-qV/kT), \qquad (8.1)$$

where V is the voltage upon which B depends and

$$I_s = c + (mkT/q) \qquad (8.2)$$

is the "saturation" value of the current for large positive values of V and

$$I_v = mkT/q. \qquad (8.3)$$

Both I_s and I_v are readily calculated in terms of the G's. In the analysis of the data the measured I_s and I_v values are compared with values computed from the G's, and the dependence of I upon V is investigated.

TABLE 8.1. ZERO BIAS CONDUCTANCES FOR AN *n-p-n* TRANSISTOR
(CONDUCTANCES IN MICROMHOS AT $T = 22^\circ$C)

	Measured	Calculated
G_{11}	8.8 $\pm$ 0.5	8.8
G_{22}	33.3 $\pm$ 0.5	33.3
$G_{11}(1-a_1a_2)$	6.9 $\pm$ 0.5	6.9
$G_{22}(1-a_1a_2)$	26.5 $\pm$ 0.5	26.4
$a_2 = (V_c/V_\epsilon)$ for $I_c = 0$	0.86 $\pm$ 0.02	0.89
$a_1 = (V_\epsilon/V_c)$ for $I_\epsilon = 0$	0.22 $\pm$ 0.02	0.23
$G_{11} + G_{12} - 2G_{21}$	26.2 $\pm$ 0.5	26.5

It should be pointed out that the values of the G's are strongly dependent on temperature. Consider, for example,

$$G_{rl} = b\sigma_i^2 A/(1 + b)^2 \sigma_p W. \tag{8.4}$$

In this expression[15]

$$\sigma_i^2 \propto \exp(-\epsilon_G/kT) \tag{8.5}$$

where ϵ_G is the energy gap and

$$\sigma_p \propto T^{-\frac{3}{2}}. \tag{8.6}$$

Consequently the value of G_{rl} at $T_0 + \Delta T = 300°K + \Delta T$ is approximately

$$\begin{aligned} G_{rl}(T_0 + \Delta T) &= G_{rl}(T_0) \exp[(\epsilon_G/kT_0^2) + (3/2T_0)]\Delta T \\ &= G_{rl}(T_0) \exp(0.095 + 0.005)\Delta T \end{aligned} \tag{8.7}$$

so that G_{rl} increases approximately 10 percent per degree C. This increase arises chiefly from σ_i^2 and will be approximately the same for all the G's.

The fact that the G's have large temperature coefficients implies that at fixed voltages the currents will be very sensitive to temperature. This does not mean, however, that in a properly designed circuit, the behavior of the unit will be highly sensitive to temperature. The value of a_1, for example, as shown in (6.24) involves only $\sigma_b W/\sigma_e L_{pe}$ and this has only a small temperature coefficient. At a fixed emitter current, the emitter resistance is proportional to T in °K. Thus the most important quantities from a circuit point of view have small temperature coefficients.

Since in this section we are dealing with a transistor designed to have one terminal as emitter and one as collector, we shall abandon the "left" and "right" terminology and use subscript "1" for the emitter and "2" for the collector as is customary for transistors. The large signal equations are then

$$I_\epsilon = G_{11}B_1 + G_{12}B_2 \tag{8.8}$$

$$I_c = G_{21}B_1 + G_{22}B_2 \tag{8.9}$$

---

[15] n_i^2 varies as $T^3 \exp(-\epsilon_G/kT)$, see reference 2, page 475, and $\mu_n\mu_p$ as T^{-3}, see page 287.

and the small signal equations are

$$I_\epsilon = g_{11}v_\epsilon + g_{12}v_c \qquad (8.10)$$

$$i_c = g_{21}v_e + g_{22}v_c \qquad (8.11)$$

where each g depends on its corresponding voltage in the form,

$$g_{ij} = G_{ij}\exp(-qV_j/kT). \qquad (8.12)$$

The low voltage conductances were measured at 2 millivolts. For this small voltage

$$B(+2\text{ mV}) = \quad 1.95\text{ mV} \qquad (8.13a)$$

$$B(-2\text{ mV}) = -2.05\text{ mV} \qquad (8.13b)$$

so that the currents are nearly linear in this range, and the non-linearity is practically eliminated by averaging the two polarities. With the collector grounded, I_ϵ was measured and G_{11} computed from I_ϵ/V_ϵ. With the collector open circuited, I_ϵ and V_c were measured; for this case $I_\epsilon/V_\epsilon = G_{11}(1 - a_1a_2)$ and $V_c/V_\epsilon = -G_{21}/G_{22} = a_2$. Similar data were taken with voltage applied to the collector. Finally collector and emitter were connected together and the combined currents measured; this gives

$$(I_\epsilon + I_c)/V_\epsilon = G_{11} + G_{22} - G_{12} - G_{21}. \qquad (8.14)$$

The values selected for the G's were: Conductances in micromhos at 22°C

$$G_{11} = 8.8, \quad G_{22} = 33.3, \quad G_{12} = G_{21} = -7.8. \qquad (8.15)$$

These three values fit the seven measurements within the limits of experimental accuracy as shown in Table 8.1. The fact that the fit can be achieved with three constants is not a real test of the theory of Sec. VI, however, since any passive three terminal device in the absence of magnetic fields should satisfy the reciprocity condition and be described by three constants. What the table shows essentially is the consistency of the measurements.

Accurate values for the constants for the base layer were not available for the unit studied. However, the orders of magnitude of the G's are in reasonable agreement with values expected for a structure with constants lying in the ranges expected from the method of fabrication. We shall not attempt to obtain a perfect fit[16] but will choose as an example a structure with $A = 0.003$ cm^2, $W = 2.5 \times 10^{-3}$ cm, $\sigma_\epsilon = 20$, $\sigma_b = 10$, $\sigma_c = 0.1$, $\sigma_l = (1/60)$ ohm^{-1} cm^{-1}, and lifetimes $\tau_{pc} = 40$ and $\tau_{p\epsilon} = 10$ microseconds. The resulting values for the G's based on Eqs. (6.2), (6.22), and (6.25) are

$$G_{11n} = 7.3 \text{ micromhos} \tag{8.16a}$$

$$G_{11p} = 0.5 \text{ micromhos} \tag{8.16b}$$

$$G_{22p} = 45 \text{ micromhos.} \tag{8.16c}$$

The value of β is greater than 0.99 for $\tau_n = 40$ microseconds and may be taken as unity so far as the G's are concerned. These values lead to

$$G_{11} = G_{11n} + G_{11p} = 7.8 \tag{8.17a}$$

$$-G_{12} = -G_{12n} = \beta_1 G_{11n} = \beta_2 G_{22n} = 7.3 \tag{8.17b}$$

$$G_{22} = G_{22n} + G_{22p} = 7.3 + 45 = 52. \tag{8.17c}$$

According to this interpretation the failure of a_1 to be unity is due chiefly to hole flow across J_ϵ and a similar condition is true of a_2. The base current arises almost entirely from these hole flows with recombination in the base being nearly negligible.

Figures 5 and 6 show the internal contact potential effect. In Fig. 5 the potential V_ϵ is applied and V_c measured while zero current flows to the collector terminal. The data are seen to be in general agreement with the theory and with the value of a_2, corresponding to the collector junction, obtained at low voltage for Table 8.1. Figure 6 shows similar data with the voltage applied to the collector. The data are seen to differ slightly from the theoretical curves for reverse biases. The values of a obtained by applying (7.19b) to these data are

$$a_2 = 0.226 \quad \text{and} \quad a_2 = 0.894, \tag{8.18}$$

[16] For the simpler case of a p–n junction, the electrical properties have been predicted with an accuracy of about 20 percent from the independently measured constants describing the junction.

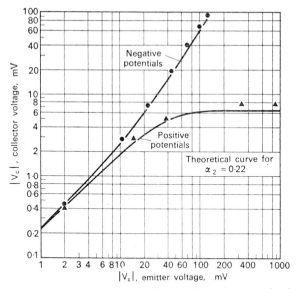

FIG. 5. Internal contact potential developed on the open circuited collector.

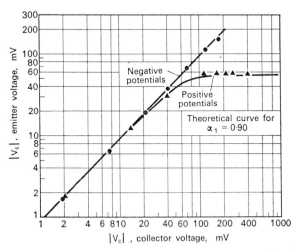

FIG. 6. Internal contact potential developed on the open circuited emitter.

which shows that the fit is very sensitive to small variations in value of α. The test of Eq. (7.17b), which applies to forward bias, cannot be carried out as satisfactorily because under these conditions the currents are relatively large and the voltage drops across the series resistances of the specimen are not negligible compared to the effects studied. The values obtained are, however, approximately the same as those of Table 8.1.

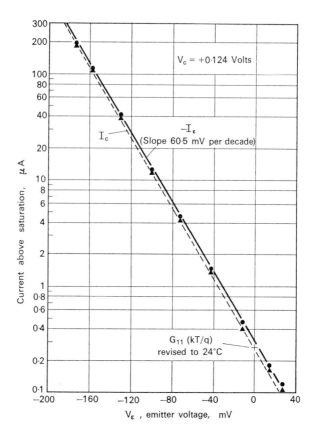

FIG. 7. Emitter and collector currents for the collector biased to saturation.

In Fig. 7, the collector is biased to saturation and I_c and I_ϵ are plotted as functions of V_ϵ. For this case the formulas should be

$$I_\epsilon = G_{11}B_1 + G_{12}(kT/q)$$
$$= G_{11}(1 - a_1)kT/q - (G_{11}kT/q)\exp(-qV_\epsilon/kT) \quad (8.19a)$$

$$I_c = G_{12}B_1 + G_{22}(kT/q)$$
$$= G_{22}(1 - a_2)(kT/q)$$
$$+ (a_1G_{11}kT/q)\exp(-qV_\epsilon/kT). \quad (8.19b)$$

It is seen that the lines agree well with the exponential forms and, furthermore, that the slope is in good agreement with theory which requires that for one decade of change in the current the voltage change should be

$$\Delta V = 2.30 \times kT/q = 2.30/39.4 = 59.0 \text{ mV} \quad (8.20)$$

for $T = 297°\text{K}$, the temperature at which the data were taken. The values of I_S and I_ν deduced from Table 8.1 (corrected for a ΔT of 2°C) and from the data on which Fig. 7 was based are:

	Fig. 7	Table 8.1
$G_{11}(1 - a_1)kT/q$	0.021 μA	0.025 μA
$G_{11}(kT/q)$	0.30 μA	0.27 μA
$G_{22}(1 - a_2)kT/q$	0.88 μA	0.78 μA
$a_1G_{11}kT/q$	0.27 μA	0.24 μA.

The slope terms are simply the values for $V_\epsilon = 0$ in Fig. 7. The saturation values were deduced directly from the data. In the voltage range used, the saturation for the collector was not perfect and the collector saturation values were corrected for a "leakage" term of about 1 megohm. (The origin of this leakage effect is not clear and it tends to saturate at higher reverse biases.)

In Fig. 8 the dependence of emitter current upon emitter voltage is again shown. The unit was at somewhat higher temperature and was measured at a higher collector voltage in one case and with the collector floating in the other. The ratio of the two terms should be

$$G_{11}/G_{11}(1 - a_1a_2) = 1.25. \quad (8.21)$$

The observed ratio is 1.30 at $V_\epsilon = 0$ which is satisfactory agreement.

In Fig. 9 the dependence of collector current upon collector voltage is shown for two cases similar to those of Fig. 8. The ratio of the two values is again 1.30 in good agreement with the prediction. It should be noted, however, that the slope requires 74 millivolts per decade, a value appropriate to an unreasonably

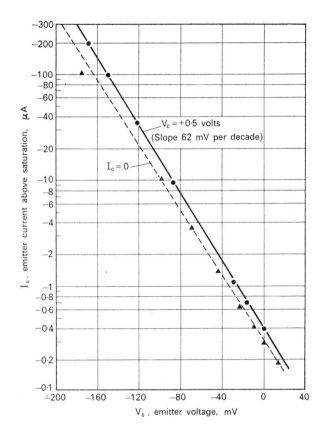

FIG. 8. Emitter current for two conditions of collectors.

high temperature of 103°C. This slope is established for such low currents that it seems difficult to explain it by spurious effects of series resistances.

There is an important difference in the nature of the currents of Fig. 7, which fit the theoretical slope, and those of Fig. 9, which do not. The currents of Fig. 7 consists chiefly of electrons which diffuse through the base layer and arrive at the collector; the

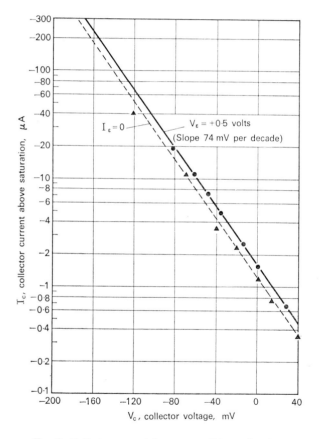

FIG. 9. Collector current for two conditions of emitter.

evidence for this conclusion is the value 0.89 for α_1, which implies that only 11 percent of the current is carried by electrons recombining in the base layer or holes diffusing into and recombining in the emitter body (or the reverse processes, depending on the polarity). On the other hand, most of the collector current is probably carried by holes which recombine in the collector body. (This reasoning is in agreement with the attempt to interpret the G's in terms of the structure discussed in connection with (8.17a, b, c).) It is to be expected theoretically that if the recombination process involves trapping on recombination centers,[17] then the rate of recombination will increase less rapidly than linearly with injected carrier density because at high densities the traps tend to saturate. This view has received some experimental support from the work of F. S. Goucher and J. R. Haynes who find an apparent increase in lifetime with increasing carrier density. It may be that this mechanism accounts for failure of the currents to increase as rapidly as they should with increasing voltage in Fig. 9.

Further evidence for nonlinearity in the recombination of holes in the emitter is furnished by the dependence of α_1 upon emitter current. This can be seen in Fig. 7. As the emitter current increases, the ratio of collector to emitter current (above saturation) increases from 0.9 to about 0.95. This is interpreted as being due to the failure of hole current to increase as rapidly with voltage as does emitter current.

The tendency of α to increase with emitter current appears to be a general feature of n–p–n transistors. Wallace and Pietenpol[3] report values as high as 0.995 for α.

Phototransistors made of n–p–n structures are extremely responsive to light and exhibit apparent quantum efficiencies of at least several hundreds. In accordance with the interpretation of Sec. VII C, these efficiencies would lead to α_1 values deduced from $1 - (1/\alpha^*)$ comparable to or larger than the highest observed in n–p–n transistors.

[17] See reference 2, page 342.

IX. Some Design Considerations

It has been the principal purpose of the preceding sections to examine the consequences of the diffusion theory and compare them with experiment. For this purpose the experimental conditions considered were the simplest: small currents and zero frequency. For practical applications high frequency and larger currents are also of interest. In this section we shall discuss briefly some of the factors of importance in design considerations.

Of great interest is the frequency cutoff. This may be determined by the external circuit or by one or another of several internal features of the transistor. The most fundamental of these latter is that set by the diffusion time through the base layer. This time is

$$\tau_D = W^2/D_n. \tag{9.1}$$

At a circular frequency ω, solutions for n_1 in the base layer are of the form,

$$\exp(i\omega t \pm x(1 + i\omega\tau_n)^{\frac{1}{2}}/L_n) \tag{9.2}$$

and this leads to a β value of

$$\beta = \operatorname{sech}(1 + i\omega\tau_n)^{\frac{1}{2}}W/L_n. \tag{9.3}$$

For frequencies such that $\omega\tau_D \gg 1$, this reduces to

$$B = 2/[\exp(1 + i)(\omega\tau_D/2)^{\frac{1}{2}} + \exp(-1 - i)(\omega\tau_D/2)^{\frac{1}{2}}]. \tag{9.4}$$

From this it is evident that for $\omega\tau_D \gg 2$ there is a phase lag of $(\omega\tau_D/2)^{\frac{1}{2}}$ radians and an equal attenuation in nepers. The power gain, which is proportional to β^2 in many cases, drops about 3 db when $\omega\tau_D = 2$ or $f = D_n/\pi W^2 \doteq 30/W^2$. For $W = 10^{-3}$ inch or 2.5×10^{-3} cm this is about 5×10^6 cps.

In addition to this fundamental limitation, there may be limitations due to capacitance and ohmic resistances. We shall illustrate this by considering the grounded emitter form of circuit, which is analogous to a grounded cathode vacuum tube circuit. For this case ac signals are applied to the base and ac voltages are developed on the collector. These voltages charge the capacitance of the base collector junction and this charging current must be furnished by hole flow in the base layer. For a layer with $\sigma_b = 10$ ohm^{-1} cm^{-1} and $W = 2.5 \times 10^{-3}$ cm, the resistance from edge to opposite edge of a unit square is 40 ohms. If the capacitance is 2000 $\mu\mu$F/cm^2 and the voltage gain is 10, then the input signal will dominate the voltage on the base layer only if the width of the unit is less than

$$(10 \times \omega \times 2 \times 10^{-9} \times 40)^{-\frac{1}{2}} = (\omega 8 \times 10^{-7})^{-\frac{1}{2}}.$$

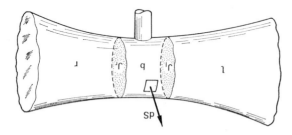

FIG. 10. The base region over whose surface the integration is made.

For a frequency of 5×10^6 cps, this leads to a width of 2 mm. The current through the base layer must also charge the emitter capacitance which may be much larger than the collector capacitance due to the effects of diffusion.

If the unit is too wide, the signal applied at the electrode on the base layer will be attenuated so that only a portion of the base layer will be operative in the desired way. The remainder of the base layer will be dominated by the capacitative voltages and these will induce currents which will lead to large "active" capacitances appearing between emitter and collector.

It is evident that the effects involved will lead to rather detailed calculations for any particular case but that the physical principles required to design n–p–n transistors are simply extensions of those well established for p–n junctions and n–p–n transistors for the low bias, low frequency conditions.

The low noise figures of these transistors cannot be said to be explained in the absence of an established theory of noise generation. They are, however, in rough agreement with a theory based on noise modulation of the recombination mechanism.[17] This theory predicts that each element of volume is a source of (noise current)^2 proportional to the square of the deviation of minority carrier density from its normal value. Applying this criterion to the *n–p–n* structure and comparing it to the type A indicates that the observed difference of 40 db or more between noise figures can be accounted for in terms of the change in current densities and geometries.

X. Acknowledgments

We are indebted to a number of our colleagues for encouragement and assistance. In particular, we recognize the contribution of J. A. Morton of the transistor development group, whose encouragement resulted in the techniques that made good *p–n* transistors possible. We are grateful to E. Buehler and R. M. Mikulyak who processed the germanium, to W. J. Pietenpol who prepared the particular unit studied, to R. L. Wallace for help with the measurements and the manuscript, and to W. van Roosbroeck for a critical reading of the manuscript.

APPENDIX

Proof of the Equality $G_{lr} = G_{rl}$

We shall prove this equality subject to the assumption that the electron density in the base layer is small compared to the thermal equilibrium hole density. Under these conditions, the effect of injected electrons on the potential distribution may be neglected so that the variation of the electron density from its equilibrium value may be treated by linear equations. In Fig. 10 we represent the situation considered. We shall denote by $I_{nl}(B_l, B_r)$ the current across J_l into the base carried by electrons. The symmetry relation $G_{lr} = G_{rl}$ is then established by proving that

$$I_{nl}(0, B) = I_{nr}(B, 0). \tag{A1}$$

In the base layer we shall suppose that the electrostatic potential ψ and the lifetime τ are arbitrary functions of position. The boundary condition on the external surfaces and at the metal contact will be taken as

$$I_n \cdot dS = -qn_1 s |dS|, \tag{A2}$$

where dS is the outward normal, s the surface recombination velocity and

$$n_1 = n - n_p \tag{A3}$$

is the deviation of n from the thermal equilibrium value.

We shall denote the solutions corresponding to potentials applied to the two junctions as follows:

$$B_l = B, \quad B_r = 0 \qquad n_1, I_n \tag{A4}$$

$$B_l = 0, \quad B_r = B \qquad n_1', I_n'. \tag{A5}$$

The currents in question are then

$$I_{nl}(0, B) = -\int_{J_l} I_n' \cdot dS \tag{A6}$$

$$I_{nr}(B, 0) = -\int_{J_r} I_n \cdot dS. \tag{A7}$$

The desired theorem is proved by considering the vector A:

$$A = (n_1/n_b)I_n' - (n_1'/n_b)I_n. \tag{A8}$$

Since $I_n \cdot dS$ is proportional to n_1 on the external surfaces, $A \cdot dS = 0$ on these surfaces. Hence, the integral of $A \cdot dS$ over the surface of the base region is

$$\int A \cdot dS = (qB/kT)[-I_{nl}(0, B) + I_{nr}(B, 0)] \tag{A9}$$

since on J_l and J_r we have

$$\begin{aligned} n_1/n_b &= (qB/kT) \text{ on } J_l \\ &= 0 \text{ on } J_r \end{aligned} \tag{A10}$$

$$\begin{aligned} n_1'/n_b &= 0 \text{ on } J_l \\ &= (qB/kT) \text{ on } J_r. \end{aligned} \tag{A11}$$

Furthermore, it can be shown that $\nabla \cdot A = 0$ in the base region and hence that (A9) is zero by Gauss's theorem so that (A1) is proved. The proof that $\nabla \cdot A = 0$ is accomplished by showing that $\nabla \cdot (n_1/n_b)I_n'$ is symmetrical in n_1 and n_1' so that the two terms in (A8) have canceling divergences:

$$\nabla \cdot (n_1/n_b)I_n'$$
$$= (1/n_b) (\nabla n_1 - n_1 \nabla \ln n_b) \cdot I_n' + (n_1/n_b) \nabla \cdot I_n'$$
$$= (1/n_b)[(\nabla n_1 + n_1 qE/kT) \cdot (q\mu_n n_1' E + qD_n \nabla n_1')$$
$$-q(n_1 n_1'/\tau)], \quad \text{(A12)}$$

which is seen to be symmetrical.

PAPER 11

Theory of Alpha for *p-n-p*
Diffused Junction Transistors†‡

EARL L. STEELE§

ASSOCIATE, I.R.E.

Summary

Equations are developed for the emitter and collector currents for this
type of transistor, and the resulting expressions are then used to obtain
the current-gain factor. The low-frequency value of the current-gain
factor and its high-frequency cutoff value are shown to depend strongly
on the width of the base region, the behavior at high frequencies being
better for small base width. The high-frequency behavior when used in
grounded emitter applications depends more directly on the lifetime of
holes in the germanium and shows only a second-order dependence on
the base width; the lower the lifetime the higher the frequency cutoff
value.

Introduction

THE transistors which form the basis for the discussion to follow
differ from the devices made by other methods in both intrinsic
properties and geometry. The general characteristics are very
similar to those described in the literature,[1, 2] but the new geo-

† *Proceedings of the I.R.E.* **40,** 1424 (1952).

‡ Decimal classification: R282.12. Original manuscript received by the
Institute, July 7, 1952. This work was supported, in part, by the Air Material
Command, the Signal Corps, and the Bureau of Ships, under Contract AF-33
(600)17793.

§ Electronics Laboratory, General Electric Co., Syracuse, N.Y.

[1] W. Shockley, "Theory of *p–n* junction in semiconductors and *p–n* junction
transistors, *Bell Sys. Tech. Jour.*, **28,** p. 435 (1949).

[2] W. Shockley, M. Sparks, and G. K. Teal, *p–n* junction transistors, *Phys.
Rev.* **83,** 151 (1951).

metry brings into the picture some modified boundary conditions in the design equation. The necessary equations are developed in the following discussion.

General Description

A brief description of the transistor will be given with the aid of Fig. 1. The unit consists of emitter and collector regions of p-type

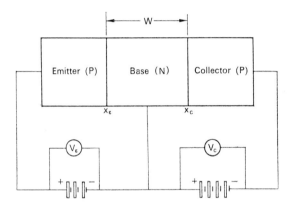

FIG. 1. Schematic diagram or $p–n–p$ transistor with bias supply shown.

germanium and a base region of n-type germanium. Ohmic contacts are made to these three regions and voltage biases applied as shown. The three regions are separated by diffused-type $p–n$ junctions which, in general, are rather abrupt. These junctions arise from acceptor-type impurities diffusing into relatively high-purity, single-crystal germanium.[3] The diffused material forms the barrier region behind which exists a region of p-type germanium, usually very thin. One of these p-type regions exists on either side of the n-type region, thus forming the transistor structure.

In this device the conduction is of the deficit type, that is, by

[3] R. N. Hall and W. C. Dunlap, *P–N* junctions prepared by impurity diffusion, *Phys. Rev.* **80,** 467 (1950).

holes. The potential-energy diagram for these holes in the above-described device is shown in Fig. 2.

The holes in the emitter region can be treated as a gas of free particles with a Boltzmann-type energy distribution. Some of these have energies high enough to lift them up the potential hill into the base region. Now, if a voltage is applied to the emitter, making it positive relative to the base, the potential hill will be decreased and more holes can get up this hill and into the base region. This is called "hole injection." Since there is essentially no

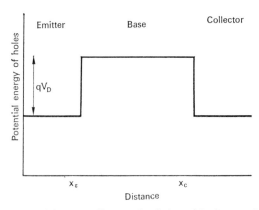

FIG. 2. Potential-energy diagram for holes with the transistor in thermal equilibrium, without bias voltages applied.

field in the base region away from the junction, the holes will drift away from the emitter junction by a diffusion process influenced only by the concentration gradient of the holes and not to any appreciable extent by a field-induced drift. As these holes drift, some will be lost by recombination with electrons, but most of them will reach the collector junction.

The collector voltage is applied so as to make the collector negative relative to the base. This causes an increase in the height of the potential wall at the collector junction. It will be seen that this forms a very good sink for holes so that once they arrive at this junction they fall through the potential drop and are collected.

Of course, at the same time as holes are being injected into the base region, electrons are being injected from the base into the emitter region. As it turns out, these electron effects are small but not negligible, and will be taken into account in the calculations. This, however, does not alter the basic nature of the device operation.

Basic Considerations

The flow of carrier through the base region can be described by the diffusion equations for the one-dimensional case as follows:

$$I(p) = -qD_p \frac{dp}{dx} + qp\mu_p E \tag{1}$$

$$\frac{dp}{dt} = -\frac{(p - p_B)}{\tau_B} - \frac{1}{q}\frac{dI}{dx}, \tag{2}$$

where the charge on holes (q), hole current $(I(p))$, hole density (p), diffusion constant (D_p), lifetime of holes in base before recombination $(\tau_B,$ hole mobility (μ_r), and electric field (E) are related as shown. Quantity (p_B) is the number of holes normally in the base region under thermal equilibrium conditions. The physical meaning of (2) can be given as follows: The rate at which hole density in a small region changes (dp/dt) is equal to number of holes per second lost by recombination, $((p - p_B)/\tau_B)$, plus the net number per second which flow away as current $[(1/q)\,(dI/dx)]$. The recombination rate is assumed proportional to the density of injected carriers.

The assumptions which will be used in solving the above equations can be rather simply stated.

1. The electric field (E) can be neglected in the regions away from the junctions. All the voltage applied between two regions appears only across the junction between those regions.
2. The junctions are very abrupt, we shall assume them to be step functions.

3. The density of holes in the base region is small compared to the electron density there. This means that physical parameters, such as mobility and lifetime, are not influenced by the injected carriers. Also, the conductivity in a given region is governed primarily by the majority carriers in that region and not by minority or injected carriers; that is, in the base the conductivity is due to electrons only and in the emitter and collector the conductivity is due only to holes.

4. Carrier densities are small compared to density of states in germanium and the energies are sufficiently large to enable one to use the Boltzmann approximation to Fermi statistics. This is a valid assumption for germanium at room temperature.

The boundary conditions can now be ascertained. Let the density of holes in the emitter region be (p_ϵ); then under thermal equilibrium conditions the hole density in the base region (p_B) can be obtained from the Boltzmann law by

$$p_B = p_\epsilon e^{-qV_D/kT}, \tag{3}$$

where the diffusion potential (V_D) is shown in Fig. 2. If an emitter voltage (V_ϵ) is now applied as shown in Fig. 3, the hole density in

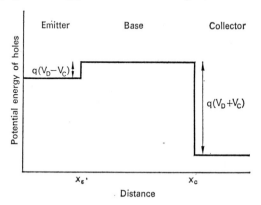

FIG. 3. Potential-energy diagram for holes with bias voltages applied to transistor.

the base region at the emitter junction (x_ϵ) will be increased to (p_1), given by

$$p_1 = p_\epsilon e^{-q(V_D - V_\epsilon)/kT} = p_B e^{qV_\epsilon/kT}. \tag{4}$$

The same sort of argument can be applied at the collector junction (x_c). Thus,

$$p_2 = p_B e^{-qV_c/kT}, \tag{5}$$

where the collector voltage (V_c) is applied so that the collector is negative to the base.

Steady-State Solution of Diffusion Equations

The substitution of (1) into (2), combined with the assumption of a field-free region, gives the following relation:

$$\frac{dp}{dt} = -\frac{(p - p_B)}{\tau_B} + D_p \frac{d^2 p}{dx^2}, \tag{6}$$

which is to be solved subject to the boundary conditions stated by (4) and (5).

We shall first solve the steady-state problem, where $dp/dt = 0$. The time-dependent solution, which will be solved later, will yield information on frequency response.

$$\frac{d^2 p}{dx^2} - \frac{(p - p_B)}{D_p \tau_B} = 0. \tag{7}$$

The solution for this is obviously of the form

$$p - p_B = A_1 e^{-x/\sqrt{D_p \tau_B}} + A_2 e^{x/\sqrt{D_p \tau_B}}. \tag{8}$$

Putting in the boundary conditions and noting that $x_c = x_\epsilon + w$ where (w) is the width of the base region, (8) becomes

$$p - p_B = (p_2 - p_B) \frac{\sinh\left(\dfrac{x - x_\epsilon}{L_B}\right)}{\sinh\left(\dfrac{w}{L_B}\right)}$$

$$- (p_1 - p_B) \frac{\sinh \left(\dfrac{x - x_\epsilon - w}{L_B} \right)}{\sinh \left(\dfrac{w}{L_B} \right)}, \tag{9}$$

where we have defined the "diffusion length" for holes in the base region as (L_B) and

$$L_B = (D_p \tau_B)^{1/2}.$$

The emitter current density due to holes $I_\epsilon(p))$ can be obtained by combining (1) and (9) at $(x = x_\epsilon)$. This will be the hole current diffusing into the base region from the emitter junction.

$$I_\epsilon(p) = - q D_p \frac{dp}{dx} \bigg|_{x=x\epsilon}$$

$$= \frac{q D_p p_B}{L_B} \left[(e^{q V_\epsilon /kT} - 1) \coth \left(\frac{w}{L_B} \right) \right.$$

$$\left. - (e^{-q V_c /kT} - 1) \operatorname{csch} \left(\frac{w}{L_B} \right) \right]. \tag{10}$$

The expression reduces to

$$I_\epsilon(p) = \frac{q D_p p_B}{w} \left(e^{q V_\epsilon /kT} - \frac{1}{2} \left(\frac{w}{L_B} \right)^2 \right)$$

for large collector voltages $(V_c > 2 \text{ volts})$ when $[(w/L_B) \ll 1]$.

It will be noted that this emitter-current equation differs slightly from the standard diode-current equation as typified by (16). The term which accounts for the back saturation current is reduced by the factor $[(1/2)/(w/L_B)^2]$. This comes about because of the influence on the emitter by the collector.

The collector current density due to holes diffusing out of the base region into the collector can be obtained in the same manner, except that (dp/dx) is evaluated at at $(x = x_c)$.

$$I_c(p) = - q D_p \frac{dp}{dx} \bigg|_{x=x_c=x_\epsilon+W}$$

$$= \frac{qD_p p_B}{L_B} \left[(e^{qV_\epsilon/kT} - 1) \operatorname{csch} \left(\frac{w}{L_B} \right) \right.$$

$$\left. - (e^{-qV_\epsilon/kT} - 1) \coth \left(\frac{w}{L_B} \right) \right]. \tag{11}$$

Now, of course, at the emitter junction there will be electrons injected from the base into the emitter by the same mechanism as for the hole injection. This electron flow into the emitter will increase the emitter current, but will tend to decrease the efficiency of the device because this electron component of current yields nothing at the collector, and thereby cuts down the ratio of collector to emitter current.

This electron component can be computed as follows: Let (n_ϵ) represent the density of electrons normally in the emitter. Then by an argument similar to that for (5) we get the electron density in the emitter at the junction as

$$n_1 = n_\epsilon e^{qV_\epsilon/kT}, \tag{12}$$

and similarly, for electron injection into the base from the collector,

$$n_2 = n_\epsilon e^{-qV_c/kT}. \tag{13}$$

The diffusion equation for the electrons is

$$\frac{d^2 n}{dx^2} - \frac{(n - n_\epsilon)}{L_\epsilon^2} = 0. \tag{14}$$

At the emitter, this can be solved subject to (12) with the additional condition that the electron density be (n_ϵ) far in the emitter region. Physical quantities, diffusion length for electrons in the emitter region (L_ϵ), diffusion constant for electrons (D_n), and lifetime of electrons in the emitter (τ_ϵ), are related by the expression

$$L_\epsilon = (D_n \tau_\epsilon)^{1/2}.$$

The solution of (14) with the prescribed boundary conditions at the emitter is

$$n - n_\epsilon = n_\epsilon (e^{qV_\epsilon/kT-1}) (e^{(x-x_\epsilon)/L_\epsilon}), \tag{15}$$

from which the current of electrons into the emitter can be obtained from

$$I_\epsilon(n) = qD_n \frac{dx}{dn}\bigg|_{x=x_\epsilon}$$

$$= \frac{qD_n n_\epsilon}{L_\epsilon}(e^{qV_\epsilon/kT} - 1). \qquad (16)$$

Calculation of Transistor Parameters

We shall now utilize the results so far obtained to evaluate the transistor parameters concerned with (a), the current-gain factor.

A. Current Gain (a)

From the definition, the current-gain factor (a) is given by

$$a = -\frac{\partial I_c}{\partial I_\epsilon}\bigg|_{V_c}. \qquad (17)$$

The total emitter current involves both hole and electron flow. This is given by the sum of (10) and (16),

$$I_\epsilon = I_\epsilon(p) + I_\epsilon(n)$$

$$= \frac{qD_n n_\epsilon}{L_\epsilon}(e^{qV_\epsilon/kT} - 1)$$

$$- \frac{qD_p p_B}{L_B}\left[e^{-qV_c/kT} - 1)\operatorname{csch}\left(\frac{w}{L_B}\right)\right.$$

$$\left. - (e^{qV_\epsilon/kT} - 1)\coth\left(\frac{w}{L_B}\right)\right]. \qquad (18)$$

The total collector current is obtained from (11) and an electron component similar to (16), which yields

$$I_c = I_c(p) + I_c(n)$$

$$= \left[\frac{qD_n n_c}{L_c} - \frac{qD_p p_B}{L_B} \coth\left(\frac{w}{L_B}\right) \right] (e^{-qV_c/kT} - 1)$$

$$+ \frac{qD_p p_B}{L_B} \operatorname{csch}\left(\frac{w}{L_B}\right) (e^{qV_\epsilon/kT} - 1). \tag{19}$$

If the term $(e^{qV_\epsilon/kT} - 1)$ is eliminated between (18) and (19) and the differentiation is carried out as indicated in (17), we obtain

$$\alpha = \frac{1}{\cosh\left(\dfrac{w}{L_B}\right) + \left(\dfrac{D_n}{D_p}\right)\left(\dfrac{n_\epsilon}{p_B}\right)\left(\dfrac{L_B}{L_\epsilon}\right)\sinh\left(\dfrac{w}{L_B}\right)}. \tag{20}$$

For the case of $[(w/L_B) \ll 1]$, this reduces to

$$\alpha = \frac{1}{\cosh\left(\dfrac{w}{L_B}\right) + \left(\dfrac{D_n}{D_p}\right)\left(\dfrac{n_\epsilon}{p_B}\right)\left(\dfrac{w}{L_\epsilon}\right)}. \tag{21}$$

In diffused-junction transistors, made with indium as acceptor material, we may conservatively estimate the following:

$$n_\epsilon/p_B \lesssim 10^{-6}; \quad (w/L_\epsilon) < 100; \quad (w/L_B) < 10^{-1}.$$

The denominator of (21) can be approximated as

$$1 + \frac{1}{2}\left(\frac{w^2}{L_B{}^2}\right) + \left(\frac{D_n}{D_p}\right)\left(\frac{n_\epsilon}{p_B}\right)\left(\frac{w}{L_\epsilon}\right),$$

and the last term is seen to be almost negligible, compared with the second term which is itself of second order.

B. Injection and Diminution Factors

By disregarding second-order terms, the above expression for (α) can be put into the approximate form

$$\alpha = \left[\operatorname{sech}\left(\frac{w}{L_B}\right)\right] \times \left[\frac{1}{1 + \left(\dfrac{D_n}{D_p}\right)\left(\dfrac{n_\epsilon}{p_B}\right)\left(\dfrac{w}{L_\epsilon}\right)}\right] = \beta\gamma. \tag{22}$$

This is similar to the form described by Shockley, *et al.*[2] These factors (β), (γ), can be identified as follows: The first term (β) is a diminution factor which results from the loss of hole current due to recombination of holes with electrons while passing through the base. The second term (γ) is an injection factor and results from the fact that not all of the current injected at the emitter is in the form of holes. There is some electron current injected into the emitter which is undesirable. The factor (γ) can be defined as the fraction of the total emitter current which is in the form of holes.

C. Frequency Dependence of (α)

If we assume the injected hole density to have a small ac variation in time of the form $\exp(i\omega t)$, then the term (dp/dt) from (6) becomes $i\omega(p - p_B)$. This time variation will be satisfied if the periodic ac signal voltage applied to the emitter is small and superimposed on the dc bias. The diffusion equation simply transforms into

$$D_p \frac{d^2p}{dx^2} - \left(\frac{1}{\tau_B} + i\omega\right)(p - p_B) = 0. \qquad (23)$$

Thus, the solution for the steady-state problem can be utilized with the substitution of $(1/L_B)(1 + i\omega\tau_B)^{1/2}$ in place of $(1/L_B)$. The frequency dependence of (α) can then be written immediately. Since the diminution factor (β) is the only term requiring significant modification, we have from (22)

$$\alpha = \beta = \mathrm{sech}\left((1 + i\omega\tau_B)^{1/2}\frac{w}{L_B}\right). \qquad (24)$$

A plot of this relation is shown in Fig. 4.

Again, for the case of $[(w/L_B) \ll 1]$ we can expand the expression for (β) and obtain

$$\alpha = \beta = \frac{1}{1 + \frac{1}{2}(1 + i\omega\tau_B)\frac{w^2}{L_B^2}}, \qquad (25)$$

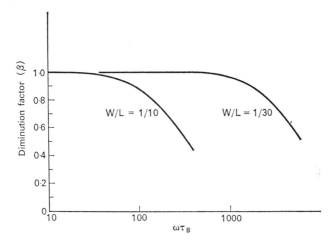

FIG. 4. Semilog plot showing the frequency dependence of diminution factor (β) for two different values of (wL_B).

which yields for the frequency cutoff:

$$\omega_0 = \frac{2}{\tau_B} \left(\frac{L_B}{w}\right)^2 = \frac{2D_p}{w^2} \qquad (26)$$

after noting that $(L_B = (D_p \tau_B)^{1/2})$. For high purity, but fairly thick base regions ($w < 10^{-2}$ cm), we obtain $\omega_0/2\pi = 140$ kc/s.

It can be seen from (25) that the factor, $(a/(1-a))$ is much more sensitive to the phase, or frequency term, than (a), above. Thus, to the same approximation as (25), we obtain

$$\frac{a}{1-a} = \frac{2L_B^2}{w^2} \left[\frac{1}{1 + \frac{1}{12}\frac{w^2}{L_B^2} + i\omega\tau_B \left(1 + \frac{1}{6}\frac{w^2}{L_B^2}\right)} \right]. \qquad (27)$$

The cutoff frequency (ω_1) for the factor ($a/(1-a)$) can be obtained from (27)

$$\omega_1 = \frac{1}{\tau_B} \left(1 - \frac{1}{12}\frac{w^2}{L_B^2}\right).$$

This can be as low as a few kc/s for high lifetime base material. Since this factor enters into the gain for grounded emitter amplifiers, it is seen that the frequency response should be much poorer for this circuit. This turns out to be the case. Calculations along the same lines as indicated here by Pritchard[4] indicate essential agreement with the results.

D. Evaluation of Hole Density (p_B)

We wish now to get an expression for the hole density in the base (p_B) in terms of measurable physical parameters of the bulk germanium.

The conductivity of the base (σ_B) is given in terms of the hole mobility (μ_p), the electron mobility (μ_n), and electron density (n_B), in the form

$$\sigma_B = q(n_B\mu_n + p_B\mu_p). \tag{28}$$

In intrinsic germanium, the electron density (n_i), which is equal to the hole density (p_i) and the intrinsic conductivity (σ_i), is related in the same manner as mentioned above,

$$\sigma_i = qn_i(\mu_n + \mu_p). \tag{29}$$

By the method of detailed balancing, it can be shown that the product of the hole density and that of electron density in a given region are related by

$$n_B p_B = n_i^2. \tag{30}$$

Using the three relationships (28), (29), (30), and simplifying, we get

$$p_B = \frac{\sigma_B}{2q\mu_p}\left[1 - \left\{1 - 4\left(\frac{\sigma_i}{\sigma_B}\right)^2\left(\frac{\mu_p}{\mu_n + \mu_p}\right)^2\left(\frac{\mu_n}{\mu_p}\right)\right\}^{1/2}\right], \tag{31}$$

which further simplifies to the following when ($\sigma_B \gg \sigma_i$)

$$p_B = \frac{1}{q\mu_p}\frac{\sigma_i^2}{\sigma_B}\left(\frac{\mu_p}{\mu_n + \mu_p}\right)^2\left(\frac{\mu_n}{\mu_p}\right). \tag{32}$$

[4] R. L. Pritchard, private communication.

This simply means that nearly all the conductivity in the base is due to electrons. This will be a good approximation for material in which the resistivity is less than 30 ohm-cm. For this resistivity, $p_B = 6 \times 10^{12}$ holes/cc at room temperature.

Conclusions

The equations for the p–n–p diffused-junction transistors indicate that the current gain (α) is influenced principally by the diminution factor (β) rather than the injection factor (γ). This is due to the relatively high-purity base material used in addition to the highly doped emitter and collector regions.

The high-frequency response is influenced by the lifetime of holes in the base region as well as the width of the base region itself. For grounded emitter uses, the lifetime is the predominant influence on the frequency cutoff, while for other uses, the base-region width plays a much more important part.

List of Symbols

p_e, p_B, p_c Hole density (carriers/cc) in emitter, base, collector region under thermal equilibrium.

n_e, n_B, n_c Same as above but for electron densities.

D_p, D_n Diffusion constants for holes and electrons (cm²/sec).

μ_p Mobility of holes (1700 cm/s/volt/cm.)

μ_n Mobility of electrons (3600 cm/s/volt/cm.)

q Charge on carriers (1.6 $\times$ 10^{-19} coulomb).

I_e, I_c Emitter and collector current density (amp/cm²).

τ_B Lifetime of minority carriers (holes) in base region (sec).

τ_e Lifetime of minority carriers (electrons) in emitter region (sec).

L_B, L_e Diffusion length of holes in base and electrons in emitter (cm).

ω Angular frequency (radians/sec).

ω_0 Cutoff frequency of (α) (radians/sec).

ω_1 Cutoff frequency of $(\alpha/(1 - \alpha))$ (radians/sec).

w Width of base region (cm).

x_e, x_c Distance along axis at which the emitter and collector junctions are located.

V_e, V_c DC bias voltage on emitter and collector (volts).

V_D Diffusion potential.

σ_B Conductivity of base region (ohm-cm)$^{-1}$.

σ_i Conductivity of intrinsic germanium (ohm-cm)$^{-1}$.

β Diminution factor.

γ Injection factor.

α Current gain factor.

n Electron density.

p Hole density.

PAPER 12

A High-frequency
Diffused Base Germanium Transistor†

CHARLES A. LEE

(Manuscript received November 15, 1955)

Summary

Techniques of impurity diffusion and alloying have been developed which make possible the construction of p–n–p junction transistors utilizing a diffused surface layer as a base region. An important feature is the high degree of dimensional control obtainable. Diffusion has the advantages of being able to produce uniform large area junctions which may be utilized in high power devices, and very thin surface layers which may be utilized in high-frequency devices.

Transistors have been made in germanium which typically have alphas of 0.98 and alpha-cutoff frequencies of 500 mc/s. The fabrication, electrical characterization, and design considerations of these transistors are discussed.

Introduction

Recent work[1, 2] concerning diffusion of impurities into germanium and silicon prompted the suggestion[3] that the dimensional control inherent in these processes be utilized to make high-frequency transistors.

One of the critical dimensions of junction transistors, which in many cases seriously restricts their upper frequency limit of operation, is the thickness of the base region. A considerable advance in

---

† *The Bell System Technical Journal*, **35**, 23 (1956).
[1] C. S. Fuller, *Phys. Rev.* **86**, 136–137 (1952).
[2] J. Saby and W. C. Dunlap, Jr., *Phys. Rev.* **90**, 630 (1953).
[3] W. Shockley, private communication.

transistor properties can be accomplished if it is possible to reduce this dimension one or two orders of magnitude. The diffusion constants of ordinary donors and acceptors in germanium are such that, within realizable temperatures and times, the depth of diffused surface layers may be as small as 10^{-6} cm. Already in the present works layers slightly less than 1 micron (10^{-4} cm) thick have been made and utilized in transistors. Moreover, the times and temperatures required to produce 1 micron surface layers permit good control of the depth of penetration and the concentration of the diffusant in the surface layer with techniques described below.

If one considers making a transistor whose base region consists of such a diffused surface layer, several problems become immediately apparent:

(1) Control of body resistivity and lifetime during the diffusion heating cycle.
(2) Control of the surface concentration of the diffusant.
(3) Making an emitter on the surface of a thin diffused layer and controlling the depth of penetration.
(4) Making an ohmic base contact to the diffused surface layer. One approach to the solution of these problems in germanium which has enabled us to make transistors with alpha-cutoff frequencies in excess of 500 mc/sec is described in the main body of the paper.

An important characteristic feature of the diffusion technique is that it produces an impurity gradient in the base region of the transistor. This impurity gradient produces a "built-in" electric field in such a direction as to aid the transport of minority carriers from emitter to collector. Such a drift field may considerably enhance the frequency response of a transistor for given physical dimensions.[4]

The capabilities of these new techniques are only partially realized by their application to the making of high frequency transistors, and even in this field their potential has not been com-

[4] H. Krömer, *Archiv. der Elek. Übertragung* **8**, (5) 223–228 (1954).

pletely explored. For example, with these techniques applied to making a p–n–i–p structure the possibility of constructing transistor amplifiers with usable gain at frequencies in excess of 1,000 mc/sec now seems feasible.

Description of Transistor Fabrication and Physical Characteristics

As starting material for a p–n–p structure, p-type germanium of 0.8 ohm-cm resistivity was used. From the single crystal ingot rectangular bars were cut and then lapped and polished to the approximate dimensions: $200 \times 60 \times 15$ mils. After a slight etch, the bars were washed in deionized water and placed in a vacuum oven for the diffusion of an n-type impurity into the surface. The vacuum oven consisted of a small molybdenum capsule heated by radiation from a tungsten coil and surrounded by suitable radiation shields made also of molybdenum. The capsule could be baked out at about 1,900°C in order that impurities detrimental to the electrical characteristics of the germanium be evaporated to sufficiently low levels.[5]

As a source of n-type impurity to be placed with the p-type bars in the molybdenum oven, arsenic doped germanium was used. The relatively high vapor pressure of the arsenic was reduced to a desirable range (about 10^{-4} mm of Hg) by diluting it in germanium. The use of germanium eliminated any additional problems of contamination by the dilutant, and provided a convenient means of determining the degree of dilution by a measurement of the conductivity. The arsenic concentrations used in the source crystal were typically of the order of 10^{17}–10^{19}/cc. These concentrations were rather high compared to the concentrations desired in the diffused surface layers since compensation had to be made for losses of arsenic due to the imperfect fit of the cover on the capsule and due to some chemical reaction and adsorption which occurred on the internal surfaces of the capsule.

The layers obtained after diffusion were then evaluated for sheet

[5] R. A. Logan and M. Schwartz, *Phys. Rev.*, **96,** 46 (1954).

conductivity and thickness. To measure the sheet conductivity a four-point probe method[6] was used. An island of the surface layer was formed by masking and etching to reveal the junction between the surface layer and the p-type body. The island was then biased in the reverse direction with respect to the body thus effectively isolating it electrically during the measurement of its sheet conductivity. The thickness of the surface layer was obtained by first lapping at a small angle to the original surface ($\frac{1}{2}°-1°$) and locating the junction on the beveled surface with a thermal probe; then multiplying the tangent of the angle between the two surfaces by the distance from the edge of the bevel to the junction gives the desired thickness. Another particularly convenient method of measuring the thickness[7] is to place a half silvered mirror parallel to the original surface and count fringes, of the sodium D-line for example, from the edge of the bevel to the junction. Typically the transistors described here were prepared from diffused layers with a sheet conductivity of about 200 ohms/square, and a layer thickness of $(1.5 \pm 0.3) \times 10^{-4}$ cm.

When the surface layer had been evaluated, the emitter and base contacts were made using techniques of vacuum evaporation and alloying. For the emitter, a film of aluminum approximately 1,000 Å thick was evaporated onto the surface through a mask which defined an emitter area of 1×2 mils. The bar with the evaporated aluminum was then placed on a strip heater in a hydrogen atmosphere and momentarily brought up to a temperature sufficient to alloy the aluminum. The emitter having been thus formed, the bar was again placed in the masking jig and a film of gold–antimony alloy from 3,000 to 4,000 Å thick was evaporated onto the surface. This film was identical in area to the emitter, and was placed parallel to and 0.5 to 1 mil away from the emitter. The bar was again placed on the heater strip and heated to the gold–germanium eutectic temperature, thus forming the ohmic base contact. The masking jig was constructed to permit the simultaneous evaporation of eight pairs of contacts on each

[6] L. B. Valdes, *Proc. I.R.E.*, **42**, 420–427 (1954).

[7] W. L. Bond and F. M. Smits, to be published.

bar. Thus, using a 3-mil diamond saw, a bar could be cut into eight units.

Each unit, with an alloyed emitter and base contact, was then soldered to a platinum tab with indium, a sufficient quantity of indium being used to alloy through the n-type surface layer on the back of the unit. One of the last steps was to mask the emitter and base contacts with a 6- to 8-mil diameter dot of wax and form a small area collector junction by etching the unit attached to the platinum tab, in CP4. After washing in solvents to remove the wax, the unit was mounted in a header designed to allow electro-lytically pointed wire contacts to be made to the base and emitter areas of the transistor. These spring contacts were made of 1-mil phosphor bronze wire.

Electrical Characterization

Of the parameters that characterize the performance of a transistor, one of the most important is the short circuit current gain (alpha) versus frequency. The measured variation of α and

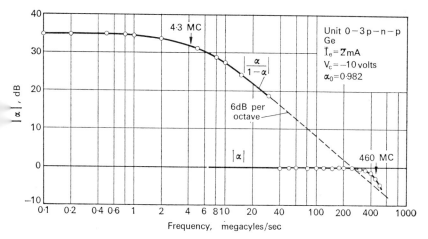

FIG. 1. The grounded emitter and grounded base response versus frequency for a typical unit.

$a/(1 - a)$ (short-circuit current gain in the grounded emitter circuit) as a function of frequency for a typical unit is shown in Fig. 1. For comparison the same parameters for an exceptionally good unit are shown in Fig. 2.

In order that the alpha-cutoff frequency be a measure of the transit time of minority carriers through the active regions of the transistor, any resistance-capacity cutoffs, of the emitter and collector circuits, must lie considerably higher than the measured f_a. In the emitter circuit, an external contact resistance to the aluminum emitter of the order of 10 to 20 ohms and a junction transition capacity of 1 $\mu\mu$fd were measured. The displacement current which flows through this transition capacity reduces the emitter efficiency and must be kept small relative to the injected hole current. With 1 milliampere of current flowing through the emitter junction, and consequently an emitter resistance of 26 ohms, the emitter cutoff for this transistor was above 6,000 mc/sec. One can now see that the emitter area must be small and the current density high to attain a high emitter cutoff frequency. The fact that a low base resistance requires a high level of doping

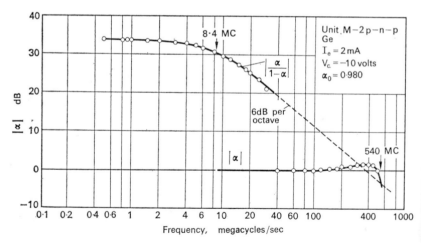

FIG. 2. The grounded emitter and grounded base response versus frequency for an exceptionally good unit.

in the base region, and thus a high emitter transition capacity, restricts one to small areas and high current densities.

In the collector circuit capacities of 0.5 to 0.8 $\mu\mu$fd at a collector voltage of -10 volts were measured. There was a spreading resistance in the collector body of about 100 ohms which was the result of the small emitter area. The base resistance was approximately 100 ohms. If the phase shift and attenuation due to the transport of minority carriers through the base region were small at the collector cutoff frequency, the effective base resistance would be decreased by the factor $(1 - \alpha)$. The collector cutoff frequency is then given by

$$f_c = \frac{1}{2\pi C_c R_c}$$

where $C_c =$ collector transition capacity and $R_c =$ collector body spreading resistance.

However, in the transistors described here the base region produces the major contribution to the observed alpha-cutoff frequency and it is more appropriate to use the expression

$$f_c = \frac{1}{2\pi C_c(r_b + R_c)}$$

where $r_b \equiv$ base resistance. This cutoff frequency could be raised by increasing the collector voltage, but the allowable power dissipation in the mounting determines an upper limit for this voltage. It should be noted that an increase in the doping of the collector material would raise the cutoff since the spreading resistance is inversely proportional to N_a, while the junction capacity for constant collector voltage is only proportional to $N_a^{1/2}$.

The low-frequency alpha of the transistor ranged from 0.95 to 0.99 with some exceptional units as high as 0.998. The factors to be considered here are the emitter efficiency γ and the transport factor β. The transport factor is dependent upon the lifetime in the base region, the recombination velocity at the surface immediately surrounding the emitter, and the geometry. The geometrical factor of the ratio of the emitter dimensions to the base layer thickness is > 10, indicating that solutions for a planar geometry may be assumed.[8] If a lifetime in the base region of 1 microsecond and a surface recombination velocity of 2,000 cm/sec is assumed a perturbation calculation[9] gives

$$\beta = 0.995$$

The high value of β obtained with what is estimated to be a low base region lifetime and a high surface recombination velocity indicates that the observed low frequency alpha is most probably limited by the emitter injection efficiency. As for the emitter injection efficiency, within the accuracy to which the impurity concentrations in the emitter regrowth layer and the base region are known, together with the thicknesses of these two regions, the calculated efficiency is consistent with the experimentally observed values.

Considerations of Transit Time

An examination of what agreement exists between the alpha-cutoff frequency and the physical measurements of the base region involves the mechanism of transport of minority carriers through the active regions of the transistor. The "active regions" include the space charge region of the collector junction. The transit time through this region[10] is no longer a negligible factor. A short calculation will show that with -10 volts on the collector junction, the space charger layer is about 4×10^{-4} cm thick and that the frequency cutoff associated with transport through this region is approximately 3,000 mc/sec.

The remaining problem is the transport of minority carriers through the base region. Depending upon the boundary conditions

[8] E. S. Rittner, *Phys. Rev.*, **94**, 1161 (1954).
[9] W. M. Webster, *Proc. I.R.E.*, **42**, 914 (1954).
[10] J. M. Early, *B.S.T.J.*, **33**, 517–533 (1954).

existing at the surface of the germanium during the diffusion process, considerable gradients of the impurity density in the surface layer are possible. However, the problem of what boundary conditions existed during the diffusion process employed in the fabrication of these transistors will not be discussed here because of the many uncertainties involved. Some qualitative idea is necessary though of how electric fields arising from impurity gradients may affect the frequency behavior of a transistor in the limit of low injection.

If one assumes a constant electric field as would result from an exponential impurity gradient in the base region of a transistor, then the continuity equation may be solved for the distribution of minority carriers.[4] From the hole distribution one can obtain an expression for the transport factor β and it has the form

$$\beta = e^{\eta} \, \frac{Z}{\eta \sinh Z + Z \cosh Z}$$

where

$$\eta \equiv \frac{1}{2} \ln \frac{N_e}{N_c} = \frac{1}{2} \frac{qE}{kT} \, w,$$

$$Z \equiv [i\varphi + \eta^2]^{1/2}$$

$$\varphi \equiv \omega \frac{w^2}{D_p}$$

$N_e \equiv$ donor density in base region at emitter junction

$N_c \equiv$ donor density in base region at collector junction

$E \equiv$ electric field strength

$D_p \equiv$ diffusion constant for holes

$w \equiv$ width of the base layer

A plot of this function for various values of η is shown in Fig. 3. For $\eta = 0$, the above expression reduces to the well known case of a uniformly doped base region. The important feature to be

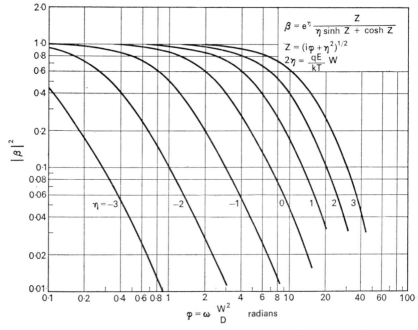

FIG. 3. The variation of $|\beta|$ versus frequency for various values of a uniform drift field in the base region.

noted in Fig. 3 is that relatively small gradients of the impurity distribution in the base layer can produce a considerable enhancement of the frequency response.

It is instructive to calculate what the alpha-cutoff frequency would be for a base region with a uniform distribution of impurity. The effective thickness of the base layer may be estimated by decreasing the measured thickness of the surface layer by the penetration of the space charge region of the collector and the depth of the alloyed emitter structure. Using a value for the diffusion constant of holes in the base region appropriate to a donor density of about 10^{17}/cc,

$$300 \text{ mc/s} \leqq f_\alpha \leqq 800 \text{ mc/s}$$

This result implies that the frequency enhancement due to "built-in" fields is at most a factor of two. In addition it was observed that the alpha-cutoff frequency was a function of the emitter current as shown in Fig. 4. This variation indicates that at least intermediate injection levels exist in the range of emitter current shown in Fig. 4. The conclusion to be drawn then is that electric fields produced by impurity gradients in the base region are not the dominant factor in the transport of minority carriers in these transistors.

The emitter current for a low level of injection could not be determined by measuring f_α versus I_e because the high input impedance at very low levels was shorted by the input capacity of the header and socket. Thus at very small emitter currents the measured cutoff frequency was due to an emitter cutoff and was roughly proportional to the emitter current. At $I_e \geqq 1$ ma this effect is small, but here at least intermediate levels of injection already exist.

A further attempt to measure the effect of any "built-in" fields by turning the transistor around and measuring the inverse alpha proved fruitless for two reasons. The unfavorable geometrical

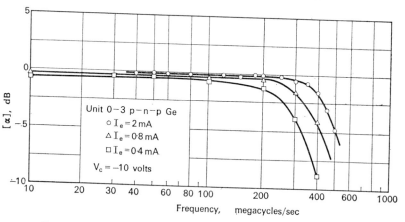

FIG. 4. The variation of the alpha-cutoff frequency as a function of emitter current.

factor of a large collector area and a small emitter area as well as a poor injection efficiency gave an alpha of only

$$a = 0.1$$

Secondly, the injection efficiency turns out in this case to be proportional to $\omega^{-1/2}$ giving a cutoff frequency of less than 1 mc/sec. The square-root dependence of the injection efficiency on frequency may be readily seen. The electron current injected into the collector body may be expressed as

$$J_e = qD_nN \left[\frac{1 + i\omega\tau_e}{L_e^2}\right]^{1/2}$$

where $q \equiv$ electronic charge

$D_n \qquad \equiv$ diffusion constant of electrons

$$N = \frac{q}{kT} v_1 n_c$$

$v_1 \equiv$ voltage across collector junction

$n_c \equiv$ density of electrons on the p-type side of the collector junction

$\tau_e \equiv$ lifetime of electrons in collector body

$L_e \equiv$ diffusion length of electrons in the collector body

Since the inverse cutoff frequency is well below that associated with the base region, we may regard the injected hole current as independent of the frequency in this region. The injection efficiency is low so that

$$\gamma \approx \frac{J_p}{J_e} \ll 1$$

Thus at a frequency where

$$\omega\tau_e \gg 1$$

then

$$\gamma \propto \omega^{-1/2}$$

An interesting feature of these transistors was the very high current densities at which the emitter could be operated without appreciable loss of injection efficiency. Fig 5 shows the transmission of a 50 millimicrosecond pulse up to currents of 18 milliamperes which corresponds to a current density of 1800 amperes/cm². The injection efficiency should remain high as long as the electron density at the emitter edge of the base region remains small compared to the acceptor density in the emitter regrowth layer. When high injection levels are reached the injected hole density at the emitter greatly exceeds the donor density in the base region. In order to preserve charge neutrality then

$$p \approx n$$

where $p \equiv$ hole density, $n \equiv$ electron density

As the injected hole density is raised still further the electron

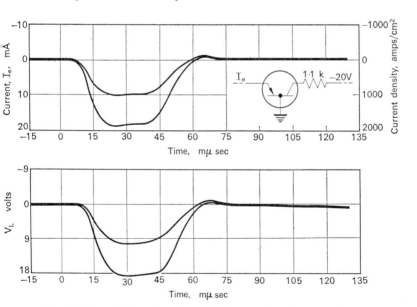

FIG. 5. Transmission of a 50 millimicrosecond pulse at emitter currents up to 18 mA by a typical unit. (Courtesy of F. K Bowers.)

I—I

density will eventually become comparable to the acceptor density in the emitter regrowth layer. The density of acceptors in the emitter regrowth region is of the order of

$$N_A \approx 10^{20}/\text{cc}$$

and this is to be compared with injected hole density at the base region side of the emitter junction. The relation between the injected hole density and the current density may be approximated by[8]

$$J_p = \frac{2qD_p p_1}{w}$$

where p_1 = hole density at emitter side of base region

w = width of base region

A short calculation indicates that the emitter efficiency should remain high at a current density of an order of magnitude higher than 1,800 amp/cm^2. The measurements were not carried to higher current densities because the voltage drop across the spreading resistance in the collector was producing saturation of the collector junction.

Conclusions

Impurity diffusion is an extremely powerful tool for the fabrication of high frequency transistors. Moreover, of the 50-odd transistors which were made in the laboratory, the characteristics were remarkably uniform considering the variations usually encountered at such a stage of development. It appears that diffusion process is sufficiently controllable that the thickness of the base region can be reduced to half that of the units described here. Therefore, with no change in the other design parameters, outside of perhaps a different mounting, units with a 1000 mc/s cutoff frequency should be possible.

Acknowledgment

The author wishes to acknowledge the help of P. W. Foy and W. Wiegmann who aided in the construction of the transistors, D. E. Thomas who designed the electrical equipment needed to characterize these units, and J. Klein who helped with the electrical measurements. The numerical evaluation of alpha for drift fields was done by Lillian Lee whose assistance is gratefully acknowledged.

The Surface-Barrier Transistor†‡

PART I. PRINCIPLES OF THE SURFACE-BARRIER TRANSISTOR§

W. E. BRADLEY††
FELLOW, I.R.E.

Summary

This paper, consisting of five parts, describes the principle, fabrication, circuit application, and theoretical bases of a new semiconductor transducer, the surface-barrier transistor. This device, produced by precise electrochemical etching and plating techniques, operates at frequencies in excess of 60 mc while displaying the low-voltage, lower-power-consumption and low-noise properties of transistors hitherto confined to much lower frequencies.

Part I describes the basic discovery which led to the new transistor: a new mode of hole injection produced by a broad-area metal electrode in intimate contact with a single crystal of N-type germanium. The mechanisms of hole emission, conduction, and collection are discussed, and the effect on performance of precise fabrication of germanium sections a few microns in thickness is explained.

Part II describes typical fabrication methods. A germanium blank is etched by directing to its surfaces two opposed jets of a metal salt solution, through which current passes in such polarity as to remove germanium. In addition to etching away material and disposing of the reaction products, the flowing solution cools the work. The etching is allowed to continue until the thickness of the germanium is reduced to a

---

† *Proceedings of the I.R.E.* **41,** 1702 (1953).

‡ The research leading to the development of the surface-barrier transistor was supported in part by the Bureau of Ships, Department of the Navy, under Contract NObsr 57322.

§ Decimal classification: R282.12. Original manuscript received by the Institute, October 14, 1953.

†† Philco Corp., Research Div., Philadelphia, Pa.

few microns with a tolerance of ±5 per cent of the remaining thickness. A sudden reversal of polarity then stops the etching action and immediately initiates electroplating of metal electrodes from the salt onto the freshly cleaned germanium surfaces.

Part III describes the circuit parameters of the surface-barrier transistor and the performance of typical amplifiers: a compensated video amplifier having a bandwidth of 9 mc and a gain-bandwidth product of 45 mc per stage and a neutralized bandpass rf amplifier centered at 30 mc having an insertion stage gain of 15 db. Switching times in typical switching circuits are less than 0.1 microsecond.

Part IV describes quantitatively the geometrical concepts on which the extended high-frequency performance of the device is based, namely the effect of a flat, thin section of semiconductor between emitter and collector electrodes. Part V gives the theoretical treatment of the basic internal actions of the surface-barrier transistor, hole injection, and hole-current enhancement. Experimental verification of the quantitative predictions of the theory is reported.

Introduction

In THE course of research in the Philco Corporation laboratories a new form of transistor, the surface-barrier transistor, has been discovered. This device differs from previously discovered transistors in that it contains only one form of germanium, whereas earlier devices contained at least two forms. Alloy junction transistors, for example, are described as p–n–p or n–p–n types, while the point-contact transistor has regions of modified germanium produced by the forming process near the point contacts. The new surface-barrier transistor is an N-type transistor.

The name "Surface-Barrier Transistor" is derived from the fact that the interfaces of the transistor which perform the functions of emission and collection of the useful current are located *at the surface* of a uniform crystal-base electrode. The development of an active interface located at the crystal surface results in a new mode of operation upon the charge carriers of the crystal permitting the use of metal electrodes of relatively large area.

The fact that the electrodes are applied to the surface of the crystal after the crystal has been shaped permits accurate control of the geometry of the transistor to a degree unheard of in prior art. Accurately controlled fabrication of N-type germanium in sections a few microns in thickness is readily achieved, for example, by the electrochemical techniques described by Tiley and Williams.[1]

The practical result of this new principle and the associated techniques is a transistor of unprecedented performance characteristics. Efficient operation on a power supply of three volts or less at frequencies above 60 megacycles has been achieved and

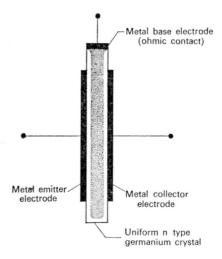

Metal base electrode
(ohmic contact)

Metal emitter
electrode

Metal collector
electrode

Uniform n type
germanium crystal

FIG. 1. Schematic cross section of a surface-barrier transistor.

substantially higher frequency operation is anticipated with further refinement of the fabrication method. Band-pass amplification centered at a frequency of 30 megacycles has been demonstrated and low-pass amplification from zero to 9 megacycles has been achieved. In brief, the surface-barrier transistor combines low-voltage, low-power-consumption, low-noise-figure operation at frequencies higher by more than an order of magnitude than can be attained with available alloy-junction transistors.

The principles and techniques embodied in the surface-barrier

[1] *Proc. I.R.E.*, pp. 1706–1708; this issue.

transistor are applicable not only to the particular type described herein but also to other forms, as those familiar with the art will readily appreciate from the detailed description of the electrochemical technique in the associated paper.[1]

The Surface Barrier of N-type Germanium

The useful current of the surface-barrier transistor is a current of holes moving from the emitter to the collector. The free electrons which are normally present in large quantity in N-type germanium would short-circuit the device if it were not for the action of the surface barrier which tends to push the free electrons back from the surface.

The surface barrier includes the surface and a layer of germanium just beneath the surface of the crystal which is about one ten-thousandth of an inch thick and contains almost no free charge carriers, either electrons or holes. This layer (shown schematically in Fig. 1) is practically an insulator, but contains a strong electric field, like a charged condenser, in such a direction as to move a free electron from the surface toward the interior.

The formation of the surface barrier is related to the fact that electron energy levels, or orbits, may exist on the surface of a crystal which are quite different from those in the interior of the crystal. Inside the crystal the orderly array of atoms of a single element gives rise to an orderly arrangement of bands of allowed electron energy separated by forbidden bands.

Many excellent expositions of bulk properties of semi-conductors exist in the literature and no repetition will be attempted here. Not so much attention has been paid so far to the surface of the crystal. Here the left-over bonds of the germanium atom, together with any atoms of other substances on the surface, may form a sort of two-dimensional solid with properties entirely different from the interior. Thus insulating crystals may exhibit high surface conductivity due to a layer only one or two atoms thick which can pass electrons from atom to atom along the surface freely. It is possible that no orderly structure of energy bands exists on such a surface, since it may be composed of many kinds of atoms, or ions, in many orientations. It is fairly safe to assume that the energy levels of such a layer form a rear continuum, with no forbidden bands at all.

Inside a crystal of N-type germanium the free electrons move in a high-energy, nearly empty band. Lower in energy is a forbidden band and below that the so-called valence band which is filled completely. The free electrons tend to descend in energy to fill any available vacancy and hence are attracted to the surface. So many electrons may move to the surface in this way that it acquires a strong negative charge repelling free electrons toward the interior and causing a nearly insulating region containing a strong electric field, just beneath the surface.

Electron Current Through a Surface Barrier

A metal electrode in intimate contact with such a germanium crystal makes firm electrical connection to the surface layer but communicates with the main body of the crystal only through the surface barrier. Making the metal negative tends to repel the free electrons even more, thickening the insulating layer so that little current flow takes place. Making the metal positive attracts free electrons, making the insulating layer thinner, permitting current to flow.

Hole Current Through a Surface Barrier

While the above mechanism explains rectification at a surface contact, it is not sufficient to explain the surface-barrier transistor because it ignores the current of holes which is the only useful current component. The existence of a set of energy levels at the surface which are intermediate between the conduction band and the valence band implies that thermal agitation will frequently excite valence electrons of the crystal into the surface levels. It will be recalled that even in the interior of the crystal electrons are occasionally thermally excited from the valence band to the conduction band. Remembering that the probability of such a transition varies exponentially with the energy difference, changing by about a factor of e for each 1/40 of a volt, and that the band spacing of germanium totals about $\frac{3}{4}$ electron volts, it is clear that if intermediate levels are available, electrons from the valence band will be excited into them fairly frequently so there will be, under equilibrium conditions, a population of holes just under the germanium surface.

Some metal contacts produce a denser hole population under the surface of the germanium than others. Differences between metals in their propensity to emit holes into N-type germanium have been found, in apparent contradiction to results obtained elsewhere, when the metals are deposited electrolytically upon a freshly etched surface of germanium. The mechanism by which the potential of the surface layer adjusts itself with respect to the metal is difficult to treat theoretically in quantitative fashion. Upon the adjustment of the metal potential with respect to that of the germanium depends the height of the surface barrier and the density of holes under the surface.

The effect of the surface barrier is to force these holes to remain near the surface just as it forces free electrons to remain in the interior. When a metal contact to the crystal is made positive it repels these holes through the barrier just as it attracts the free electrons. The result is that the forward current of the rectifier is made up of two currents in parallel, the hole current and the electron current. For transistor purposes it is desirable to reduce the electron current as much as possible since only the hole current is received at the collector.

It is clear that a back-biased metal contact can serve as a collector of holes since the surface-barrier field augmented by the back bias will infallibly draw holes coming within its reach out to the surface.

Enhancement of Ratio of Hole Current to Electron Current

Some precautions are necessary for a metal contact to serve as emitter of holes with the electron current reduced to a low value.

In the first place, the metal should have the property that when applied to the surface it produces a satisfactorily high density of holes in the adjoining germanium. Among the metals found to be satisfactory for this purpose are indium, zinc, cadmium, tin, and copper.

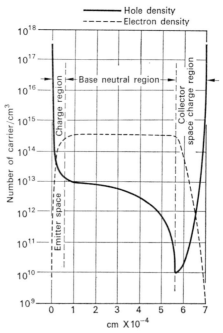

FIG. 2. Variation of densities of hole and electrons with distance in the space between emitter and collector electrodes.

Inside the body of the germanium crystal the large number of charge carriers present makes the electric field very small. The absence of any substantial electric field causes the holes to move to the collector *principally by thermal diffusion*. Such a diffusion current flows only when a gradient of hole density exists. Such a gradient implies a larger density of holes in the bulk material near the emitter barrier than near the collector barrier. Unfortunately, the effect of high density of holes near the emitter barrier, coupled with the random nature of the diffusion process, tends to cause a large proportion of holes to diffuse back to the emitter reducing the net hole current. Worse yet, the increased hole population attracts an equal number of electrons by its space charge, increasing the electron population near the surface barrier and, hence, the undesired electron current. The distribution of holes and electrons during operation is shown in Fig. 2.

The most effective means of enhancing the hole current for large-area contacts is to make the hole-density gradient through the base as steep as possible. A high value of gradient increases the current directly without increasing the hole density and, therefore, without increasing the electron current. By bringing the collector close to the emitter the gradient can be proportionately increased since the hole density is reduced by the action of the collector.

Application to Surface-Barrier Transistor

In the surface-barrier transistor the spacing between the metal electrodes has been successfully reduced to a few microns with good control of the process. This excellent control is possible because the electrodes are applied to the *surface*, so that it is possible to shape the germanium crystal itself to the required geometry and apply the electrodes afterward.

Unfortunately, most shaping processes strain the surface of the structure being shaped and, as can be seen from the discussion above, it is important for a surface-barrier transistor to have undisturbed germanium all of the way out to the surface. Chemically or physically inhomogeneous germanium crystals or uneven metal contacts tend to produce inefficient and variable operation because of nonuniform structure at the resulting surface barrier.

Electrochemical Fabrication

Accurate shaping of the crystal, together with intimate electrode contact without disturbance of more than one atomic layer of crystal, has been achieved by a process of "electrolytic machining." Tiny jets of metal salt solution with current passing through them dissolve germanium from the crystal wafer until cavities of the right size and shape have been excavated. By a mere reversal in polarity, and without any interruption, the same jets are made to electroplate the electrodes directly upon the freshly etched surface of germanium. Many salt solutions are suitable for the electrolytic processes. A cross section of the resulting structure is shown in Fig. 3(a).

Experimental Results with Electrochemically-Deposited Surface Electrodes

The uniformity of the surface barrier produced by the electrolytic assembly process is proved by the shape of the current versus

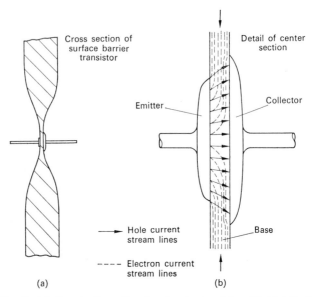

FIG. 3. (a) Crosssection of surface-barrier tranistor. (b) Detail of center section.

voltage curves of an electrode with respect to the base. The theory of metal-to-semiconductor contacts predicts that the current should consist of a constant (the saturation current), plus a term which increases exponentially with forward bias.[2] The important thing is that this exponent should be numerically equal to about forty times the voltage. Exponents as large as this have not been found with any other type of metal-to-germanium contact so far as we have been able to determine. Exponents of forty times the voltage are usually obtained with high-quality alloyed or pulled junctions, although with these accuracy of dimensional control is much more difficult. Exponents of this value are normally obtained with metal electrodes applied by the electrochemical process, showing that the increased dimensional accuracy of the surface-barrier transistor has been achieved without sacrifice of essential barrier uniformity.

Unlike the point-contact transistor, the hole current of the surface-barrier transistor is protected from exposure to uncovered germanium surface. The action of such an exposed surface as a collector or as a conductor of holes is subject to variation with time because of variations of the chemical composition of the surface layer of adsorbed atoms on the crystal. The stream lines of flow of hole current in the surface-barrier transistor Fig. 3(b)) are all nearly equal in length and extend directly from emitter to collector without any appreciable diffusion to the exposed crystal surface.

The extreme uniformity of the barrier gives another useful result. The high exponent value implies that, like alloy- or pulled-junction transistors, the device will operate on very low voltages. The characteristic curves of the surface-barrier transistor in Fig. 4 show that the collector impedance becomes high for potentials above one-quarter of a volt.

Not only does the close spacing of emitter and collector cause the emitter current to consist almost entirely of holes, but it permits operation with low voltages at frequencies, which it has

[2] For example, see H. C. Torrey and C. A. Whitmer, *Crystal Rectifiers*, p. 77, Section 4.3, McGraw-Hill Book Co., 1948.

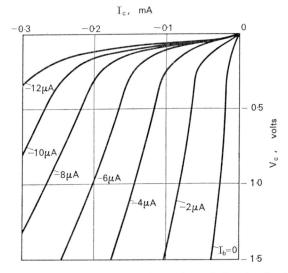

FIG. 4. Grounded-emitter characteristics of a typical surface-barrier transmitter.

proved impractical to obtain with other forms of transistors. Operation on a 3-volt power supply at 30 megacycles with a power gain of 18 db has readily been obtained.

TABLE 1. PARAMETERS OF SURFACE-BARRIER TRANSISTORS MEASURED AT $V_c = -3$ VOLTS $I_c = -0.5$ mA.

Unit	$f_{c\alpha}$ (mc)	α^0	r_e (ohms)	r_c (kilohms)	r_b (ohms)	r_b' (ohms)	C_b ($\mu\mu$f)
148	40	0.912	21	200	800	320	2.0
149	41	0.925	47	280	730	180	1.5
150	36	0.913	18	155	780	160	2.1
152	47	0.910	23	210	610	185	2.7
200	37	0.912	31	160	560	200	2.2
214	40	0.961	33	265	1120	190	2.5
217	49	0.905	11	160	650	130	2.2
219	47	0.962	13	330	1500	235	1.7
226	47	0.925	59	220	970	220	1.3
227	44	0.922	17	210	920	190	1.0

The most important characteristics of a group of ten surface-barrier transistors are tabulated in Table 1. The column labeled $f_{c\alpha}$ is the frequency at which the hole current falls to seven-tenths of its low-frequency value with constant signal input.

The surface-barrier transistor is at present a low-power device. This is not inherent but reflects the fact that our research program was guided partly by our dissatisfaction with the high-frequency performance and uniformity of existing low-power transistors. The power output of the transistors in Table 1 is of the order of milliwatts.

Future Prospects

It is clear that the discovery that unformed surface electrodes of substantial area when properly applied are suitable for transistor use, together with the fact that semiconductors can be accurately shaped by electrochemical techniques, opens up a promising new area of research and development in the already vigorous field of applied semiconductor physics.

Unipolar and Analog Transistors†

W. Shockley

9. Unipolar and Analog Transistors

Although transistors and vacuum tubes are different in structure and mode of operation, vacuum-tube concepts have often been used to describe the functioning of transistors. Usually the analogy between the two is rather strained. In this section, however, we shall describe a new class of *unipolar transistors*, some of which are so conveniently described by analogy with vacuum tubes that they are referred to as *analog transistors*. We shall present the material of this section in terms of these analogies.

As a starting point for describing these new transistors by analogy with vacuum tubes, we shall discuss an analogy between a *p–n* junction biased in the reverse direction and a vacuum condenser. In a vacuum condenser there is a potential difference between the two metal plates. Between the plates there is an electric field, and under ordinary conditions of operation the electron emission from the plates can be neglected. Thus in the vacuum condenser the space between the two plates is free of charge. As we discussed in the last section, when a *p–n* junction is biased in the reverse direction a region of carrier depletion is formed. If the effect of the small number of carriers in the region of depletion is negligible, then the structure will behave as a condenser. However, in general there will be an appreciable space charge in the depletion region and the electric field will not be the same as in a true vacuum condenser.

† *Proceedings of the I.R.E.* **40,** 1311 (1952).

A closer approximation to a true vacuum condenser can be produced by suitably adjusting the donor and acceptor concentrations. In Fig. 28 we represent a situation in which the structure consists of a p-type region, a region which is substantially pure or intrinsic, and an n-type region. If an electric field which produces

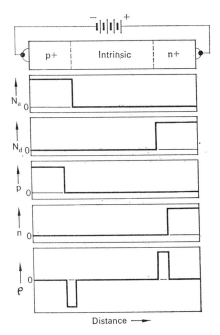

Fig. 28. Semiconductor analog to a vacuum condenser.

a potential difference is applied across the structure, then the distribution of charge will be as shown in Fig. 28. In this case the dipole layer consists of two separated distributions of charge much as it does in the case of a metal parallel plate condenser. Thus we see in this example that the p- and n-regions act as the metal condenser plates and the substantially pure region as the vacuum. This analogy will hold so long as reverse potentials are applied. For forward potentials, however, there will be injection of majority carriers from both sides into the middle region.

From the reasoning presented above, it is evident that heavily doped p- and n-regions are like cold nonemitting electrodes in a vacuum-tube structure, provided that the electrical fields at their surfaces are properly chosen. The choice must be such that the electric fields at the boundaries of the regions are *majority carrier retaining* so that the p- and n-type regions will furnish only small saturation currents of minority carriers. For suitably designed structures, these small currents can be neglected. On the basis of these ideas we can understand how a transistor may be made whose mode of operation will be closely analogous to that of a vacuum-tube triode. We shall refer to such a transistor as an analog transistor.

The mode of operation of the analog transistor may be described by reference to the state of affairs in the vacuum-tube triode. If normal operating voltages are applied to a vacuum-tube triode whose cathode is cold and nonemitting, then at the grid and cathode the electric field is electron extracting and at the plate it is electron retaining. If the cathode is heated so that electron emission occurs, then the field at the cathode is reduced by the space charge of the emitted electrons. However, the fields at the electrodes still remain electron extracting at grid and cathode and electron retaining at the plate.

In the analog transistor the geometrical structure of the vacuum tube is converted to semiconductor, as represented in Fig. 29, by replacing the cathode and anode by $n+$ regions, the grid by a $p+$ region, and the space by pure germanium. Potentials of the same polarities are applied. Under these conditions the analog-grid will draw only a small saturation current since the field at its surface is hole retaining so that the majority carriers do not flow out of it. Likewise, the majority carriers are retained in the analog-plate. At the analog-cathode, however, the field is such as to extract majority carriers. Electrons will thus flow out of the analog-cathode, setting up a negative space charge. Since the analog-grid is negative in respect to the analog-cathode, none of these electrons will reach it and the grid will be surrounded by a depletion region. The electron flow between the grid "wires" can evidently be controlled by a signal voltage applied to the analog-grid. Thus a mode of operation closely analogous to that of a vacuum tube is achieved.

A space-charge law strictly similar to Child's Law can be derived for the space-charge limited emission of the $n+$ region of

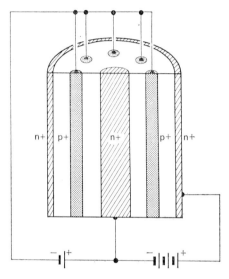

FIG. 29. Compositional structure of an analog transistor.

Fig. 29. For this purpose, as in the case of Child's Law, the complex geometry of Fig. 29 is replaced by a plain parallel model. Under these conditions one finds that the current emitted per unit area is given by the formula

$$I = 9\kappa\epsilon_0\mu V^2/8x^3, \tag{55}$$

where κ and ϵ_0 are the dielectric constant of germanium and the permittivity of free space, respectively, μ is the mobility of an electron, V is the voltage between the parallel planes, and x is their spacing. In similar notation the conventional expression for Child's Law is

$$I = (4/9)\epsilon_0(2q/m)^{1/2}V^{3/2}/x^2. \tag{56}$$

The analog for Child's Law governs the current flow in the analog transistor in much the same way that Child's Law does in the case of a vacuum tube.

It should be pointed out, however, that there are important differences between the two laws. In the case of the analog of Child's Law it should be noted that there is no conservation of momentum of the electrons. After traveling one mean-free path they are scattered so that no coherent motion is preserved in the direction of the electric field from one collision to the next. One interesting consequence of this is that electron flow to the analog-grid need not occur when the analog-grid is positive in respect to the analog-cathode, provided that the field is electron extracting at the analog-grid. It should also be pointed out that the analog of Child's Law presented above is valid only for relatively low electric fields. For high electric fields the relationship between drift velocity and electric field ceases to be linear, with the result that, in effect, the mobility decreases. This fact must also be taken into account in designing transistors making use of space-charge limited emission.

The transistor of Fig. 29 is a strict analog of a vacuum-tube triode so far as the polarities and nature of the electron currents are concerned. It is possible of course to have an anti-analog transistor in which the roles of donors and acceptors are interchanged. In such an anti-analog transistor the source of holes would be the anode and the electrode to which they flow would be the cathode. This situation poses certain difficulties in nomenclature for analog transistors. It is evident that the words cathode and anode are unsuitable since the role played by an electrode will be opposite in a hole-flow analog or p-type analog transistor from what it is in an electron-flow or n-type analog transistor.

It is evident that the analog transistor works according to principles somewhat different from those of the ordinary type of transistor. As was mentioned above, the phenomenon of minority carrier injection into a region where majority carriers are present does not occur. Thus the conventional role assigned to an emitter electrode in an ordinary transistor is not played by any of the electrodes of the analog transistor. Furthermore, except for ac charging currents and small reverse saturation currents, practically all of the current flowing in the transistor is carried by carriers of one sign. This is different from the point-contact transistor and the filamentary transistor in which both signs are involved to a significant degree. In the junction transistor, also, both controlled and controlling currents flow in the base layer at the same time. Thus a difference between the analog transistor and the more conventional type is a separation in space of the two kinds of current flow.

In order to distinguish between the more conventional transistors and the analog types, we propose to use the words *bipolar* and *unipolar*. In terms of this terminology the *analog* transistor structures are the *unipolar* type. This is true for both the type in which the current is carried by electrons and the type in which the current is carried by holes. Elsewhere in this issue we discuss another type of unipolar transistor, referred to as the *field-effect* transistor.[44] This transistor differs from the analog type in having unbalanced chemical impurity densities in the region where the carriers flow. These chemical impurities neutralize some of the space charge of the current carriers in a way somewhat reminiscent of the behavior of positive gas ions in a gas-discharge tube.

Since the role of emitter is not played in the normal way in the unipolar transistor and since the collector also functions somewhat differently, it appears advantageous to introduce new terminology for the electrodes in the unipolar types. The choice proposed for the electrodes is as follows: *Source* for the electrode from which the carriers enter the region of relatively high electric fields; *drain* for the electrode at which they arrive and out of which they flow; in the analog transistor the control electrode will be called the *grid*

---

[44] W. Shockley, A unipolar "field-effect" transistor, *Proc. I.R.E.*, **40**, 1365–1377; this issue.

because of its close analogy with vacuum-tube structures. In the field-effect transistor it is proposed to call the control electrode the *gate.* The fact that gate and grid have the same initial letter leads to the use of a common subscript for these two similarly functioning electrodes. The choice of these names has been based partly on an attempt to find names which describe functions and partly on the value of the names from a phonetic and abbreviational point of view. It should be noted that none of the new subscripts are the same as those encountered in bipolar transistors. Furthermore, it may be noted that the names selected are all monosyllabic.

Conclusion

This article has attempted to show how the basic mechanisms of current flow in semiconductors arise from imperfections. Another purpose has been to show that the theoretical concepts of the hole and the electron, known for over two decades since the pioneering theories of Wilson were published, have reached the stage of acquiring quantitative attributes usable for engineering design. This quantitative status has become possible largely as a result of new experiments in transistor physics made possible by the growth of transistor technology. Although not all of the physical principles that may have engineering utility have been discussed at length, enough examples have been presented to show that transistor electronics is a large and diversified field. New combinations of principles may be expected to lead to new and useful devices. One new class of devices is constituted by the unipolar transistors, first published in this article. The conclusion is that transistor electronics is a large and diverse field. It may be expected to show rapid growth for many years to come.

PAPER 15

A Unipolar "Field-effect" Transistor†‡

W. Shockley§

Summary

The theory for a new form of transistor is presented. This transistor is of the "field-effect" type in which the conductivity of a layer of semiconductor is modulated by a transverse electric field.

Since the amplifying action involves currents carried predominantly by one kind of carrier, the name "unipolar" is proposed to distinguish these transistors from point-contact and junction types, which are "bipolar" in this sense.

Regarded as an analog for a vacuum-tube triode, the unipolar field-effect transistor may have a mμ of 10 or more, high output resistance, and a frequency response higher than bipolar transistors of comparable dimensions.

1. Unipolar Transistor and Field-effect Modulation

PRIOR to the invention by Bardeen and Brattain of the point-contact transistor at Bell Telephone Laboratories, the hope that purely electronic amplification might be obtained in semiconductors was strongly bolstered by the concept of the "field-effect" amplifier.[1] The field-effect transistor was conceived as consisting of a thin layer of semiconductor separated from another conducting electrode by a layer of dielectric. A potential applied across the dielectric would then charge the layer of semiconductor, and this change in charge would alter the number of holes and electrons

† *Proceedings of the I.R.E.* **40**, 1365 (1952).

‡ Decimal classification: R282.12. Original manuscript received by the Institute, August 18, 1952.

§ Bell Telephone Laboratories, Inc., Murray Hill, N.J.

[1] For a brief history see W. Shockley, *Electrons and Holes in Semiconductors*, chap. 2; D. van Nostrand, New York, N.Y. 1950.

available for conduction, thus altering the conductivity of the layer.

This effect was found to take place in experiments carried out by Pearson.[2] it was much less than that expected on the basis of an elementary theory, and the difference was attributed to surface states. These surface states were assumed, in a theory proposed by Bardeen,[3] to trap, in an immobile condition, the added charge induced on the layer of semiconductor.

It is the purpose of this article to show that transistor structures are possible in which the adverse effects of surface states are eliminated and to show how, in certain ways, these structures have advantages over previously described transistors.

One of the important characteristics which distinguishes the "field-effect" transistors described here from the more conventional types is that the working current is substantially "unipolar." In the point-contact, filamentary, and junction types an important process is the injection of minority carriers into regions having relatively high concentrations of majority carriers. In the region of injection, space-charge neutrality is maintained to a high degree by currents of majority carriers which neutralize the space charge of the minority carriers. Since carriers of both signs are involved, these processes may be referred to as "bipolar." In a "field-effect" transistor, the current flow is carried by one type of carrier only. The changed conductance between input and output terminals results from changing numbers of carriers of this one type. For this reason the name "unipolar transistors" is proposed.

One feature which should be emphasized about field-effect transistors is the possibility of voltage gain in addition to current gain. We shall show that voltage gain is indeed possible and that $m\mu$ values of ten or higher can be obtained.

Another feature of importance is the efficiency for high-frequency response of these devices compared to bipolar types of

[2] W. Shockley and G. L. Pearson, Modulation of conductance of thin films of semiconductors by surface charges, *Phys. Rev.* **74**, 232–233 (1948).

[3] J. Bardeen, Surface states and rectification at metal semiconductor contact, *Phys. Rev.* **71**, 717–727 (1947).

comparable dimensions. The reason for this difference is that in the bipolar types, the electric field is either very low, as in the base layer of a junction transistor, or else is effective in producing a current of majority carriers, as in the filamentary and point-contact transistors. In the latter cases, the majority carrier current is an important source of power dissipation being produced by the electric field that gives the minority carriers a desirably high drift velocity. In the unipolar types, even higher drift velocities can be produced without similar disadvantages.

It should be remarked in passing that the unipolar transistors considered here are essentially different from devices of the "fieldistor" type such as that discussed by Stuetzer.[4] The theory proposed by Stuetzer does involve modulation by electric fields, but otherwise bears, at most, a distant relationship to the structures considered here.

2. Modulation of a Conducting Channel by Electric Fields

In Fig. 1 we represent an example of a unipolar field-effect transistor. It is a three-terminal device, and consists principally of

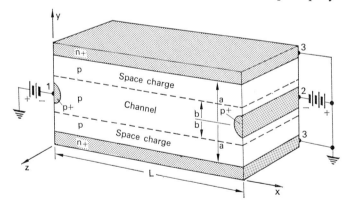

FIG. 1. Space-charge regional and channel in a $(n++)p(n+)$ structure.

---

[4] O. T. Stuetzer, A crystal amplifier with high input impedance, *Proc. I.R.E.*, **38,** 868–871 (August 1950).

a layer of p-type material sandwiched between two layers of n-type material, the doping being much stronger in the n-type material, which is designated as $n+$. The "working current" is carried by holes flowing in the x-direction in the p-layer. The terminals are inserts of heavily doped p-type material, designated $p+$. Under operating conditions, reverse bias is applied across the p–n junctions, and space-charge regions form in which the carrier concentration is negligible. As a consequence, the current flows in a *channel* of p-type material bounded by the space-charge regions.

If the reverse bias at one $p+$ terminal is larger than at the other, the channel will be narrower at the one terminal. How the channel varies in width between the terminals will be discussed in subsequent sections.

In passing, we shall point out that the unipolar transistor of Fig. 1 is in some ways a closer analog to a vacuum tube than are the bipolar transistors. If we imagine that a signal is applied between terminals 3 and ground, then the effect will be to widen and narrow the channel which carries current between 1 and 2. This is closely analogous to the action of a grid which controls the current flow in a "channel" of thermionic electrons flowing between the grid wires. As in the bipolar case, the control is exerted by flow of electrons by one mechanism on flow by another mechanism; in this case, flow by excess electrons in the $n+$ regions controls flow of holes in the channel. A difference from the bipolar case is that the controlling and controlled currents differ not only in conduction mechanism but also in spatial location.

In this section we shall consider only the case in which the reverse bias is almost the same on the two terminals so that the channel has substantially uniform width. We shall derive the dependence of conductance of the channel upon

$$W = \text{the magnitude of the reverse bias} \qquad (1)$$

applied across the p–n junctions.

In Fig. 1, the space-charge region is represented as lying entirely in the p-region. This is only an approximation; but it is a good one, as we shall show below if the $(n+)$-regions are much more heavily doped than the p-region. The doping of the regions defines two "chemical" charge densities

$$p\text{-region} \qquad \rho_0 = q(N_a - N_d) \qquad (2a)$$

$$(n+)\text{-region} \quad \rho_n = q(N_d - N_a), \qquad (2b)$$

where q is the electronic charge, N_d and N_a densities of donors and acceptors. The charge density of the holes in the conducting part of the p-region is equal to ρ_0 and the conductivity is $\sigma_0 = \mu_0 \rho_0$, where μ_0 is the mobility of a hole. The choice of signs in (2a) and (2b) makes both ρ_0 and ρ_n positive so that ρ_n corresponds to the chemical charge density in the n-region while ρ_0 corresponds to the carrier charge density in the p-region.

The distribution of charge density in the space-charge region is represented in Fig. 2(a). The middle plane of the p-region is $y = 0$, the edge of the space-charge layer is at $y = b$, and the p–n junction at $y = a$. The space-charge region is a dipole layer in which the charges add to zero. (If this were not the case, Gauss' theorem would require an electric field to exist beyond the boundaries of the layer.) Consequently, the shaded rectangles of Fig. 2(a) are equal in size and the depth of penetration is much less in the n-region.

Mathematically, this result may be deduced from Poisson's equation. If we let $V(y)$ represent the electrostatic potential, $E_y(y)$ the electric field, and y distance from the center of the p-layer, then Poisson's equation is

$$\kappa\epsilon_0 d^2 V/dy^2 = -\kappa\epsilon_0 dE_y/dy = -\rho(y), \qquad (3)$$

where $\rho(y)$ is the charge density. For y less than b, E_y is zero. Near $y = b$ there is a transition region in which ρ changes from zero to $-\rho_0$. This transition region is about one "Debye Length" thick, and in it the potential changes by about kT/q, where k is Boltzmann's constant and T the absolute temperature.[5] These quantities are both very small compared to a and W, respectively, and may

[5] W. Shockley, "The theory of p–n junctions in semiconductors and p–n junction transistors," *Bell Sys. Tech. Jour.* **28**, 441 (1949).

be neglected. Consequently, we assume that at the edge of the space-charge layer we have

$$E_y = 0 \quad \text{at} \quad y = b, \tag{4}$$

and within the p region

$$dE_y/dy = \rho/\kappa\epsilon_0 = -\rho_0/\kappa\epsilon_0 \quad y > b, \tag{5}$$

so that

$$E_y = -\rho_0(y - b)/\kappa\epsilon_0. \tag{6}$$

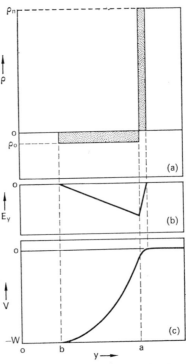

FIG. 2. Penetration of the space-charge region into the p and $n+$ regions. (a) Space charge. (b) Electrical field. (c) Electrostatic potential.

This leads to the variation of E_y shown in Fig. 2(b) for $y < a$. For $y > a$, the charge density changes from a small negative to a large positive value, ρ_n. Evidently, E_y will vanish when $(a - b)\rho_0 = \rho_n \times$ (thickness of space-charge layer in n-region). This equation requires the equating of areas shown in Fig. 2(a).

Since the average value of the electric field is the same in both regions, as may be seen by inspection of Fig. 2(b), the potential differences across the two regions will be proportional to the thickness of the space-charge layers. We shall neglect the thickness in the n-region and assume that the potential drop occurs wholly in the p-region. This leads to the value

$$V = -\int E_y dy$$
$$= (\rho_0/2K)\,[(y - b)^2 - (a - b)^2], \tag{7}$$

where the constant of integration has been chosen to make $V = 0$ when $y = a$, corresponding to grounding the n-region, and we have introduced

$$K = \kappa \epsilon_0 \tag{8}$$

as the dielectric constant.

K may be conveniently expressed in farads/cm rather than farads/m. Since we shall make no use of magnetic quantities in this article, it is not necessary to have a magnetically consistent set of equations. The use of K in farads/cm permits the use of dimensions in cm, mobilities in cm^2/volt sec, and conductivities in ohm/cm, while retaining currents and voltages in amp and volt. (These conclusions may be verified for any equations given here simply by deriving them in mks and then converintg the length unit to cm.)

With $\kappa = 16$ and 12 for germanium and silicon, respectively, the values of K are

$$\text{Ge} \qquad K = 1.42 \times 10^{-12} \text{ farads/cm} \tag{9}$$

$$\text{Si} \qquad K = 1.06 \times 10^{-12} \text{ farads/cm}. \tag{10}$$

The potential in the channel is

$$V(b) = -(\rho_0/2K)\,(a - b)^2. \tag{11}$$

We shall find it advantageous to use W, a positive quantity representing this reverse bias,

$$W = -V(b) = [1 - (b/a)]^2 W_0, \qquad (12)$$

where

$$W_0 \equiv \rho_0 a^2 / 2K. \qquad (13)$$

W_0 is the magnitude of reverse bias required to make the space charge penetrate the entire p-region. We shall refer to it as the "pinch-off voltage" since it is the voltage that will reduce the channel to zero and pinch off the conducting path between terminals 1 and 2.

In Fig. 3, the potential distribution in the p-region is shown and related to the values of W and W_0. The dashed line shows the limiting case of $W = +W_0$. The solid line shows a case in which $W = W_0/4$.

We shall next apply these considerations to the treatment of the

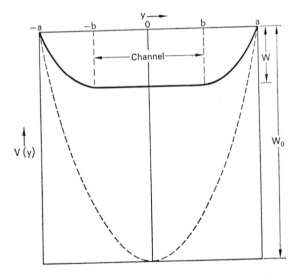

FIG. 3. Potential distribution for channel with $W = W_0/4$ (and $b = a/2$) and limiting case of $W = W_0$.

transistor structure represented in Fig. 1. We shall denote the reverse biases at terminals 1 and 2 by W and $W + \Delta W$, respectively. These biases cause a current I per unit length in the z-direction to flow from terminal 1 to terminal 2. We shall require ΔW to be small compared to $W_0 - W$ so that the channel will be of substantially uniform width and can be treated simply as a layer of p-type semiconductor of conductivity

$$\sigma_0 = \mu_0 \rho_0, \tag{14}$$

where μ_0 is the mobility of holes. If the electric field in the layer is E_x, the current density will be $\sigma_0 E_x$ and the current per unit length in the z-direction will be

$$I = 2b\sigma_0 E_x = g(W)E_x, \tag{15}$$

where $g(W)$ is the conductance of a unit square of the layer $2b$ thick.

For the case in which ΔW is small compared to W and to $W_0 - W$, the channel will be of uniform width and the conductance per cm in the z-direction of a structure of length L in the x-direction will then be

$$G = g(W)/L. \tag{16}$$

However, if ΔW is not small compared to $W_0 - W$, then the channel will change its width appreciably, and this must be taken into account. We do this by considering the dependence of g upon W.

Equation (12) gives a relationship between W and b. This can be transformed into a relationship between g and W;

$$g(W) = 2\sigma_0 b(W) = [1 - (W/W_0)^{1/2}]g_0, \tag{17}$$

where

$$g_0 \equiv 2\sigma_0 a \tag{18}$$

is the conductance of a square of the p-region at zero bias. In Fig. 4, the dependence of $g(W)$ upon W is shown. In terms of this dependence it is possible to calculate the current flowing in the channel when there is a large voltage difference between the ends of the channel. This calculation is presented in Section 4.

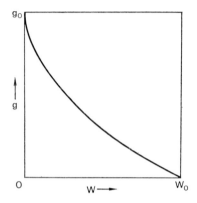

FIG. 4. Conductance of square of channel versus W.

3. Proposed Unipolar Transistor Terminology

As was stressed in the introductory section, the principles of operation of the unipolar transistor are substantially different from those of the bipolar types. For this reason, it seems appropriate to consider choosing a new set of names for the three terminals. An advantageous choice would be one which involves no overlapping of subscripts with the emitter, base, collector combination in use for bipolar transistors. The choice selected is "source" for the electrode through which the carriers flow into the channel, "drain" for the electrode into which the carriers flow out of the channel, and "gate" for the control electrodes that modulate the channel. One reason for selecting "gate" rather than something else is that the subscript "g" is reminiscent of "grid" and the analogy is close between the two. Voltages applied to and currents flowing into these electrodes are denoted by

$$V_s, \ V_g, \ V_d \quad \text{and} \quad I_s, \ I_g, \ I_d \tag{19}$$

for dc values, small letters being used for small-signal or ac values.

A symbol for this type of transistor is shown in Fig. 5. As with the bipolar transistor, the arrow indicates the *direction of conventional current* flow, and is *located near source* where working carriers enter the structure.

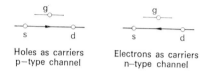

Holes as carriers   Electrons as carriers
p–type channel   n–type channel

FIG. 5. Symbols for unipolar field-effect transistor.

When it is convenient to use numerical subscripts to indicate the three terminals, system will be that shown in Fig. 1, with 1 for source, 2 for drain, and 3 for gate.

In the treatment of this article, we shall, in general, deal with low frequencies and shall neglect the current to the gate both due to reverse currents and to charging currents and shall set I_g equal to zero. Consequently, I_s and I_d are equal and opposite. We shall use I to mean

$$I = I_s = -I_d, \tag{20}$$

these quantities being *currents per unit length* of structure in the z-direction

The relationship between the V's and the W's is evidently

$$W_s = V_g - V_s \tag{21}$$

$$W_d = V_g - V_d, \tag{22}$$

and small changes in these quantities, which we shall treat as differentials, are

$$\delta W_s = v_g - v_s \tag{23}$$

$$\delta W_d = v_g - v_d \tag{24}$$

$$\delta I = i = i_s = -i_d. \tag{25}$$

T.—K

We shall use these relationships in the next section in deriving an equivalent circuit for the unipolar transistor.

4. The Gradual Case

A. Introduction

When current flows in the plus x direction in the channel, an electric field with a component E_x must be present. This requires that the potential changes along the channel. Since the gate electrodes carry no current (we shall consider small reverse junction current later), they are equipotentials. Hence the reverse voltage between channel and $(n+)$- region varies with x and hence the channel width varies. In calculating the relationship between channel width b and reverse voltage W in Section 2, we assumed that

$$\partial^2 V/\partial x^2 = 0, \tag{26}$$

so that a one-dimensional Poisson equation could be used. Since when current flows,

$$E_x = -\partial V/\partial x \neq 0, \tag{27}$$

in general $\partial^2 V/\partial x^2$ will not vanish. However, if $\partial^2 V/\partial x^2$ is very small compared to ρ_0/K, then the one-dimensional approximation can be used for $V(y)$ and the reverse potential $W(x)$ will be the same function of $b(x)$ as in the case of $I = 0$. The approximation that W and b are related in this way is valid if conditions along the channel vary gradually. We refer to this situation as the *gradual case*.

The situation that prevails in the gradual case is illustrated in Fig. 6. Current flows to the right so that in the $+x$ direction the potential becomes more negative, the reverse bias increases, and the channel narrows. Consider a particular value of x and a length a centered about x. In this length $b(x)$ is supposed to vary by a small fraction of itself. Now the potential difference between the points $(x, 0)$ and (x, a) will depend on the entire distribution of charge in the structure and the potentials applied to source and

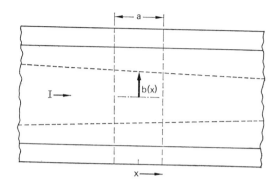

FIG. 6. Condition in a "gradual" channel. Note interval marked *a* should be slightly wider than shown, so as to be one half the width of the *p* layer.

drain. However, the $(n+)$-regions exert a shielding action so that the potential at $(x, 0)$ is determined chiefly by charges lying within the interval a about $(x, 0)$, unless, of course, there are very much larger charge densities relatively near. If the channel changes relatively gradually, the potential will thus be that determined by the average value of b in the interval a, and this is substantially the same as the value of $b(x)$ at x. Hence the reverse voltage is

$$W = W[b(x)], \qquad (28)$$

where W has the functional dependence on b derived for $I = 0$.

In several parts of this section we shall take the potential on the gate as zero. This is especially convenient when considering how the potential varies along the channel.

One of the assumptions involved in establishing the function $W(b)$ in Section 2 was that $E_y = 0$ at $y = b$. This assumption is not exactly fulfilled for the gradual case, but is a good approximation. Inside the channel the electric field is predominantly in the x direction. At the edges there is a component in the y direction which produces the inward component of hole-drift velocity that corresponds to the narrowing of the channel. Thus at the edge of the channel

$$-E_y:E_x = db/dx. \tag{29}$$

For the gradual approximation, db/dx must be much less than unity; if it were not, the channel would narrow abruptly. As will be shown below, E_x is also small compared to typical values of E_y in the region between the channel and the gate. Hence the value of E_y at the surface of the channel may be neglected so far as calculations of $W(b)$ are concerned. Since E_y is even smaller in the interior of the channel, where the current flow is more nearly parallel to the x-direction, the equipotential surfaces in the channel are well approximated by planes perpendicular to the x-axis; the electrostatic potential on these planes is $-W(x)$ since this is the potential difference between the $(n+)$-regions, which are equipotentials and taken to be at zero potential, and the channel.

We are now in a position to analyze the gradual case in terms of $W(x)$ and g. Since g is a function of b and since b and W are related as discussed in Section 2, g is the same function of W as in Section 2. This leads at once to the equation

$$I = g(W)dW/dx. \tag{30}$$

This is the basic equation on which the theory of the gradual case is developed. It is applicable not only to the structure of Fig. 1 but to others in which there may be concentration gradients rather than abrupt transitions. For such other cases, new functions $g(W)$ can be derived. Once the appropriate $g(W)$ is known, the analysis is similar to that presented below.

Before discussing the consequences of (30) we shall point out that such an equation does not apply if the gradual condition is badly violated. We shall illustrate this by supposing that the channel width varies rapidly. Then the potential at x is not determined by $b(x)$ alone but by the much larger charges that lie to the left of x. Under these conditions, then, W cannot be expressed as a function of b alone and, consequently, b and hence g are not functions of W alone, but depend also on derivatives of W. Another case in which

W and b are not directly related may occur if the potential at x is determined in large measure by the potential applied to the end electrode. In this case it is evident that there is no unique relationship between $b(x)$ and $W(x)$. This latter case will be examined in detail in subsequent sections in which we suppose that W exceeds W_0 near one electrode.

B. The Current–Voltage Relationships

Returning to the gradual case, we assume that (30) is valid and integrate it formally by multiplying by dx. We thus obtain

$$I \int dx = \int g(W)dW. \tag{31}$$

Denoting the values of W at source and drain by W_s and W_d and letting L represent their separation, we obtain

$$I = (1/L) \int_{W_s}^{W_d} g(W)dW. \tag{32}$$

The current–voltage characteristics based on this equation may be conveniently expressed in terms of a function of one variable having the dimensions of a current

$$J(W) \equiv \int_0^W g(W)dW$$
$$= g_0 W[1 - (2/3)(W/W_0)^{1/2}], \tag{33}$$

the last expression following from (17). In terms of J, the current per unit length I takes the form

$$I = [J(W_d) - J(W_s)]/L$$
$$= [J(V_g - V_d) - J(V_g - V_s)]/L. \tag{34}$$

If I is plotted as a function of V_d with V_d as a parameter and $V_s = 0$ (analogous to a collector family for a bipolar transistor or a plate family for a vacuum-tube triode), then all of the curves have the same shape but are simply translated parallel to each other along the I and V_d axes. Such a plot is shown in Fig. 7, absolute values of V_d being used so the curves fall in the first quadrant.

These characteristics cannot be continued beyond

$$W_d = V_g - V_d = W_0 \qquad (35)$$

on the basis of (34) since for such potentials pinch-off occurs at the drain and the gradual approximation fails. The continuation shown in Fig. 7 is based on a treatment given in Section 5. The

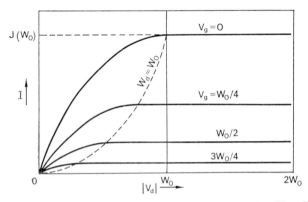

FIG. 7. Receiver family with source at zero potential. (Note $W_2 = W_0$ line.)

critical condition for pinch-off at the drain is indicated by the dashed line. This curve has the equation

$$I = J(W_0)/L - J(W_0 - |V_d|)/L. \qquad (36)$$

From this it follows that the dashed curve is the same as the curve for $V_g = 0$, except that it is rotated through 180° and has its origin at $|V_d| = W_0$ and $I = J_0(W_0)/L$.

The small-signal behavior corresponding to (32) is readily obtained by making small changes v_s, v_d, and v_g in the V's. This leads to a small change i in I of

$$\begin{aligned} i &= (g_d \delta W_d - g_s \delta W_s)/L \\ &= (g_s/L)v_s - (g_d/L)v_d - (g_s - g_d)v_g/L, \qquad (37) \end{aligned}$$

where

$$g_s \equiv g(W_s) = g(V_g - V_s) \tag{38}$$

$$g_d \equiv g(W_d) = g(V_g - V_d). \tag{39}$$

Making use of the notation

$$G_{dg} = g_s/L \tag{40}$$

$$R_d = L/g_d \tag{41}$$

$$\mu_{dg} = G_{dg}R_d = g_s/g_d, \tag{42}$$

the current equation may be put in the form

$$i_d = -i = G_{dg}[(v_g - v_s) + (v_d - v_g)/\mu_{dg}], \tag{43}$$

which is the same as that for a vacuum-tube triode, provided we note the ac current into the drain from outside is $i_d = -i_s = -i$.

The equivalent circuit corresponding to (43) is shown in Fig. 8, with the nonreciprocal element represented as a current generator.

It is evident that a high mμ will be obtained by operating with

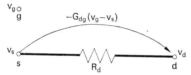

FIG. 8. Equivalent circuits for unipolar field-effect transistor.

W_d nearly equal to W_0 so that the channel is nearly "pinched-off" at the drain and $g_d = g(W_d)$ is much less than g_s. We shall return to this subject in more detail in Section 5. The circuit is incomplete owing to the absence of capacitative elements. These omitted elements will play an important role at frequencies as high as those discussed in Section 7, and at these frequencies a lumped constant treatment becomes a poor approximation.

C. Natural Parameters

Although the circuit characteristics for the gradual case can be obtained from (32) as soon as $g(W)$ is known as a function of W, it is desirable to understand the behavior of the channel in greater detail. For this purpose, we shall derive expressions for the dependence of W upon x along the channel and the shape of the channel in the x-y plane. It is convenient to use certain natural parameters associated with the constants of the structure.

The natural unit of voltage, W_0, has already been derived. The natural unit of field, E_0, is that at the plane $y = a$ when W_0 is applied. The natural unit of conductance is g_0. The natural unit for current per unit length is the current associated with g_0 and a field E_0. The natural unit of time, τ_0, is the time required for a hole to travel a distance a in a field E_0. The equations for these quantities are

$$W_0 = \rho_0 a^2 / 2K \tag{44}$$

$$E_0 = \rho_0 a / K = 2W_0/a \tag{45}$$

$$g_0 = 2\rho_0\mu_0 a \tag{46}$$

$$I_0 = g_0 E_0 = 2\rho_0{}^2\mu_0 a^2/K = 8\mu_0 K W_0{}^2/a^2 \tag{47}$$

$$\tau_0 = a/\mu_0 E_0 = K/\mu_0 \rho_0 = K/\sigma_0. \tag{48}$$

Several forms have been given for some of the quantities above. These are convenient for subsequent manipulations.

The expression K/σ_0 for τ_0 should be noted. This expression is simply the "dielectric relaxation time" for material characterized by σ_0 and K.

D. Expressions for the Solution

It is convenient not to solve for W as a function of x but instead for x as a function of b. Since the relationship between b and W has already been derived, this establishes the relationship between x and W. In order to find x as a function of b, we note that, from (12) and (13),

$$dW = -(a - b)\rho_0 db/K. \tag{49}$$

Using this equation to eliminate dW, we obtain

$$Idx = g(W)\,dW$$
$$= -g_0(a - b)\,(b\rho_0/aK)db$$
$$= -I_0 a(1 - u)u\,du, \tag{50}$$

where

$$u \equiv b/a \tag{51}$$

is the fraction of the p layer occupied by channel. It should be noted that dx/du is zero at $u = 0$ and $u = 1$. Formally, this means that the channel is changing its width with an infinite value of db/dx at those points. When u is between 0 and 1, dx/du is symmetrical about $u = 0.5$. The equation for dx is readily integrated to give

$$x = -(aI_0/I)\,[(u^2/2) - (u^3/3)], \tag{52}$$

where the integration constant has been chosen so that $x = 0$ when $u = 0$. The resultant shape of the channel is shown in Fig. 9(a) for two values of I_0/I. In Fig. 9(b), the variation of potential

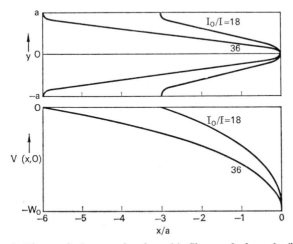

FIG. 9. The gradual approximation. (a) Shape of channel. (b) Electrostatic potential.

along the channel is shown. These curves are obtained by computing values of the electrostatic potential $V(x, y)$, which may be denoted as $V(x, 0)$ in the channel,

$$V(x, 0) = -W(x) = -W_0(1 - u)^2, \qquad (53)$$

for the same values of u as were used to compute x for Fig. 9(a) and then by plotting related V and x values.

The total length of the channel is

$$L(I) = (a/6) (I_0/I). \qquad (54)$$

It is evident that the conditions for the gradual case can hardly be considered to hold unless $L(I)$ is about $3a$ or more, corresponding to I_0/I greater than 18. Even if $L(I)$ is equal to $3a$, the gradual condition will hold only in the middle of the channel. Where the channel narrows rapidly, the gradual condition will not hold.

As an approximate criterion for the limit of validity of the gradual approximation we shall require that over a distance a the fractional change in channel width shall be small. This leads to

$$adb/dx < b \qquad (55)$$

or to

$$(a/b)db/dx < 1. \qquad (56)$$

This seems a reasonable condition. If it holds, then db/dx is small and the arguments given early in this section for the relationship between b and W apply. On the other hand, if the condition fails, then b may differ by a factor of 2 or more in a distance a. Under these conditions it is not evident that the potential at a point x is determined by b at that value of x, since it will be strongly influenced by variations of b to both sides.

We shall use the criterion in form

$$1 > (a/b) (db/dx) = I/(1 - u)u^2I_0. \qquad (57)$$

If I_0/I is 18, then the inequality is satisfied for values of u in the neighborhood of 0.5 For larger values of I_0/I and longer channels, the gradual condition will be satisfied over a wider range of channel widths. In all cases, however, the gradual condition will fail when u approaches unity or zero. The failure of the gradual condition near $u = 1$ is of little importance since the value of g is large there and the electric field E_x is small. Near $u = 0$, however, the electric field is high; furthermore, $u = 0$ will be approached in all cases in which W_d is greater than W_0.

Near $u = 0$, the term $1 - u$ is practically unity and the inequality may be written in the form

$$1 > I/u^2I_0. \tag{58}$$

In this range the u^3 term can be neglected in (52) for x so that

$$-x \doteq I_0au^2/2I. \tag{59}$$

Inserting the inequality here leads to

$$-x > a/2, \tag{60}$$

which implies that the gradual condition is applicable at distances greater than $a/2$ away from the end of the channel.

Actually the electric field does not approach infinity at $x = 0$ and the number of holes per unit length does not go to zero as implied by the gradual approximation. Thus the pinch-off condition at $x = 0$ does not really occur. Nevertheless, it is convenient to define a certain point as $x = 0$ and to refer to it as the *extrapolated pinch-off point*, or the *expop* for short. The expop is defined as the point at which u would vanish and W would equal W_0 if the gradual solution were continued beyond its range of validity.

In the next section we shall consider what occurs at and beyond the expop.

5. Conditions in the Expop Region

Before considering the conditions prevailing at the expop, we shall consider the conditions somewhat beyond it corresponding to $x > 0$. In this region, the charge per unit length due to holes will be very small compared to that due to $q(N_a - N_d)$. Thus that part of the electrostatic potential which is due to the charges may be well approximated by

$$V_0(x, y) = -W_0[1 - (y/a)^2], \tag{61}$$

which satisfies Poisson's equation and vanishes for $y = \pm a$. This potential is independent of x and produces no field which causes the holes to flow. The cause of the field E_x is the potential applied to the drain.

If we assume that the drain is located at a relatively large value of x and has a large negative charge, then we can approximate the field which it exerts near $x = 0$ by a relatively simple expression. This expression may be obtained by considering a Fourier expansion of potential on the plane $x = x_d$ at which the drain is located. If the potential is symmetrical about $y = 0$, it can be expanded in a cosine series with terms of the form

$$\cos [\pi(2n + 1)y/2a]; \, n = 0, 1, 2. \qquad (62)$$

Each term vanishes at $y = \pm a$. Each term can be combined with a function of x so as to obtain a solution of Laplace's equation, the complete terms being

$$T_n = \exp [\pi(2n + 1)x/2a] \cos [\pi(2n + 1)y/2a]. \qquad (63)$$

Each such term satisfies

$$d^2T_n/dx^2 + d^2T_n/dy^2 = 0. \qquad (64)$$

Terms with negative exponentials would satisfy Laplace's equation also, but would increase towards the left and would not represent properly a field due to the potential on the drain. The term with $n = 0$ decays by a factor of $\exp(-\pi/2) = 0.21$ in each interval a towards the left. The next term with $n = 1$ decays similarly but by a factor of $\exp(-3\pi/2) = 0.009$. From this it is evident that, except in the immediate neighborhood of the drain, the potential due to the drain can be represented by a single term

$$T_0 = (\exp \pi x/2a) \cos \pi y/2a. \qquad (65)$$

This term gives rise to a set of equipotentials of the form represented in Fig. 10.

In the region in which the charge due to holes is small the potential can thus be well represented by

$$V(x, y) = V_0(x, y) - AT_0(x, y). \qquad (66)$$

The coefficient A must be chosen so that $V = -W_d$ at the drain. Actually near the drain, other terms in the Fourier expansion should be included. However, if the drain has a shape somewhat

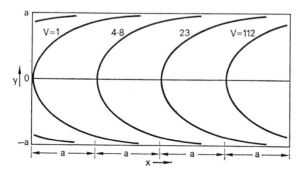

FIG. 10. Equipotentials for field satisfying Laplace's equation.

like the equipotentials for T_0, these other terms may be quite small. We shall, therefore, neglect them and determine A by requiring that $V = -W_d$ at the point $(x_d, 0)$. This leads to

$$W_d = W_0 + A \exp (\pi x_d/2a), \tag{67}$$

or

$$A = (W_d - W_0) \exp (-\pi x_d/2a). \tag{68}$$

We shall next consider how operating conditions affect the value of x_d, the distance between the extrapolated pinch-off and the drain.

In Fig. 11 we represent the dependence of $V(x, 0)$ upon x including a range of x in which the approximations that

$$x \doteq (I_0a/2I)u^2 \tag{69}$$

and

$$\begin{aligned} W &= W_0(1 - u)^2 \doteq W_0 - 2W_0u \\ &= W_0 - W_0(8Ix/I_0a)^{1/2} \end{aligned} \tag{70}$$

are valid. This solution will be valid for $x < -a$, where the gradual approximation holds. For positive values of x, it must join

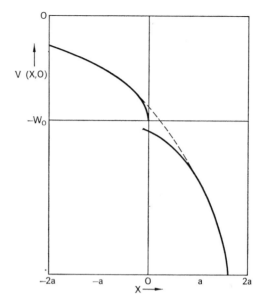

FIG. 11. Approximate joining of gradual solution to exponential.

smoothly onto the solution in the space-charge region. The problem of joining is discussed more fully in an Appendix. It may be helpful to give an estimate of the coefficient A based on simpler reasoning.

In the gradual region, the longitudinal electric field is produced by the variation in hole-charge per unit length. This variation produces a changing potential along the channel. As the expop is approached, the hole charge becomes negligible and further variation from this cause is impossible. Consequently, the electric field must be furnished from the potential on the drain. Since the gradual solution begins to fail badly at $x = -a/2$, it is reasonable to assume that the T_0 term makes an appreciable contribution to the field at that point. As an approximate joining condition at $x = -a/2$ we shall let the contribution of T_0 be 25 per cent as large as that of the gradual solution. This leads to the approximation shown in Fig. 11 and to

$$
\begin{aligned}
dW/dx &= W_0(8I/I_0a)^{1/2}x^{-1/2}/2 \\
&= E_0(I/I_0)^{1/2} = 4AdT_0/dx \\
&= 4(\pi A/2a)\exp(-\pi/4).
\end{aligned}
\tag{71}
$$

This leads to a value for A of

$$
\begin{aligned}
A &= (W_0/\pi)(I/I_0)^{1/2}\exp(\pi/4) \\
&= 0.7W_0(I/I_0)^{1/2}.
\end{aligned}
\tag{72}
$$

On the basis of this value of A, the distance between the expop and drain can be estimated as a function of W_d and I.

From (67) we find

$$
x_d = (2a/\pi)\ln[(W_d - W_0)(I_0/I)^{1/2}/0.7W_0].
\tag{73}
$$

As an example, we shall take $I_0/I = 18$, which gives a value of $3a$ for the maximum channel length, from full width to expop, and shall take W_d as $2W_0$. This leads to

$$
x_d = (2a/\pi)\ln(4.25/0.7) = 1.1a.
\tag{74}
$$

Hence the drain lies approximately a distance a beyond the expop.

On the basis of the gradual solution and the expression for x_d it is possible to develop the circuit theory for operation beyond the pinch-off condition in much the same way as was done for operation entirely in the gradual condition. The following presents this theory.

6. Equivalent Circuit for Low Frequencies

In Section 2 we considered a structure of length L between the source and drain and introduced a function $J(W)$ defined by

$$
J(W) = \int_0^W g(W)dW.
\tag{75}
$$

In terms of this function the current per unit length flowing into the source from outside is

$$
I = [J(V_g - V_d) - J(V_g - V_s)]/L.
\tag{76}
$$

Curves based on this formula were shown on Fig. 7. For $V_d - V_g$ more negative than $-W_0$, the curves were continued with a constant value of

$$I = [J(W_0) - J(V_g - V_s)]/L. \tag{77}$$

We now examine the justification of this continuation.

If we suppose that W_s is sufficiently large compared to W_0, then we may use (73) to estimate x_d. This means that the effective length of the channel should be taken as L_s with

$$L_s = L - x_d. \tag{78}$$

In other words the channel adjusts its current until the expop falls short of the drain by a distance x_d. Under these conditions the equation

$$I dx = g(W) dW \tag{79}$$

holds along the gradual part of the channel. Furthermore, if the expression is integrated from W_s to W_0, then the integral of dx must simply be L_s, since by definition L_s is the distance from the source to the expop when (79) is integrated to W_0. This gives

$$IL_s = \int_{W_s}^{W_0} g(W) dW = J(W_0) - J(W_s). \tag{80}$$

This leads to

$$I = [J(W_0) - J(V_g - V_s)]/L_s. \tag{81}$$

It is evident that this current is larger than that used previously by the ratio

$$L/L_s = [1 - (x_d/L)]^{-1}. \tag{82}$$

This ratio will be nearly unity if L is 5 or more times a since x_d will in general be comparable to a. Thus the extrapolation used in Fig. 7 is seen to be reasonable.

We may use these expressions to obtain differential forms for small-signal effects. For this purpose we write the equation in the form

$$I(L - x_d) = \int_{W_s}^{W_0} g(W) dW. \tag{83}$$

We then take total differentials of both sides, letting

$$\delta I = i, \ \delta W_s = v_g - v_s, \ \delta W_d = v_s - v_d, \tag{84}$$

and note that

$$I/g(W_s) = E_{xs}, \tag{85}$$

the electric field at the source. Because of the exponential dependence of term T_0, we note also that the electric field at the drain is

$$E_{xd} \doteq \pi(W_d - W_0)/2a. \tag{86}$$

The contributions of $x_d(W_d, I)$ to the differential is

$$\delta x_d = -(ai/\pi I) + \delta W_d/E_{xd}. \tag{87}$$

These considerations lead to

$$i = I \left(\frac{v_s}{E_{xs}} - \frac{v_d}{E_{xd}} + v_g \left(\frac{1}{E_{xd}} - \frac{1}{E_{xs}} \right) \right)$$
$$\div [L - x_d + a/\pi]. \tag{88}$$

From these we see that the $m\mu$ is

$$\mu_{gd} = (E_{xd}/E_{xs}) - 1. \tag{89}$$

The meaning of this expression may be seen by thinking in terms of Fig. 11. Here we consider the curve of $V(x, 0)$ versus x for current I. A change in potentials which keeps the currents the same corresponds to changing W_s and W_d by amounts δW_s and δW_d while having L fixed. Thus L_s must decrease and x_d increase by equal amounts. The changes of δW_s and δW_d are evidently in the ratios of E_{xs} and E_{xd}. This leads to (89).

The dominant term in $\mu_g d$ is

$$E_{xd}/E_{xs} = [\pi(W_d - W_0)/2a]g(W_s)/I$$

$$= \frac{\pi(W_d - W_0)}{2a} \cdot \frac{I_0 b_s}{E_0 I a}$$

$$= \frac{\pi}{4} \left(\frac{W_d}{W_0} - 1 \right) \frac{I_0}{I} \frac{b_s}{a}. \tag{90}$$

If W_d is $2W_0$ and $I_0/I = 18$ and $W_s = (1/4)W_0$ so that $b_s/a = 1/2$, the value of μ_{gd} is

$$\mu_{gd} = 7.1 - 1 = 6.1. \tag{91}$$

Higher values of $m\mu$ can be obtained by operating with smaller values of I/I_0 or larger values of W_d.

The transconductance is dominated by the term in E_{xs} and is negative with magnitude

$$G_g = \mu_{gd}g_s \div (L - x_d + a/\pi)(1 + \mu_{gd})$$
$$= 2\sigma_0 b_s \mu_{gd}(L - x_d + a/\pi)(1 + \mu_{gd}). \tag{92}$$

The value is substantially that of a p-layer $2b_s$ thick and L long.

The resistance looking into the drain is

$$R_d = 1/G_g\mu_{gd}, \tag{93}$$

and is thus substantially that of a p-layer $2b_s$ thick and $\mu_g d$ long.

7. Effects at High Frequency

Although the gradual case lends itself to analysis from the transient point of view, the analysis is somewhat tedious. We shall, therefore, discuss in simple terms the frequency at which the circuit constants deviate substantially from their dc values. For this purpose we shall consider a structure operated with the drain beyond pinch-off. We shall also assume that W_s is approximately $W_0/4$ so that $b_s = a/2$. The structure then may be regarded as consisting of a distributed resistance of total value somewhat greater than

$$R = L/2b_s\sigma_0 = L/a\sigma_0, \tag{94}$$

which charges a pair of capacitances of length L and spacing somewhat more than $a/2$. The value of the resultant capacity is thus less than

$$C = 2LK/(a/2). \tag{95}$$

If we consider that the charging current flows through about $R/2$, then the effective time constant of the combination is thus

$$\tau = RC/2 = 2(L/a)^2K/\sigma_0 \tag{96}$$

$$= (I_0/I)^2\tau_0/18. \tag{97}$$

If we imagine that an input signal at frequency $f = \tau/2\pi$ is applied to the gate, then the input power will be

$$i_g^2R/2 \tag{98}$$

and the voltage will be

$$v_g = i_gR/2^{1/2}. \tag{99}$$

If we neglect transit-time effects, this voltage would produce a current to the drain, if grounded, of

$$i_d = G_gv_g = (a\sigma_0/L)v_g \tag{100}$$

and this output current generator can furnish power of magnitude

$$i_d^2\mu_{gd}/4G_g \tag{101}$$

to a matched load of μ_gd/G_g. The power gain is thus

$$\mu_{gd}G_g/4R = \mu_{gd}/4. \tag{102}$$

Thus power gain may still result even at frequencies as high as $1/2\pi\tau$ corresponding to

$$f = (2.9)\,(I/I_0)^2/\tau_0. \tag{103}$$

At lower frequencies, the power gain is higher since the input impedance is largely capacitative and increases with decreasing frequency so that for a given voltage there will be less current and less input power.

At higher frequencies there can still be power gain, but it is necessary to treat the channel as a wave-transmitting medium rather than as a lumped constant circuit.

8. Some Quantitative Design Considerations

For purposes of example we shall consider a structure comprising a layer of n-type germanium bounded by p-type gates. Under operating conditions, the electric field in the specimen may well be as large as $2E_0$ in the neighborhood of the drain. One design consideration is that this field should not be as large as the "Zener field" at which appreciable field generation of hole electron pairs occur.[6]

In order for the theory developed in the previous sections to apply, the electric field along the channel should be less than E_c, the critical field at which Ohm's law fails due to inability of the electrons to dissipate their energy sufficiently rapidly. This field is about 900 volts/cm for electrons in n-type germanium at room temperature,[7] and for it the drift velocity is about

$$3.1 \times 10^6 \text{ cm/sec.} \tag{104}$$

Above this field, the drift velocity varies approximately as the square root of the electric field.

If we require that the constant mobility region extend to the point where the gradual approximation fails, we can write from (71)

$$dW/dx = E_c = E_0(I/I_0)^{1/2}$$

so that for $I_0/I = 18$, $E_0 \doteq 4,500$ volts/cm. This condition is considerably more stringent than the Zener field condition, which would permit E_0 values at least 10 times larger to be used.

Throughout the discussion we have neglected currents flowing to or from the gate. In the case of a p-layer structure a reverse current of thermally generated electrons will flow from the p-layer to the electrodes and a current of holes will flow from the n-regions into the p-layer. These currents will be of the same order of magnitude as those met with in p–n junctions biased reverse. The current of electrons will tend to be somewhat larger than a normal saturation current because of the large size of the space-charge

[6] K. B. McAfee, E. J. Ryder, W. Shockley, and M. Sparks, Observations of Zener current in germanium p–n junctions, *Phys. Rev.*, **83**, 650–651 (1951).

[7] E. J. Ryder and W. Shockley, Mobilities of electrons in high electric fields, *Phys. Rev.*, **81**, 139 (1951). Also, W. Shockley, Hot electrons in germanium and Ohm's law, *Bell Sys. Tech. Jour.*, **30**, 990 (1951). See also E. Conwell, Properties of silicon and germanium, *Proc. I.R.E.*, **40**, 1327–1338; this issue.

region and enhanced generation therein,[8] and will tend to be somewhat smaller because usually the p-layer will be considerably less than one diffusion length thick. A typical reverse current in a p–n junction in germanium[9] may be of the order of 10^{-3} amp/cm^2.

We shall illustrate orders of magnitudes for an n-type unipolar transistor by taking n-type material having 4×10^{13} electrons/cm^3 and a charge density and conductivity of

$$\rho_0 = 1.6 \times 10^{-19} \times 4 \times 10^{13}$$
$$= 6.4 \times 10^{-6} \text{ coulombs/cm}^3 \qquad (105)$$

$$\sigma_0 = 3600\rho_0 = 2.3 \times 10^{-2} \text{ mho/cm.} \qquad (106)$$

We shall take a field E_0 of 10^4 volts/cm, but shall operate with $I_0/I = 60$ so that throughout most of the channel the mobility is constant. The resulting value of a is

$$a = KE_0/\rho_0 = 1.41 \times 10^{-12} \times 10^4/6.4 \times 10^{-6}$$
$$= 2.2 \times 10^{-3} \text{ cm} \qquad (107)$$

and

$$W_0 = aE_0/2 = 11 \text{ volts.} \qquad (108)$$

The characteristic current I_0 will be

$$I_0 = 2a\sigma_0 E_0 = 1.0 \text{ amp/cm.} \qquad (109)$$

If this structure is operated with a spacing L between source and drain of $5a$, and $W_s = W_0/4$ so $b_s = a/2$, and $W_d = 2W_0$, the following characteristics are found:

$$L = 1.1 \times 10^{-2} \text{ cm} \qquad (110)$$

$$W_s = 3 \text{ volts} \qquad (111)$$

$$W_d = 22 \text{ volts} \qquad (112)$$

$$I = I_0/60 = 17 \text{ mA/cm} \qquad (113)$$

[8] W. Shockley and W. T. Read, Jr., Statistics of the recombinations of hole and electrons, *Phys. Rev.* **87**, 835 (1952).

[9] F. S. Goucher, G. L. Pearson, M. Sparks, G. K. Teal, and W. Shockley, p–n junction rectifier and photo-cell, *Phys. Rev.* **81**, 637 (1951). Also, W. J. Pietenpol, *Phys. Rev.* **82**, 120 (1951).

$$\text{power dissipation} = 0.38 \text{ watts/cm} \qquad (114)$$

$$\mu_{gd} = 23 \qquad (115)$$

$$G_g = 4,600 \text{ micromhos/cm} \qquad (116)$$

$$G_g/I = 0.27 \text{ volts}^{-1} \qquad (117)$$

$$\text{output resistance} = 5,000 \text{ ohms cm} \qquad (118)$$

$$\tau_0 = 6.1 \times 10^{-11} \text{ sec} \qquad (119)$$

$$f = 9 \times 10^6 \text{ cps from (103)} \qquad (120)$$

The electric field at the source is 300 volts/cm and at $a/2$ short of the expop it is 1,300 volts/cm; hence, as stated above, the assumption of constant mobility in the channel is a good one.

The area of p–n junction per cm of length is $L = 1.1 \times 10^{-2}$. For a reverse current of 1 mA/cm^2 for these junctions, the reverse current would be about 10^{-2} mA/cm for the structure. This value would be negligible compared to the working current of 17 mA/cm.

These very superficial design considerations have been presented to illustrate the theory and to show that a favorable relationship between size and frequency applies for unipolar transistors.

Appendix

The problem of obtaining an accurate solution for the pattern of flow in a field-effect transistor appears to be a difficult one. The approximation of electrical neutrality within the channel itself can be shown to be seriously in error at a distance of about $a/2$ from the expop. The solution would thus require finding the charge density for the carriers as a function of x and y, which vanished outside the boundaries of the channel.

It is possible to give physical reasoning, however, that shows that once the channel has become relatively narrow, one can eliminate one of the variables. Suppose that instead of allowing the carriers to flow over a channel of finite width we imagine them to be constrained to the plane $y = 0$, keeping the same number of carriers per unit area of the plane. The effect of this shift of charge on the potential is quite small. If we consider a case in which the channel is $a/4$ wide, then the value of W is $W_0(3/4)^2$ or $0.56W_0$. If the same number of carriers are compressed into the $y = 0$ plane, the potential is W_0 due to the fixed charge minus $aE_0/4$ due to the field $E_0/4$ of the carriers acting over a distance a. This results in a potential at the $y = 0$ plane of $0.50W_0$, or about 10 per cent less than the correct value. For narrower channels, the error will be proportionally smaller.

The advantage of assuming that the carriers all flow in one plane is that the charge density of the carriers can now be described by a function of x alone rather than by a function of both x and y.

If we assume that the mobile carriers are restricted to the central plane at $y = 0$, then it is possible to show that a very simple scaling law applies for the case of constant mobility. For this case we may advantageously write the potential in the form

$$V(I, x, y) = (\rho_0/2K)(y^2 - a^2) + V_m(I, x, y).$$

The ρ_0 term satisfies Poisson's equation for $0 < |y| < a$ and gives a uniform potential $-W_0$ at $y = 0$. The V_m term thus represents the fields due to the mobile charges and due to the potentials applied to the end electrodes. The simple result, which we shall now establish, is as follows: If

$$V_1(x, y) \equiv V_m(I_1, x, y)$$

is one function which satisfies the conditions of the problem for current I_1, then a solution that holds for current I_2 is obtained by replacing V_1 by

$$V_2(x, y) = (I_2/I_1) = (I_2/I_1)^{1/2}V_1(x, y).$$

This follows from the fact that if V_1 satisfies Laplace's equation for $0 < |y| < a$, then so does V_2. Furthermore, the mobile carrier charge density in the $y = 0$ plane is evidently

$$-2K\partial V/\partial y,$$

and this is larger for V_2 than for V_1 by the ratio $(I_2/I_1)^{1/2}$. Furthermore, the longitudinal field is larger for V_2 by the same ratio. Hence the current is larger in the ratio of charge times field and hence is larger by the ratio I_2/I_1. Hence if V_1 satisfies boundary conditions and gives current I_1, then V_2 satisfies them also and gives current I_2.

We shall next consider what the solution is for this case in which the mobile carriers are assumed to move in the $y = 0$ plane with constant mobility. For these assumptions, the solution in the gradual region takes a very simple form. It also takes a very simple form in the region beyond the expop. We shall discuss both of these cases and then present a simplified treatment of the transition of one solution to the other.

Solution is readily obtained for the gradual region. The electric field in a region where charge density per unit area is uniform with value P, which corresponds to $2b\rho_0$ in the earlier discussion, is simply

$$-\partial V/\partial y = E_y = P/2K.$$

This gives for the potential

$$V_m = (P/2K)(a - y) \equiv - W_m[1 - (y/a)],$$

where W_m is a quantity analogous to W as used in the text. The longitudinal field at $y = 0$

$$E_x = -\partial V/\partial x = - (a/2K)dP/dx = dW_m/dx.$$

The current equation is

$$I = \mu P E_x = (2K\mu/a)W_m dW_m/dx,$$

which integrates to give

$$W_m{}^2 = - (aI/\mu K)x$$

provided the integration constant is chosen so as to make the extrapolated pinch-off point come at $x = 0$.

The potential at any value of x arises chiefly from P values within a distance of a about that value of x. A condition for the validity of the gradual approximation will thus be that the value of $P(x)$ does not differ greatly from its average value between $x - a$ and $x + a$. Near some point x_0 we may take

$$P(x) = P(x_0) + P'(x - x_0) + (1/2)P''(x - x_0)^2.$$

Average value of $P(x)$ in the interval of $\pm a$ about x_0 is

$$\langle P \rangle = P(x_0) + (a^2/6)P''(x_0).$$

If this average is to differ only slightly from $P(x_0)$, then

$$1 < a^2 P''/6P = a^2/24x^2.$$

Hence the gradual approximation should hold quite well until x is less than a distant from the expop.

Well to the right of the expop, the potential due to the mobile carriers must be small compared to that due to the potentials applied to the drain electrode. This latter potential will be of the form

$$\cos (\pi y/2a) \exp (\pi x/2a),$$

and may be referred to as "charge-free" potential since it satisfies Laplace's equation for all values of x, y

In the neighborhood of the extrapolated pinch-off point, the potential will make a transition from the gradual case to the charge-free case. In Fig. 12, the limiting forms are shown, the scale of potential being selected so that unity comes at $W_m(a)$. A solution of the space-charge equations would be necessary in order to determine the coefficient of the charge-free solution which joins correctly to the gradual solution. Four charge-free curves are drawn so that they take values of -1, $-\frac{1}{2}$, $-\frac{1}{4}$ and $-\frac{1}{8}$ times $W_m(a)$ at the extrapolated pinch-off point. Since these curves are exponentials, the difference between them is equivalent to a shift by $(2a/\pi) \ln 2 = 0.45a$ along the x-axis. From inspection, it is seen that joining can be accomplished most smoothly for the case of $-W_m(a)/4$. We shall accordingly assume that this curve does represent the correct joining relationship. An exact calculation would be necessary to determine the relationship accurately, but

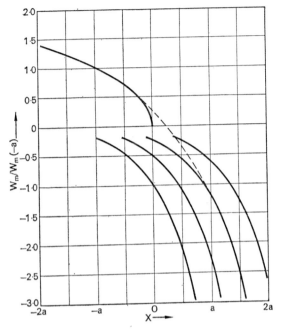

FIG. 12. Graphical fitting of gradual solution to an exponential solution.

it seems unlikely that the result would correct the present guess by more than about $a/2$ for the translational position of the charge-free solution.

On the basis of the reasoning above, we take as an approximation for $W(x)$ the following forms:

For $x < 0$,

$$W(x) = W_0 - (ai/\mu K)^{1/2}(- x)^{1/2}$$

For $x > 0$,

$$W(x) = W_0 + (1/4) (a^2i/\mu K)^{1/2} \exp (\pi x/2a)$$
$$= W_0[1 + (i/2i_0)^{1/2} \exp (\pi x/2a)].$$

The latter expression leads to a value of x_d, as defined in the text, of

$$x_d = (2a/\pi) \ln [(W_2 - W_0) (2i_0/i)^{1/2}/W_0].$$

This value differs by less than $0.1a$ from that given in the text. The reason for the good agreement is that the selection of $(1/4)$ for the ratio of the two fields used in the text was based on considerations of this appendix.

Acknowledgments

In conclusion, the author would like to express his appreciation to his colleagues G. L. Pearson, W. T. Read, Jr., George C. Dacey, and I. M. Ross for stimulating and helpful discussions in connection with theory and experiment on field-effect transistors. Special credit is due to P. W. Foy for laying a foundation for experimental studies of field-effect transistors.

PAPER 16

The TFT—A New Thin-film Transistor[†][‡]

PAUL K. WEIMER[§]
FELLOW, I.R.E.

Summary

A thin-film transistor, TFT, fabricated by evaporation of all components on to an insulating substrate has been developed. Operation is based upon the control of injected majority carriers in a wide-band-gap semiconductor by means of an insulated control gate. Experimental units using microcrystalline layers of cadmium sulfide have yielded voltage amplification factors greater than 100, transconductances greater than 10,000 μmho, input impedances greater than 10^6 Ω shunted by 50 pf and gain–bandwidth products greater than 10 Mc. Switching speeds of less than 0.1 μsec have been observed.

Simple evaporated thin-film circuits incorporating the TFT have been built. Direct coupling between stages is permitted since the insulated gate electrode can be biased positively as well as negatively without drawing appreciable gate current. Modified forms of the TFT have been built for use as a flip-flop, an AND gate and a NOR gate in computer applications.

I. Introduction

THE potential advantages of thin-film circuits have been largely unrealized to date because of the lack of a thin-film transistor which could be deposited by the same techniques upon an insulating substrate. The present paper will describe a new high-gain transistor[1] for which all components including the semi-

† *Proceedings of the I.R.E.*
‡ Received January 30, 1962; revised manuscript received, March 13, 1962.
§ RCA Laboratories, Princeton, N.J.
[1] The word transistor is used in its broadest sense here. The mode of operation of the device to be described is different from either the conventional unipolar or bipolar transistor.

conductor and metal electrodes are deposited by evaporation upon a glass plate.

Owing to the extremely short lifetime of minority carriers in microcrystalline films it was assumed at the start of this development that a majority carrier type of thin-film triode had a greater probability of success than a bipolar type of transistor. Majority carrier transistors were proposed [1] as long ago as 1935 and have been investigated in various laboratories [2]–[4]. The best known of these is the Shockley unipolar [2] field-effect transistor based upon the pinch-off of a conduction channel by the expansion of the depletion layer in a back-biased $p–n$ junction.

More recently, papers on a field-effect photo-transistor [5] and an analog transistor [6] using majority-carrier conduction in cadmium sulfide crystals have appeared. While the relatively low mobility of electrons in cadmium sulfide would not appear to recommend the material for a conventional transistor, cadmium sulfide offered some attractive features for exploratory studies of a thin-film triode. Single crystals of cadmium sulfide had been studied extensively [7], and considerable technological experience with thin films of cadmium sulfide had been acquired in the fabrication of photoconductive devices [8]. In addition, the wide-band-gap of cadmium sulfide made it well suited for the study of space-charge-limited currents in insulators [9], [10], a phenomenon which offered considerable potential for the development of new devices [6], [11]–[13].

The present investigation has yielded a new thin-film transistor [13] called the TFT whose performance utilizing microcrystalline layers of cadmium sulfide approaches that of commercial transistors made of single-crystal germanium or silicon. The surprisingly good performance of the TFT is due partly to the use of evaporation techniques which permit very small electrode spacings and gate widths. More important, however, has been the development of an insulating gate contact which permits operation in either the enrichment or depletion mode without drawing appreciable gate current. The enrichment mode is of particular interest from the standpoint of thin-film circuits since it permits direct coupling between stages. This mode of operation has not been used to date in commercially available transistors, although the effect was noted in some early experiments on "conductivity modulation" by Shockley and Pearson [14]. Recently, several single-crystal devices having an insulated control gate have been reported [15], [16]. The enrichment mode of operation has been discussed in connection with the "Electrolyte Field Effect" [17], "the Surface Field Effect Transistor" [15], the "Surface-Potential Controlled Transistor" [16], and the "Chargistor" [18].

The fabrication techniques employed in making the TFT are equally suitable for depositing interconnections and associated resistors, capacitors and diodes. Complete functional circuits containing many active and passive components can thus be fabricated in a single operation. As a simple illustration of the potential applications of the TFT a multistage thin-film amplifier was built. Other modifications of the TFT designed for particular circuit functions in computers will be described. These include an AND gate, a NOR gate and a simple flip-flop element.

II. Description of the Insulated-Gate TFT Structure

Fig. 1 illustrates one form of TFT which has yielded excellent results. The semiconductor film in most cases has been a micro-crystalline layer of cadmium sulfide. The "source" and "drain" electrodes are ordinarily formed of metals which make a low resistance contact to the semiconductor. Evaporated gold is suitable for cadmium sulfide. The "gate" electrode may also be of gold but the contact must be formed in such a manner that a thin film of insulator is interposed between the metal electrode and the semiconductor. The thickness of the semiconductor is usually less than one micron and the source–drain spacing has been in the range of 5 to 50 microns. The gate electrode is separated from the semiconductor by means of a thin evaporated layer of insulating material such as silicon monoxide.

A plot of drain current versus drain voltage for various values of positive gate bias is shown in Fig. 2 for one experimental unit.

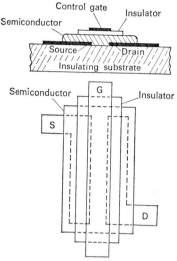

FIG. 1. Cross-sectional and plan view of an evaporated film transistor. The thickness of the evaporated layers is shown greatly exaggerated as compared with the lateral dimensions and with the thickness of the substrate.

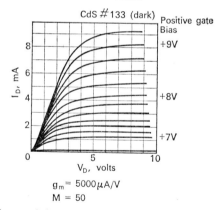

FIG. 2. Characteristic curves for an experimental cadmium sulfide TFT designed for operation in the "enrichment" mode. Drain current is plotted against drain voltage for different values of positive gate bias. (Sources grounded.) These curves were taken with the TFT in the dark.

Since the drain current increases by a factor of 10 to 1000 as the gate bias is raised from zero to several volts positive, this type of operation is called the "enrichment" or "enhancement mode." This mode is to be contrasted with the "depletion mode" used in the conventional form of unipolar transistor having a *p–n* junction at the gate. In the depletion mode maximum useful drain current is obtained at zero gate bias while a negative gate bias "pinches off" the source–drain current by expanding the depletion layer. Although the TFT's can be designed for operation in either or

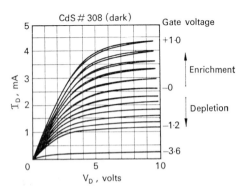

FIG. 3. Characteristic curves for an experimental TFT designed for operation in either the "enrichment" or the "depletion" mode. The hysteresis effect yielding the small loops noted in some units is now undergoing study.

both the enrichment and depletion mode, somewhat higher values of transconductance are usually obtained with the enrichment mode. The insulated gate permits operation in either mode without drawing appreciable gate current. Fig. 3 shows the characteristic curves of a TFT which operates with a gate bias near zero in either the enrichment or depletion mode.

The performance of the TFT can be predicted from the characteristic curves and a knowledge of the input capacitance. The unit shown in Fig. 2 has a transconductance of 5000 μA/V at a drain current of 6.5 mA and a gate bias approximately the same as the drain voltage. The voltage amplification factor derived from the curve is 50. The measured input capacitance of this unit was 300 pF, although this value was considerably larger than necessary. The gain–band width product can be calculated from the approximate relation,

$$\text{G.B.} = \frac{g_m}{2\pi C_g} \qquad (1)$$

where g_m and C_g are the transconductance and input capacitance, respectively. A value of 3 Mc was obtained, which is in good agreement with the measured frequency response curves on this unit.

More recently, TFT's similar to the above unit have been made with values of g_m as high as 25,000 μA/V for an input capacitance of less than 50 pF. Such units have yielded experimental gain–bandwidth products of about 12 Mc although the g_m/C ratio would indicate considerably higher capabilities. Oscillations have been obtained at frequencies up to 17 Mc, but no particular care has been taken to design the units for high frequency operation. All of the results quoted here were obtained with microcrystalline

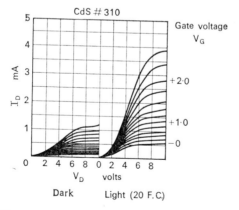

FIG. 4. Characteristic curves for an experimental TFT showing the effect of light. (Cadmium sulfide semiconductor).

films of cadmium sulfide. There is excellent reason to believe that the performance can be extended considerably beyond the present values either by improved processing of the cadmium sulfide or by the use of a different semiconductor.

Although cadmium sulfide is an excellent photoconductor, no attempt was made in the above units to process the TFT's for maximum photosensitivity. The results quoted were obtained with the units in the dark. The effect of light, however, is to increase the transconductance for operation in either the enhancement or depletion mode. Fig. 4 shows characteristic curves for a unit operating in the enhancement mode in the dark and in the presence of light.

III. Physical Processes in the TFT

An approximate description of the operation of the insulated-gate TFT can be derived from consideration of a typical field-effect experiment [19], [20] such as used in the study of semiconductor surfaces. In this type of experiment a transverse field is applied to the surface of the semiconductor by means of a close-spaced metal plate. That part of the charge induced in the semiconductor surface which is not bound in surface states or other immobile sites will appear as a change in density of the mobile carriers. The surface conductivity can thus be either enhanced or diminished by the field plate by an amount depending upon the potential applied and the nature of semiconductor–insulator contact.

The TFT differs from most of the above field-effect experiments in the use of smaller dimensions and in the choice of a wide-band-gap semiconductor such as cadmium sulfide. In such a material the thermally-generated carrier density is small compared to the density of majority carriers which can be injected from the source electrode. With a suitable low resistance contact at the source, current densities of the order of hundreds or thousands of amperes per square centimeter can be drawn through the cadmium sulfide film in spite of its normally high resistance.

Fig. 5 shows an energy band picture of the contacts used at the source and gate electrodes in a TFT. At zero bias in a unit designed particularly for operation in the enhancement mode, the bands should bend up at the semiconductor–insulator interfaces as

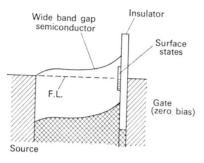

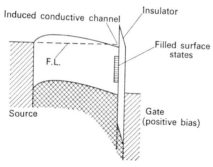

FIG. 5. An energy band picture of the "ohmic" source contact and the insulated-gate contact in a TFT designed for operation in the enrichment mode.

shown. When the gate is biased positively, electrons are drawn toward the interface, causing the bottom of the conduction band at the interface to be lowered relative to the Fermi level giving a highly conducting channel close to the insulator surface. (The small voltage drop in the semiconductor across the thickness of the layer is ignored in this drawing.) Conversely, a contact designed for the depletion mode of operation would aim to have a conducting surface channel present initially at zero gate bias which would then be depleted by operation with a negative gate bias.

An approximate expression for the transconductance of the TFT, based upon the above field-effect considerations, may be derived as follows: Consider a thin sheet of semiconductor of area $L \cdot W$ and a thickness h, separated from a close-spaced field plate by a thin dielectric spacer of thickness t. (See Fig. 6.) The dimensions L and W are assumed to be large compared to the film thicknesses, t and h. The positive potential V_g applied to the field plate

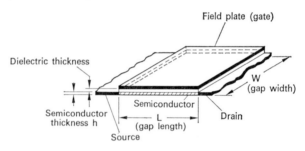

FIG. 6. Field-effect structure equivalent to the insulated-gate TFT.

(or gate) is assumed to be large compared to the potential difference between source and drain. A small increase in gate potential ΔV_g will draw Δn electrons/cm³ into the semiconductor given by

$$\Delta n = \frac{\text{total charge drawn in}}{e \cdot \text{total volume}} = \frac{C_g \cdot \Delta V_g}{e \cdot L \cdot W \cdot h}. \tag{2}$$

The resulting increase in source–drain current is approximately

$$\Delta I_D = V_D \cdot \frac{Wh}{L} \Delta \sigma = V_D \cdot \frac{Wh}{L} \Delta n e \mu_d \tag{3}$$

where

$\Delta \sigma =$ the change in conductivity of the semiconductor produced by the change in gate potential ΔV_g,

V_D = the source–drain potential difference and

μ_d = the effective drift mobility of the Δn electrons.

Combining (2) and (3) we obtain

$$\frac{\Delta I_D}{\Delta V_g} \cdot \frac{1}{C_g} = \frac{\mu_d V_D}{L^2} \quad \text{or} \quad \frac{g_m}{C_g} = \frac{\mu_d V_D}{L^2}. \tag{4}$$

The significance of small source–drain spacings is apparent since the gap length L is squared. The thickness of the dielectric spacer t and the width of the gate W appear implicitly in (4) in the gate capacitance. If we solved directly for g_m we would have

$$g_m = \frac{kW}{t} \frac{\mu_d V_D}{L} \tag{5}$$

where k is the dielectric constant of the dielectric spacer. In general, (4) is more useful than (5) since g_m/C_g may be substituted in (1) to give the gain–bandwidth product of the device. It may be noted that the right-hand side of (4) is simply the inverse of the transit time of the electrons between the source and drain if the field were uniform.

In deriving (4) it was assumed that the drift mobility μ_d was a constant independent of variations in V_g. This is true in wide band-gap materials only under certain conditions. When the semiconductor contains many traps or surface states, the large fraction of trapped electrons may cause the effective drift mobility to be much smaller than the microscopic or Hall mobility by the factor θ:

$$\mu_d = \mu_D \cdot \theta = \mu_D \frac{n_F}{n_F + n_T} \tag{6}$$

where

μ_d = effective drift mobility in the presence of traps,

μ_D = true drift mobility, which is assumed here to be equal to the Hall mobility,

n_F = is the free carrier density and

n_T = is the density of trapped carriers.

As the gate is made positive nearly all of the initial carriers drawn into the semiconductor may fall into the traps giving only a small increase in conductivity. For these electrons the effective drift mobility and the value of θ are very small. However, as the gate bias is further increased, most of the available traps should become filled (or otherwise inactivated) giving much larger increases

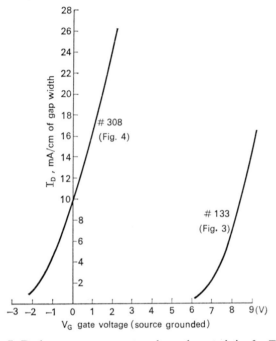

Fig. 7. Drain current versus gate voltage characteristics for TFT's of the type shown in Figs. 2 and 3.

in conductivity of the semiconductor. Under these conditions the drift mobility μ_d should approach a constant value equal to the Hall mobility ($\theta = 1$) and the g_m should become a constant independent of gate bias as predicted by (4).

The experimental results are in only partial agreement with the above analysis. The initial slow rise of drain current with gate voltage followed by a rapid rise at a large positive bias observed in Fig. 2 is consistent with the need for filling the surface states and traps to obtain adequate drift mobility. The surface state density

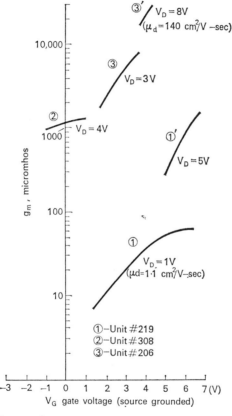

FIG. 8. Transconductance-versus-gate voltage for selected TFT's.

for this unit calculated from the gate bias and gate capacitance is of the order of 10^{12} to 10^{13} per square centimeter, a not unreasonable value. However, as shown in Fig. 3, CdS units can be made which do not require a large positive gate bias for satisfactory operation. In such units the trapping state density is either much smaller or the traps have been filled by other processes.

The incorporation of shallow donors into the surface layer or the generation of free electrons by absorption of light represent two alternative ways of filling the traps.[2] Fig. 7 shows the variation in drain current with gate voltage for units having the two types of characteristics shown in Figs. 2 and 3.

In Fig. 8 the experimental values of transconductance for widely differing units have been plotted as a function of gate bias. A log scale was chosen for g_m simply to accommodate the large range of data selected. From the above discussion one would expect g_m to reach a constant value at high positive gate biases as the effective drift mobility approaches the Hall mobility. Such a leveling off does indeed occur in curve 1 for drain voltage equal to 1 volt. The drift mobility could then be calculated from the g_m and the gate capacitance by the use of (4). For this calculation C_g was measured with an LC meter at a frequency of 150 kc and a normal positive gate bias. (The change in C_g with bias is usually less than 25 per cent.) The drift mobility computed in this manner was 1.1 cm²/V-sec, in fair agreement with independent measurements [11] of Hall mobility on polycrystalline cadmium sulfide layers. In curve 2 the g_m approaches a constant value of 1200 for $V_D = 4$ V, yielding a drift mobility of 6 cm²/V-sec. Curve 3 shows little tendency for g_m to reach a constant value even at low drain voltages.

It is clear that (4), which was derived assuming low drain voltages and a constant mobility, is inadequate for units operating with higher drain voltages as illustrated in curves 3 and 3'. Although the control mechanism in this case is probably more complex than can be explained solely by field effect considerations, it is interesting to use (4) as before to calculate the effective drift mobility. For curve 3', μ_d was found to be 140 cm²/V-sec, a value

---

[2] An entirely different process for neutralizing the effect of traps in the TFT is by emptying traps rather than by *filling* them. (See Bube [21].) Although sufficiently high fields may exist under some conditions in the gap region to empty shallow traps by impact ionization, it is not yet clear whether or not this process is a significant one in the TFT.

considerably higher than would be expected from Hall mobility measurements on polycrystalline cadmium sulfide films. The reasons for this discrepancy are now being investigated. However, regardless of the explanation this result is exceedingly encouraging from the standpoint of device performance. Such performance makes a striking contrast with the early experiments on conductivity modulation [14] with evaporated germanium where the surface state density was so large as to severely limit the control action of the gate.

At drain voltages exceeding the gate bias the drain current in the usual TFT will saturate with drain voltage as shown in Fig. 2. This saturation effect is very important from the operational standpoint, since it is required for high voltage amplification factors. A rigorous analysis of the effect for the enrichment mode of operation is not presently available. From simple field-effect considerations, however, the saturation of drain current can be "explained" in terms of the following model: When the drain voltage becomes more positive than the gate, the induced channel adjacent to the insulator would be completely pinched off at the drain end were it not for the high field extending in from the drain. Owing to the thinness of the layers, however, the lateral component of the electrostatic field from the drain can penetrate only a short distance beneath the gate. The particular equipotential surface in the channel whose potential is equal to gate voltage thus remains relatively close to the drain electrode regardless of an increasing drain voltage. The total current is limited by the electron flow *entering* this high field region, which, for drain voltages exceeding the gate voltage is consequently controlled by the gate voltage alone.[3] The failure of the drain current to completely saturate in practice would result from the gradual widening of the high field region due to incomplete shielding of the gate electrode. At much higher drain voltages (*e.g.*, 20 V in some cases) the drain current may again start rising rapidly with drain voltages. In terms of the

[3] In units which saturate at drain voltages less than gate voltage, the equipotential surface separating the low field region from the high field region will be correspondingly less than gate potential.

above picture this effect could be caused by avalanche breakdown in the high field region near the drain, hole injection from the drain, or, in poor units, by leakage across the gate insulator.

The question of saturation of drain current in the TFT is considerably more complex than the preceding discussion would indicate. Experimental units have been made which gave large enhancement currents without saturation at drain voltages considerably exceeding gate voltage (see Fig. 9). Failure to saturate can arise from the existence of non-modulated current paths

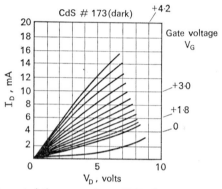

FIG. 9. Characteristic curves for a TFT showing failure of I_D to saturate.

existing in series or in parallel with the conduction channel. Such characteristics would also be expected if the high resistivity region near the drain were prevented from forming. This might occur due to a premature setting in of any of the conditions enumerated above normally giving the second rise in current at high drain voltages.

It is not surprising that all aspects of the various TFT characteristics do not appear to be accounted for by field effect considerations. The spacings involved in the insulated-gate structure are finer and the stand-off insulator considerably thinner than normally found in field-effect experiments.[4] Although such dimensions

---

[4] DeWald in [17] achieved the equivalent of a very thin insulating spacer by the use of an electrolyte as a gate electrode.

permit the relatively high values of g_m and g_m/C which have been observed, close spacings may also introduce other phenomena, such as hot electron effects, diffusion of minority carriers and tunneling phenomena. In spite of the added complexity introduced by such effects, they enhance the interest in the TFT from both the physics and the device application standpoint.

IV. Alternate Forms of TFT's

Fig. 10 illustrates structural variations of the insulated-gate TFT which can be fabricated by the same evaporation techniques used for the standard structure of Fig. 1. Although experimental units have been made it is too early to attempt to evaluate their performance. The ability to fabricate the TFT in many different forms should be an advantage in designing TFT's for particular applications and in incorporating them into thin film circuits.

The structure in Fig. 10(a) differs from the standard structure only in the sequence of evaporating the layers. In Fig. 10(b) all of the electrodes are applied on the same side of the semiconductor. Fig. 10(c) shows an interdigitated source and drain deposited upon

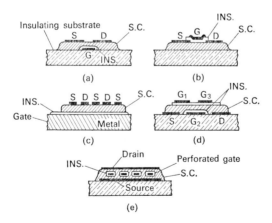

FIG. 10. Structural variations of the insulated-gate TFT.

an insulated metal gate for higher power output. Fig. 10(d) illustrates a pentode multiple gate structure designed to provide shielding between input and output.

Fig. 10(e) shows a layer-type TFT in which the control gate is a perforated metal film or an array of evaporated strips encased in insulator and embedded in the semiconductor. When biased positively or negatively with respect to the semiconductor the conductivity in the neighborhood of the apertures can be modulated, thus controlling the source–drain current. Although somewhat more lengthy to fabricate than the planar type TFT a possible advantage of the layer-type of unit may arise from a reduced source–drain transit time.

Many additional variations of the TFT will arise as the units are modified to serve particular functions in thin-film circuits. Several illustrations are given in Section VI.

V. Fabrication of the TFT

Although numerous thin-film techniques are available for fabricating the TFT, evaporation of all constituents using movable masks for defining the electrode and semiconductor patterns has proved to be satisfactory for experimental purposes. A precision masking jig of a type originally developed for making a multiple electrode television camera tube target [22] provided a simple method of achieving very fine patterns, without requiring very fine masks. As indicated by (4), close spacing of the source and drain is desirable in the TFT in order to obtain the highest possible g_m and g_m/C ratios for a given semiconductor material. This type of jig is capable of reasonable accuracy with 5 micron spacings, and the technique can be extended to electrode dimensions of less than one micron.

Fig. 11 depicts the masking arrangement employed. A fine wire grill of variable wire spacing is mounted close to the glass substrate blank, whose lateral position relative to the wires can be adjusted from outside the vacuum enclosure. By moving the glass blank between successive evaporations gap spacings considerably

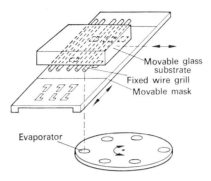

FIG. 11. Evaporation mask arrangement used in fabricating the TFT.

smaller than the wire diameter can be deposited. An additional set of movable masks positioned between the wire grill and the evaporation source serves to define the length of the evaporated strips and provides lateral connections for evaporated circuits. This procedure avoids the problems associated with the use of extremely fine wires and greatly extends the versatility of a given set of masks.

VI. Application of the TFT in Thin Film Circuits

The ability to fabricate circuits and components in the same operation points directly toward the "integrated circuit" concept [23] now being investigated in various forms in several laboratories. Although in an early stage of development, the TFT thin-film circuit is believed to offer some significant advantages when compared with existing techniques for forming transistors and circuits upon a single crystal block of silicon. An insulating substrate of nearly unlimited size permits a large array of circuits to be deposited on a single continuous support. In addition, the electrically inert base offers greater freedom in the design of the active elements and in the geometrical layout of intricate circuit patterns, since active and passive elements can be deposited in layers in any order. Both of these factors should lead not only to greater circuit density in complex devices but also to new applications where the available space for the electronics is at an absolute minimum. A TFT circuit could, in principle, be deposited upon any part of an existing device offering a few square millimeters of free surface. If the surface is a metal, a preliminary coating of insulator would be applied as substrate for the TFT.

The fabrication of thin film circuits incorporating transistors, resistors, capacitors and diodes can be carried out by the same

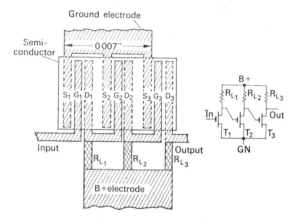

FIG. 12. A three-stage direct-coupled thin film amplifier. Direct coupling is feasible because the isolated-gate TFT does not draw appreciable gate current.

evaporation techniques as described in the preceding section for the TFT. To illustrate the method a three-stage direct-coupled thin-film amplifier was built (see Fig. 12). Since many components are deposited simultaneously the number of operations required for a complete circuit increases very slowly or not at all with increasing complexity of the circuit. Complete circuits containing hundreds or thousands of active elements deposited in one evaporation sequence appear to be entirely feasible.

Some preliminary consideration has been given to the application of the TFT in miniaturized computer circuits. Although the basic elements of a computer could be constructed using TFT triodes in combination with other thin-film components it may be advantageous to evaporate multi-electrode active elements designed particularly for the required function. Fig. 13 shows a direct-coupled flip-flop based upon the TFT. By inverting one of the triodes in the flip-flop the cross connections are simplified. Fig. 14 illustrates AND and NOR gates derived from the TFT. The semiconductor itself is used as the load resistor for the NOR gate.

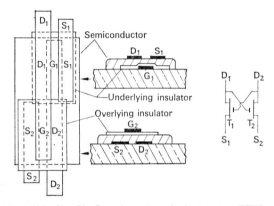

FIG. 13. A thin film flip-flop element equivalent to two TFT's with direct-coupled cross connections.

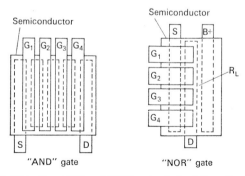

FIG. 14. Thin film AND and NOR gates derived from the TFT.

The thin film circuits of Figs. 12–14 illustrate only crudely the potentialities of the TFT in integrated circuit design. It is apparent, however, that the distinction between components and circuits will become more and more diffuse when devices of extreme complexity can be fabricated in one coherent piece. To adequately design, build and use such integrated devices a new type of engineering skill will have to be developed.

VII. Discussion and Conclusions

A striking aspect of the TFT development is the demonstration that a high-gain transistor can be built using a semiconductor as imperfect as a polycrystalline evaporated layer. Equally significant is that these transistors operate by the control of injected majority carriers with an insulated-gate structure. While the close spacing of electrodes has contributed to the surprisingly good performance the results are a convincing demonstration of the potentialities of devices utilizing injected majority carriers in wide-band-gap materials. Considering that TFT's have oscillated at frequencies up to 17 Mc using layers of the type yielding Hall mobilities of the order of 5 cm^2/V–sec, the prospect for improving the frequency response by one or two orders of magnitude appears good. This may require materials having higher mobility and structures with closer spacings.

On the basis of the results to date the TFT appears ready for evaluation in thin circuit applications. However, it is clear that much development work remains to be done. Questions such as stability, need for encapsulation, and ability to meet design tolerances, etc., have yet to be answered to fully assess the impact the TFT will have on circuit design. If these results are favorable (as preliminary tests appear to indicate) this impact could be very great indeed.

Acknowledgments

The author wishes to express his appreciation to Dr. A. Rose and Dr. D. O. North for stimulating discussions, H. Borkan for help in evaluating the performance of the TFT, H. Lambert, who performed the precision evaporations on the earliest units, Dr. F. V. Shallcross and Dr. J. Dresner for advice on preparation of CdS films and Dr. H. Johnson for helpful criticism of this paper. Others who have contributed in the fabrication and evaluation of the TFT are V. Frantz, R. Schilling, R. Pugliesi, W. S. Homa and L. Meray-Horvath.

References

[1] O. HEIL, Brit. Patent No. 439,457; 1935.

[2] W. SHOCKLEY, A unipolar field-effect transistor, *Proc. IRE*, **40**, 1365–1376 (November 1952).

[3] G. C. DACEY and I. M. ROSS, The field effect transistor, *Bell. Sys. Tech. J.* **34**, 1149–1189 (November 1955).

[4] S. TESZNER, "Le Technetron," in *Solid State Physics in Electronics and Telecommunications*, M. Desirant and J. L. Michiels, Eds., Academic Press, London, pp. 1086–1099; 1960.

[5] R. BOCKEMUEHL, Cadmium sulfide field-effect phototransistor, *Proc. IRE*, **48**, 875–882 (May 1960).

[6] W. RUPPEL and R. W. SMITH, A CdS analog diode and triode, *RCA Rev.* **20**, 702–714 (December 1959).

[7] R. W. SMITH and A. ROSE, Space-charge-limited currents in single crystals of cadmium sulfide, *Phys. Rev.* **97**, 1531–1537 (March 15, 1955).

[8] P. K. WEIMER, S. V. FORGUE, and R. R. GOODRICH, "The Vidicon—photoconductive camera tube," *RCA Rev.* **12**, 306–313 (September 1951).

[9] A. ROSE, Space-charge-limited currents in solids, *Phys. Rev.* **97**, 1538–1544 (March 1955).

[10] A. ROSE and M. LAMPERT, Photoconductor performance, space-charge-limited currents and the steady state Fermi level, *Phys. Rev.* **113**, 1227–1235 (March 1, 1959).

[11] G. T. WRIGHT, A proposed space-charge-limited dielectric triode, *J. Brit. IRE*, **20**, 337 (May 1960).

[12] J. DRESNER and F. V. SHALLCROSS, Rectification and space-charge-limited currents in CdS films, *Solid State Electronics*, to be published.

[13] P. K. WEIMER, "An Evaporated Thin Film Triode", presented at IRE-AIEE Device Res. Conf., Stanford University, Calif., June 1961; "Evaporated Circuits Incorporating Thin Film Transistors," presented at Internatl. Solid-State Circuits Conf., Philadelphia, Pa., February 1962.

[14] W. SHOCKLEY and G. L. PEARSON, Modulation of conductance of thin films of semiconductors by surface charges, *Phys. Rev.* **74**, 232–233 (July 15, 1948).

[15] M. M. ATALLA, Solid-State Device Res. Conf. at the Mellon Inst. and Carnegie Inst. of Technology, Pittsburgh, Pa.; June 1960.

[16] C. T. Sah, A new semiconductor tetrode—the surface-potential controlled transistor, *Proc. IRE*, **49**, 1623–1634 (November 1961).

[17] J. F. DeWald, A new type of semiconductor amplifier—the electrolyte field effect, *Bull. Am. Phys. Soc.*, **3**, 129 (March 1958).

[18] H. N. Yu, The chargistor, a new class of semiconductor devices, *IBM J.* **5**, 328–330 (October 1961).

[19] W. H. Brattain and C. G. B. Garrett, "Surface states" in *Methods of Experimental Physics—Solid State*, K. Lark-Horovitz and V. A. Johnson, Eds., Academic Press, London, vol. 6B, chaps. 7–8, pp. 136–143; 1959.

[20] G. Heiland, Feld Effekt und Photoleitung an ZnO-Einkirstallen, *J. Phys. Chem. Solids*. **6**, 155–168 (August 1958).

[21] R. Bube, Trap density determination by space-charge-limited currents, *J. Appl. Phys.*, to be published.

[22] P. K. Weimer, S. Gray, C. Beadle, H. Borkan, S. Ochs and H. Thompson, A developmental tricolor vidicon having a multiple electrode target, *IRE Trans. on Electron Devices*, vol. ED-7, pp. 147–153 (July 1960).

[23] T. O. Stanley, Integrated electronics, *Am. Scientist* **49**, 169–181 (June, 1961).

Index

Acceptors 24
Alpha
  current gain 43
  intrinsic 52
Anisotropic effective mass 22
Avalanche multiplication 52

Base resistance 56, 58
Bohr's theory 21
Boron 21, 24
Brillouin zones 14

Cadmium selenide 71
Cadmium sulphide 70
Chemical potential 37
Conduction band 4, 7, 15
Covalent bonding 5
Current gain, alpha 43
Cut-off frequency 56, 58

Dangling bonds 33
Density of energy states 10
Depletion layer 37
Depletion mode 72
Diamond 16
Diffusion 31, 53
  capacitance 53, 58
  potential 50
  theory 39
Diode theory 39
Donors 22
Doping 21
Drift-field 60

Effective density of stakes 19
Effective mass 9, 14
Einstein relationship 33

Electron 3
Electron-hole pair 17
Energy band 3, 7
  diagram 13
Energy gap 4
Enhancement mode 72
Extrinsic semiconductor 4

Face-centred cubic lattice 5
Fermi levels 11, 19
  shift of 24
  levelling of 37
Fermi–Dirac distribution function
  11
Field effect 34
Forbidden energy band 4
Forming 44
Frenkel defect 20

Gallium salts 71
Gate 34, 36
Germanium 4, 16, 18, 36
Gold 27

Hole 3, 4, 16
  injection 42
Hook region 44

Indium phosphide 71
Intrinsic conductivity 17
Intrinsic semiconductor 4, 16
Inversion layer 35, 41

Lattice vibrations 27
Lifetime 29

Majority carriers 22
Maxwell–Boltzmann statistics   18
Minority carriers 22
Mobility 29

Phonons 27
Phosphorus 21
Point contacts 37
Poisson's equation 38
Punch-through 58, 60

Recombination 29

Schottky defect 20
Schrödinger's equation 8
Silicon 4, 16, 18, 28, 63
Surface states 33, 37

Tamm states 33
Tetravalent bonding 6

Thermistor 35
Transistor
  analogue 66
  bipolar 66
  drift 60
  field-effect 66
  MOS-field effect 70
  n–p–i–n 61
  n–p–n 50
  photo 63
  p–n–p 50
  p–n–p–n 50, 55
  point contact 37
  power 62
  surface barrier 64
  tetrode 59
  thin film 71
  unipolar 66
Transit time 53
Transport factor β 52, 56

Valence bond 3, 7, 15